The Jungle and the Aroma of Meats

COMPARATIVE STUDIES OF HEALTH SYSTEMS AND MEDICAL CARE

For a list of titles in the series Comparative Studies of Health Systems and Medical Care, see back of book.

The Jungle and the Aroma of Meats

An Ecological Theme in Hindu Medicine

Francis Zimmermann

UNIVERSITY OF CALIFORNIA PRESS
BERKELEY LOS ANGELES LONDON

University of California Press
Berkeley and Los Angeles, California

University of California Press, Ltd.
London, England

First published in France under the title
La jungle et le fumet des viandes

Library of Congress Cataloging-in-Publication Data
Zimmermann, Francis.
The jungle and the aroma of meats.

(Comparative studies of health systems and medical care;)
Translation of: La jungle et le fumet des viandes.
Includes index.
1. Medicine, Ayurvedic—Philosophy. 2. Jungle ecology—India. I. Title. II. Series.
R606.Z5613 1987 610 87-10820
ISBN 0-520-05935-8 (alk. paper)

Printed in the United States of America

1 2 3 4 5 6 7 8 9

Contents

Preface

This is a book about the jungle in ancient India. If I may right away venture such an exorbitant request, let us please forget Kipling for a while! Not that they were unfaithful, the images with which Kipling enchanted our early days: the lianas, bamboo brakes, and the sweet flower of the *mohwa* which ripens in the shade of the teak trees . . . but that is the monsoon forest, its undergrowth, its clearings . . . that is not the jungle. Let us first record the fact (and presently we shall seek to account for it): An extraordinary misunderstanding has overtaken the history of this word. *Jāṅgala* in Sanskrit meant the "dry lands," what geographers would call "open" vegetation cover, but in the eighteenth century the Hindi *jaṅgal* and Anglo-Indian *jungle* came to denote the exact opposite, "tangled thickets," a luxuriant growth of grasses and lianas. Let us agree to abandon that misunderstanding for the time being.

Dryness, a flat terrain, sparse, scattered trees, mainly thorny ones: such are the physical features of the jungle given in the Sanskrit texts. They are not empirical observations, but norms. Every physical characteristic forms part of a binary opposition: the "dry lands" *(jāṅgala)* and the "marshy lands" *(ānūpa)*, the plain and the mountains, the savanna and the forest, thorny shrubs and palms, antelope on flat terrain and buffalo in the marshes . . . so many criteria which make it possible to set up oppositions between different soils within the same territory.

Whether it be a matter of large-scale ecological variations—over the entire Indus-Ganges plain, for example—or simply a particular microclimate, a hierarchy of the different regions within a given space always exists. The space is polarized, in two principal ways. First, a polarity exists between west and east. A key example, crucially important in our enquiry, is the polarity between the Indus and the Ganges: the superiority—repeatedly affirmed in traditional geography—of the dry lands, the jungles of the west, and the relative inferiority of Bengal, which is marshy. Second, a polarity exists between the center and the margins: agricultural civilization flourishes in the central plain, "the *jāṅgala* bursting with cereals," while the non-Aryan tribes are progressively driven out to the periphery, into forests and mountains. In the classical texts, the jungle thus appears as the positively valued pole within the framework of a normative ecology: the dry lands are better from every point of view. Salubrious, fertile, and peopled by Aryans, the jungle is the soil of brahminity.

This enquiry started from a few pages in a Sanskrit medical treatise—a catalog of meats—where animals are classified in two groups: *jāṅgala*, "those of the dry lands," and *ānūpa*, "those of the marshy lands." The meats of the jungle are light and astringent; those of the marshy lands heavy, unctuous, and liable to provoke fluxes. There is no zoology in ancient India, only catalogs of meats. The division of the various branches of knowledge favors the "utilitarian" or anthropocentric disciplines such as medicine and devalues the "pure" sciences: the rudiments of zoology and botany are literally dissolved into pharmacy. But that pharmacy in its turn presupposes a cosmic physiology: the world seen as a sequence of foods and a series of cooking operations or digestions at the end of which the nourishing essences derived from the soil are exhaled in the medicinal aroma of meats. The polarity between the dry lands and the marshy ones thus reappears at various levels. First, in the inventory of flora and fauna: acacias and coconut palms, antelopes and elephants, partridges and wild ducks; then in the field of therapeutics, as a polarity between the savors and the humors: astringency and the predominance of wind, acridity and the bilious temperament, unctuosity and a superabundance of phlegm. Eventually, medical doctrine fits into the brahminic tradition in general: the polarity between Agni and Soma, fire and water; the aridity of the jungles scorched by the sun is now associated with, now opposed to, the nourishing unctuosity of the rain. I have tried to describe here this curious wrapping of the various layers of knowledge in one another.

The purpose of these pages is thus twofold. First, it is to trace and explain through the history of collective sensibility the reversal in our (that is, modern man's) idea of the jungle, from arid and fallow land to luxuriance and tangled forest. This reversal is similar to the one Americanists have described about the prairie in the history of the United States. In our collective imagination, the trapper has usurped the position of the farmer. But we should not be duped by this Far-West mythology bequeathed to us by two centuries of romantic literature and the early years of the cinema. Literature (Fenimore Cooper, Longfellow, Thoreau, and so on) should not obscure the historical truth which, as early as the late eighteenth century, the "philosophers" clearly perceived. Crèvecoeur and Benjamin Rush despised the trapper, the frontiersman, and the man of the woods; they considered the true hero—the one who made America—to be the farmer struggling against the forest, never ceasing his labors until he had replaced it by pasture and arable land. In short, our ideas need reversing: Kipling's jungle and Fenimore Cooper's prairie are part and parcel of one and the same mirage of exoticism and primitivism. To dissipate that mirage while at the same time attempting to preserve its evocative powers is our first objective.

But in doing so, by means of a kind of archaeology of collective representations, we shall reveal the jungle in the ancient sense, to wit a system of legal and medical rules, a traditional ecology in the form of a *doctrine*, which the Sanskrit texts set out in detail. We shall then endeavor to reconstruct this doctrine, trying out first one, then another of a number of different keys: biogeography, linguistics, and a few comparisons to Greek medicine. The jungle is a medical concept. The drainage of the human body (medicine) and the cultivation of the dry lands (the jungle) make up a single, identical theme or cluster of primary images.

Looking back on it, I see this book mirroring, in its very composition, the layering of different levels of knowledge, a distinct feature of the Hindu tradition. First, it attempts to map out the jungle, distributing the flora and fauna within its space: so the first register is *geography*. Since ancient science, however, was interested only in the dietetic and therapeutic virtues of the jungle and its fauna, the enquiry then has to be pursued on the register of *pharmacy*. Chapter 4 thus embarks on an analysis of the aroma, savor, or bouquet of a particular soil and of its inhabitants, taken as potential remedies. It is an essentially linguistic analysis since it addresses not the medical substances themselves, but the phraseology used to describe them, the grouping of the adjectives which indicate their virtues. But again, the use of these remedies leads on to a superior register, tackled in chapter 6, that of *physiology*, in the ancient sense, which governs the circulation of fluids in the surrounding world, the rise of saps in plants, the aroma that is given off by the cooking of different kinds of meats, and, finally, the interplay of the humors within the human body. By way of conclusion, we return to the agricultural images that provided our starting point: the dry and fertile terrain, drainage, the sublimation of nourishing fluids—images ultimately applied to an analysis of the human body.

Acknowledgments

This book was written in the inspiring atmosphere of the Centre d'Etudes de l'Inde et de l'Asie du Sud (Paris), where I studied with two captivating teachers, Louis Dumont and Madeleine Biardeau. I also owe many thanks to various other people and institutions that helped me in research, and first of all, the Centre National de la Recherche Scientifique, of which I am most honored to be an officer. Next comes on my lips the name of my American mentor, Professor Charles Leslie, who has helped me in so many ways. I am particularly indebted to him for his acceptance of this translation in Comparative Studies of Health Systems and Medical Care, a series founded by him. We have tried to keep close to the style of the French original version. Janet Lloyd, the translator, deserves my thanks for meticulously following the sometimes long, intricate, ornate sentences aiming to describe a special mode of thought. A number of references have now been updated or completed. The most precious addition comes from a lecture by Professor A. K. Ramanujan, which I was privileged to attend in Chicago on 22 May 1985. I am most grateful to him for allowing me to quote his poem *Food Chain*, a dazzling version of the *Taittirīya Upaniṣad*'s eulogy of food studied below in chapter 8.

The Great Triad

The sources for this study are the three principal treatises of classical Indian medicine.

Suśrutasaṃhitā "Corpus of Suśruta"
Carakasaṃhitā "Corpus of Caraka"
(stabilized in the present form at the beginning of the Christian era)
Aṣṭāṅgahṛdayasaṃhitā "Corpus of the essence (of the science) with eight members"
(sixth or seventh century).

The most highly regarded Sanskrit commentaries are those composed in the Middle Ages by Cakrapāṇidatta (eleventh century) and Ḍalhaṇa (eleventh–twelfth century).

BRIEF NOTE ON THE TRANSCRIPTION OF INDIAN WORDS

In spelling current names of Indian origin, the simplest English form is used: Aryan, Himalaya, jungle, Sutlej. The diacritics are omitted (the Sarasvati, the Yamuna), except in a few passages where the ancient toponymy is studied on its own account *(Sarasvatī, Yamunā)*. Isolated Sanskrit words are transliterated in the radical form, without inflections, except when grammatical markings are relevant to the discussion.

Introduction: The Savors of the Soil

What we in Europe, in the classical period, called "the chain of being" is presented in India as a sequence of foods. Right at the end of the sequence, meats are cooked by fire, and that cooking is the last mediation, the last predigestion of foods before they are consumed by man. Inserted into this sequence, in between the plants (which they eat) and cooking (which renders them eatable), animals—eaten eaters, at once flesh and meat—are in an ambiguous position that reflects life's natural violence. "Immobile beings are the food of those which are mobile, those without teeth are the food of those with teeth, those without hands are the food of those with hands, and the cowards are the food of the brave."[1] To account for the subordination of some classes of beings to others, it is not enough to say that animals eat plants and man eats meat. In the animal kingdom and then the human one, the dialectic of the eaten eater introduces further divisions between the strong and the weak, the predator and his prey, the carnivore and the vegetarian. Vegetarianism—a brahminic ideal and a social fact in India—precisely calls into question that fateful dialectic in which every class of being feeds on another. The prohibition of flesh, which became increasingly strict in brahminic society, was one way to break the chain of all this alimentary violence and affirm that it is not really necessary to kill in order to eat. To that end, a new type of opposition between men was introduced. It was no longer a matter of courage and fear, domination and servitude; it was instead an opposition between the pure and the impure and a hierarchy of castes. Abstention from eating meat became a criterion of purity. Such is our context, what I am inclined to call the overall Hindu tradition, the principles of which are essentially juridical and religious.

However, I am interested in a particular discipline within that tradition, one which, confronted as it constantly is with physical diseases and urgency, tends more than any other to contradict the tradition's orthodoxy and ritualism. It is medicine, *Āyurveda*, "knowledge" *(veda)* for (prolonging or saving) the "continuation of life" *(āyus)*. The Ayurvedic doctors superimpose upon the religious principles of purity and hierarchy others of a different order: after all, seen from a biological point of view, flesh does nourish flesh. And the nourishment which is more fortifying and restorative than any other, for an anemic or consumptive person, is not just meat but the meat that to a brahmin is the most disgusting of all: the meat of animals that eat meat, a medication which the state of the patient sometimes renders indispensable, even if it must be disguised by being mixed with other foods and even if the patient must be told lies in order to overcome his disgust. Later, I shall illustrate this use of deceit in a good cause.

First, the medical treatises record the simple observation of a biological fact, to wit that animals compose a series of hostile couples: herbivores and carnivores, game and beasts of prey, the antelope and the lion, the partridge and the crow, and so on. Furthermore, the doctor makes use of this natural violence for therapeutic ends, and that is why hostile couples constitute one of the most important of the classificatory schemata in the nomenclature of meats. The doctor, then, cannot be free from violence, a fact which, within the civilization that invented nonviolence, *ahiṃsā*, the "absence of the desire to kill," inevitably entailed a slight lowering of his social status. We shall return to this point. We are concerned to analyze the social issues connected with this animal pharmacopoeia together with its logical structures.

Within a given area, the animals and plants share the same circumstances, climate, land relief. The existence of one group is conditioned by the presence or numbers of another, as in the following patterns of relationships: reversals of position (the eater will be eaten), reduplication (the flesh of eaters of flesh), coupling (the predator and its prey), and the sequence (moon-water-earth-plant). The chain of being is thus present in its entirety within a given landscape with its climate, land relief, trees, birds, and so on. Each of the animal or plant species char-

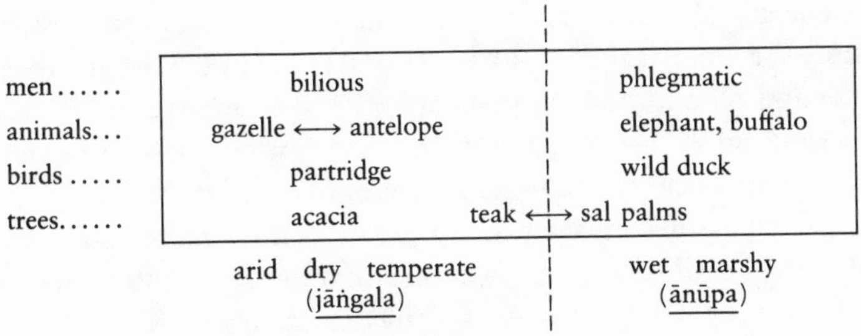

Figure 1. Bioclimatic polarities

acterizes a particular type of landscape and is at the same time part of an ecological community in which it either feeds off others or feeds them. Thus, living creatures can be distributed over two dimensions. Their stratification on a number of biological levels overlaps with their geographical distribution. They make up a table, they set up a tableau: the contrasting species—the acacia and the coconut palm, the wild partridge and the wild duck, the gazelle and the elephant—characterize the bioclimatic polarities between the arid and the marshy regions (figure 1). Teak and sal indicate two variants of a landscape that is more or less dry, ranging from tropical to deciduous forest; and in a similar fashion, the gazelle and the antelope mark out the difference between the semi-arid plains and the tree-covered savanna. But in a single landscape, thorny shrubs, bushes, and gazelles may be associated, or again, a teak forest may shelter lions and antelopes. The first chapters of this book will be devoted to charting this distribution. Animals and plants are distributed in accordance with a particular typology of soils, or *biocenoses*, if I may borrow the word used by ecologists today to refer to communities of living creatures that share the conditions of life in a given place. In ancient India, this typology did not result from empirical observation but stemmed initially from a revelation. It was the *ṛṣi*, the first sages close to the gods, the seers of Vedic times, who noted what cannot be seen in the landscape: the hidden properties of materials, their savors, or *rasa*, and it was they who taught of these things both by word of mouth and in their writings. Tradition then carries on perception so that in the landscape that nature presents to the eye each element can be named or described by the doctors and poets who know the science of the *rasa*. Although this book borrows numerous illustrations from tropical geography and contemporary studies of flora and zoology, the reader should not be misled. Its point of departure is not observation but a study of the texts; not geography or the natural sciences but a corpus of traditional notions into which it became possible to subsume the empirical data. I have tried to compare what the texts say with what is taught today by geographers and naturalists, in the hope of discovering what was at stake in Hindu scholasticism—the demands, conflicts, and world vision to which the Sanskrit texts bear witness. For a Hindu, what these texts say represents reality, reality as perceived from inside a tradition which is closed on itself. If the interpreter is not himself to become imprisoned within this tradition, he must—when faced with the words that express it—retain a sense of their strangeness. Take the word *jāṅgala*: however many the glosses, in the final analysis it remains untranslatable. Let us start by determining the terrain that it covers.

Ānūpa represents all the places where water abounds, not just marshes but also rain forests, liana forests, mangroves, with unhealthy connotations of fevers and parasites. "Marshy lands," the Indians call them. The opposite is the *jāṅgala*, defined first and foremost by a scarcity of water. At this point, we must reject all the images of a virgin forest and violence with which the romantic writers have cluttered our memories. But if it does not mean what we understood from our childhood reading, what *is* meant by the Sanskrit word for jungle? It is a technical word from medical language, denoting a land with a dry climate, which is beneficent so long as the aridity is not excessive. The definition becomes ambiguous as soon as a geographical illustration is attempted. Stretching from the borders of the desert to the monsoon forests, the spread of jungle landscapes is so vast that we must pick out one primary sense, that of dry lands, with varying extensions: pseudo-steppes, brakes, savannas, sparse forests. Let us start with a broad schema of the vegetation over the Indian subcontinent as a whole (map 1). It is based on similar schemata to be found in the three or four classic works on the vegetation and animal ecology of India: Champion and Seth (*A Revised Survey of the Forest Types of India*), Legris *(La végétation de l'Inde)*, the handbook by Spate and Learmonth, and George B. Schaller's admirable study of the wild fauna.[2]

From the Thar desert to the rain forests of Bengal and Assam, the plant formations strung out from west to east across the Indus-Ganges plain can be reduced to four principal types:

[1] steppe land with thorny shrubs covering the semiarid regions of the Punjab, Rajasthan, and Gujarat. The ligneous vegetation becomes more dense in some places, forming impenetrable thickets which the Indians call "thorn forest";

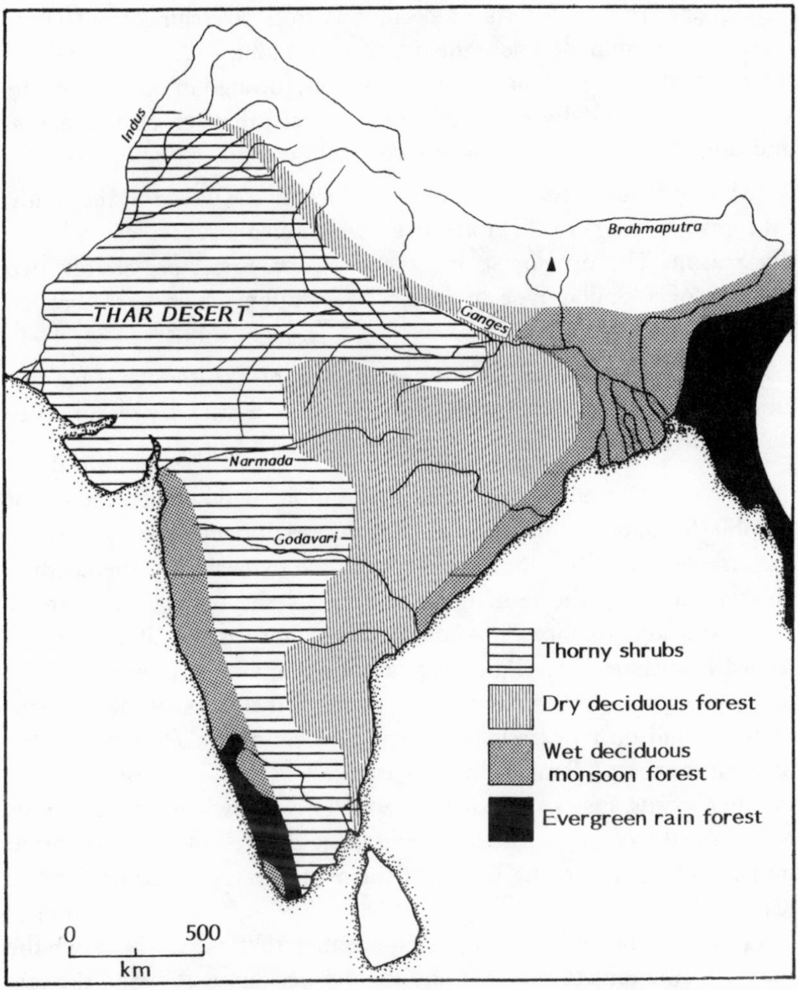

Map 1. Vegetation types. This is only a sketch. It does not indicate the edaphic formations nor the mountainous zones. *Source:* P. Legris, *La Végétation de l'Inde: Ecologie et flore* (Pondicherry, 1963), map 19.

[2] dry tropical forests of deciduous trees stretching from Uttar Pradesh to Tamilnad, where the dry season is long and intense and the total rainfall (of less than 1,500 mm) is concentrated in one-half of the year. Much of the dry forest has been reduced through human action and brushfires to more or less tree-covered savanna;

[3] monsoon forest—teak forests (drier) in the west and the south, sal forests (wetter) to the northeast—which also loses its leaves in the dry season. The dry forest and the monsoon forest are simply two variants of a similar type of tropical vegetation which goes through different seasonal periods;

[4] rain forest, which, in contrast, is evergreen. Although some species of trees do lose their leaves in the course of a brief dry season, they do so individually, and no seasonal rhythm is evident.

This is an extremely simplified description: It takes no account of edaphic formations (mangroves, liana forests) or mountainous zones. Nevertheless, it will suffice to determine the extension of the *jāṅgala*. Strictly speaking, the term is applied to [1] the semiarid regions of thorny thickets or more spaced-out thorny shrubs. But it can be extended to include [2] tree-growing savanna and even dry forest. Hence, an equivocation in the connotations of the *jāṅgala*. Sometimes the emphasis is laid on its extreme: the arid borders of the Thar desert, the Sahelian zones of Punjab and Rajasthan where dust storms blow—in other words, just a small part of zone [1].[3] Elsewhere, the emphasis is laid on the central area: dry terrain, the deforested plain colonized by peasants—that is, the whole of the area covered by zones [1] and [2].

However, the phytogeographical frontier that passes between the thorny formations to the west and the dry deciduous forest to the east assumes a capital importance as soon as one notices that it corresponds almost exactly to the ecological and medical frontier which—in the traditional geography of malaria in India and right down to the late 1940s (before the campaigns launched in 1947 to eradicate it)—separated the eastern regions, where malaria was endemic, from the western regions, where it appeared in epidemic form.[4] It is by reference to the geography of malaria and this fundamental distinction between the epidemic (in the west) and the endemic (in the east) that the traditional polarity between *jāṅgala*, the "dry land" (mostly zone [1]), and *anūpa*, the "marshy land" (mostly [2], [3], and [4]) takes on its full meaning.

The way in which the vegetation cover is divided up and distributed over the geographical map is but one aspect of the matter. In the first three chapters of this book, which consider the jungle as it were "at ground level" and as a basic element of the geography, many other aspects will one by one become the focus of attention: the relief (the geography of the plains); the hydrographic network (the division of waters between the Indus and the Ganges); and the classification of animals, agriculture, and eating customs (a polarity between wheat and rice). A whole complex of arguments, keys, classificatory grids, and cartographic procedures makes it possible for a modern Indianist to situate in space the great principles of traditional Hindu ecology, the typology of the three soils laid down in the Sanskrit medical treatises:

jāṅgala	the "dry lands"
ānūpa	the "marshy lands"
sādhāraṇa	the "middle region"

The plain, sand, rocks, and bushes: *jāṅgala*. Forests and marshes: *ānūpa*. In between, neither too wet nor too dry, the dry tropical forest of sparsely scattered trees which lose their leaves in the summer, merging with the tree-bearing savanna, a mean between two extreme climates, midway between two opposite orientations: *sādhāraṇa*, the "middle region." The whole set constitutes what Durkheim and Mauss called collective categories or forms of classification. Not only are the flora and fauna distributed between the two ecological and climatic poles but this polarity—expressed in habitat, foodstuffs, pharmacy, and bodily techniques—gives rise to two types of men: the one thin, dry, and of a bilious temperament; the other fat, rotund, and susceptible to disorders of the phlegm. Consumption in the *jāṅgala*, elephantiasis in the *ānūpa*. Given that in the traditional geography of malaria we also find this polarity, with the epidemic in the east and the endemic in the west, we must recognize it as a total social fact.

However, this polarity does not emerge immediately from the classical texts; rather, it is obscured by a plethora of adjectives. In his famous work, *La formation de l'esprit scientifique*, Bachelard described this semantic proliferation, which infests the whole of ancient scientific literature. Every medicament is literally covered in adjectives, and it comes as no surprise to find in *Āyurveda* a luxuriance of synonyms, a mixture of wordy empiricism and phantasmagoria, an omnipresent dialectic between contrary qualities, which is the very stuff of all of our old medical treatises and reflects the same unconscious reveries of prescientific thought. At first, then, this doctrine, which tells us that *the meats of dry lands are astringent and those of wet lands provoke fluxes*, strikes us as pure verbiage. In our own tradition, we have, after all, come across a similar ineradicable belief in an osmosis between living creatures and their environment. Bachelard relates how the Académie française, in 1669, dissected a civet cat in order to compare it with a beaver. The Académie concluded that the strong and unpleasant smell of the *castoreum* came "from the cold wetness of the beaver, which is half-fish"; the fluid secreted by the civet cat, in contrast, was sweet-smelling because the animal "is of a hot and dry temperament, drinks little and usually lives in the sands of Africa."[5] Wet, cold habitats go with the stench of fermenting substances; hot, dry habitats with ethereal fragrances. No need, one might surmise, to go seeking in the Hindu texts for principles which were so well formulated by the French "Immortals" of 1669. The preconceptions and mental obstacles that for so long blocked the birth of the scientific spirit appear to be the same in all civilizations, and it does not seem surprising to find here what Bachelard called the substantialist obstacle: "In general, all substantial values are internalized in life, particularly in animal life. Life deeply assimilates qualities; it firmly links them with substance. The association between the *nature* of an animal and the natural *quality* is so direct that, under the cover of idiosyncrasy, it is possible to justify the most grotesque affirmations."[6] Everything would thus appear to have already been said on the subject of the incongruities which throng the pages of the Hindu texts, as well as our own. Yet they may also be considered from a slightly different point of view. Even if the prejudices or psychological considerations surrounding the appearance of such grotesque thoughts may be universal, what is at stake is, in contrast, quite particular and diverse. While the antithesis drawn between the beaver and the civet cat may have been of little importance in the Europe of 1669, is that same antithesis purely and simply comparable in ancient India? The gazelle is light, the buffalo indigestible: Is this just the same kind of idle talk? Let us attempt to determine its medical, religious, political, and social context. A whole world looms up in the background: the jungle and the anthropological structures of space and, even more important, deeply embedded in the soil, the complex interplay of the *rasa*.

What the Rishis, the seers of Vedic times, quite literally saw was that the universe is a kitchen, a kind of chemistry of *rasa*, diluted or sublimated to feed now one, now another, of nature's kingdoms: the stars, the waters, the earth, the plants, the fauna. The cold rays of moonlight increase the unctuosity of the waters which proceed to impregnate the earth with every kind of *rasa*, nourishing essences among which sugar and salt provide easily conceivable examples. The *rasa* are six fundamental savors: sweet, acid, salty, acrid, bitter, and astringent. Savors may be invisible, as sugar and salt are in water, but they are present everywhere in the sap of plants and the juices of meats. In translating this Ayurvedic doctrine of the six *rasa*, "savors" is the word commonly used, but this conventional translation is inadequate and misleading. In our language, savors are qualities perceptible through the senses, whereas here it is not at all a matter of "sensible" qualities but rather of essences that circulate in the depths of the landscape and are diffused through the chain of being, individually taking the forms of a multitude of saps, juices or broths, remedies or poisons.

To say that all traditional knowledge has a deeply anthropocentric character is a truism. Things that are known, named, and classified in series either can be used by man or are hostile to him. The doctors of India thus declared that there is no substance in the world which may not be used as a medicament, but, equally, there is none which may not, in the hands of a charlatan, act as a poison. The ideal is to accustom oneself to hit on the right choice of regimen, learned doses, and mixtures, so that the nature of what is eaten is rendered appropriate to the nature of the one who eats it. The doctor, however, is the opposite of an empiric; his prescriptions conform with the congruences inscribed within the things themselves; his role is to interpret a hidden art which perception could not enable him to see but which words have taught him. Far from being an invention of man as a collection of empirical recipes would be, Ayurveda is beyond our powers of knowledge and submits us to laws which can be taught but cannot be discovered. Thus the individual is literally absorbed into the world that surrounds him, and the knowledge inculcated in him is designed to facilitate that integration. I hope I may be forgiven a personal observation at this point: The traveler in the Tropics truly experiences a feeling of absorption as he learns after nightfall to strike the ground with a stick or to sweep the beam of his torch over the path to disperse the snakes in the darkness, or when he shelters beneath his mosquito net surrounded by thousands of tiny, hostile, noisy, and invisible creatures. In such circumstances, he cannot help but understand how the landscape can seem to the natives a vast system of multiple environments into which man is inserted, surrounded, integrated, and absorbed, and how it is that living creatures are defined as good or bad to eat, or as biting, stinging, or venomous. Ayurvedic treatises classify fauna in two ways: in terms of meats and in terms of poisons. And who are we, the intended beneficiaries of science, if not eaters or eaten, predators or prey?

I: The Jungle and the Water's Edge

Like the veins of two joined leaves, the double hydrographic network of the Indus and the Ganges marks out a whole series of spits of land in the plain, each caught between two confluent streams. These are the interfluvial areas of Punjab and Uttar Pradesh, the doab. *Dō-āb* (Hindi, Persian): a Mesopotamia, land contained by two courses of water. Our starting point is the center of the network, in the Delhi Doab (map 2), between the Sutlej River in the north and the Yamuna River in the east, a region still known as *Jaṅgal Deś* (Hindi), "Jungle Country."

The Delhi Doab, taken as a whole, plays a fundamental geomorphological and climatic role, for it constitutes a veritable dividing line between the surface and the subterranean waters of the plain of the Indus and that of the Ganges (we shall return to this point later). The Siwalik Mountains bordering this region in the northeast today are devastated and eaten away by erosion but at the time of the Moguls were still covered by forests, which served as hunting reservations. Alongside the rivers, irrigation was effected by means of flooding, and in the north by using wells. The whole region today is crisscrossed by a huge network of canals. From the north to the south, wet and dry are divided into three zones: the well-watered plain along the base of the Siwalik Mountains, the central region irrigated by canals, and the arid lands bordering the Thar Desert. As Spate and Learmonth point out (map 2), the Jaṅgal Deś is made up of sandy lands that can tolerate drought and

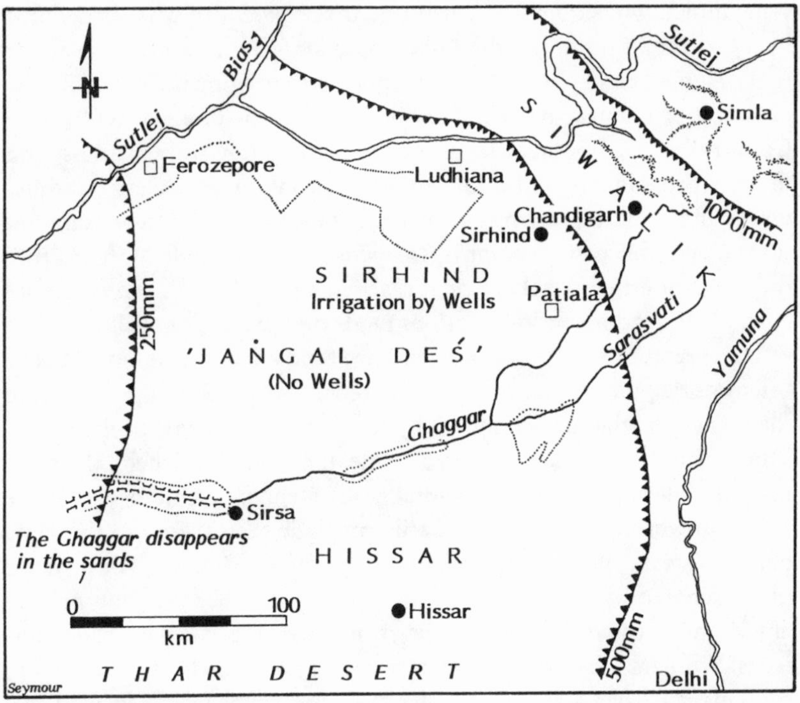

Map 2. Delhi Doab, between the Sutlej and the Yamuna rivers. Well-watered plains (at the base of the Siwalik Mountains) stretching as far as the arid margins (the Hissar): a regional polarity. This map (which has no scientific pretensions with regard to contours) shows the zones where irrigation was traditionally affected by flooding (dotted areas; based on O. H. K. Spate and A. T. A. Learmonth, *India and Pakistan*, 3d ed. [London, 1967], fig. 18.2), and the isohyets (average rains of 250, 500, and 1,000 mm per year; cf. P. Gourou, *L'Asie*, 4th ed. [Paris, 1964], fig. 69).

remain fertile despite varying conditions. Unlike the zones situated farther north, the Jaṅgal Deś can no longer use wells for irrigation purposes, but its position is not an extreme one. To find what geographers would call "arid margins," one must push farther south into the Hissar region.[1] Such is the landscape of the jungle, in the traditional sense of the word: a sandy soil, flatness, and dryness are its typical features.

It is, to be sure, a preliminary example and a very partial one. The proper nouns *Jaṅgal* (Hindi) and *Jāṅgala* (Sanskrit) denote different places at different times and in different provinces. Furthermore, the logical connection between the proper noun, *a place-name*, and the common noun, *an ecological type*, raises a methodological difficulty, always the same difficulty encountered when one tries to identify what is denoted by a vernacular term, whether it be, for example, the name of a place or that of a medicinal plant. We are trapped into begging the question: the connotations appear to justify the name. Thus the designation "Jungle Country" is used because south of the Sutlej sandy soils, flatness, and dryness predominate. Contrary examples could nevertheless be found where the same toponym is used in virtue of quite different connotations. A notable case in point is *Kurujāṅgala*, "the Jungle of the Kuru," the name of an extremely ancient place mentioned in the *Mahābhārata* epic. Identifications or localizations made on the basis of oral traditions or interpretations of the written texts are fundamentally dubious. Let us briefly anticipate a point to be considered in chapter 3. In the context of the great epic, the idea connoted by the name "the Jungle of the Kuru" is not so much a dry land (ecological meaning) as a battlefield, the territory at stake in a conflict (socioreligious meaning). One usage of the name, however, does not necessarily preclude the other, and the same name may take on different meanings in different contexts. The physical place denoted by "the Jungle of the Kuru," or rather the geographical environment to which it refers, nevertheless retains constant characteristics. Scholars are in agreement in situating the "Jungle of the Kuru" in the Ghaggar river basin, in the heart of the Delhi Doab. In medieval toponymy, the "Jungle Country" more widely refers to the semiarid lands south of the Sutlej River as a whole, a frontier region between Punjab and Rajasthan. In the ancient literature of Rajasthan, the term had an even wider application: it referred to the entire northern region of Marwar, or *Marudeśa*, the "Desert" which stretches to the west as far as the Aravalli Mountains.[2] All the same, these landscapes are of a similar type—arid, flat, and sandy. Such is the setting for this enquiry.

MENTAL CATEGORY AND GEOGRAPHICAL FACT

The word *jungle* may be grouped together with a whole series of other geographical terms—*desert*, *steppe*, and so on—which denote at once places and environments, lands and landscapes, that is to say, regions which can be located on a geographical map and, at the same time, ecological modes of organization. This double meaning is best illustrated by drawing a distinction between the localized geographical fact marked on a map and the category, the concept within which we may include a particular class of facts. I draw this distinction in order to restore to the jungle its value as a category, its richness of meaning in Hindu culture. This distinction will be understood more easily if we first consider a case closer to home. The desert, for instance, possesses just such a richness of meaning within French classical culture.

Open the dictionary. If it is both a collection of linguistic data and a formulatory of knowledge about the external world, a dictionary will provide two types of definition which are not to be confused: it defines the idea, and it defines the object. Let us consider, for example, how *désert* is treated in French dictionaries, virtually all of which give the two types of definition. For logic's sake, I will condense them as follows (the reference to the *Désert* of Port-Royal, a Jansenist place of retreat, is from the famous French dictionary by Littré):

> DÉSERT: [1] *(Archaic)* uninhabited place. Seventeenth century. To withdraw into the desert, in the language of Port-Royal: to retreat into solitude. [2] *(Geographical)* A zone that is very dry, arid and uninhabited. Cold deserts, hot deserts, Sahara Desert, etc.

Given definition [1], you could say that to some extent definition [2] is redundant, but at the same time two different perspectives are intended: [1] defines a concept; [2] denotes a geographical fact. On the one hand, definition [1] involves the formulation of a category of collective thought that subsumes a whole collection of cultural values: presence/absence, wasteland/cultivated land, life in the world/renunciation of the world, and so on; on the other hand, definition [2] presents a statement about the state of things: the dryness of the climate, the sterility of the soil, and so on. Thus the two definitions have quite different purposes.

Compared with the preceding example, the treatment of *jungle* in French dictionaries definitely seems incomplete. All of them limit themselves to the formula of a type [2] definition. Thus the definition in Littré's dictionary reads: "JUNGLE: In the East Indies, a thickly wooded plain covered by reeds." All other French dictionaries have elaborated on this formula, all of them failing to see its inaccuracy. They forget to mention that the word *jungle* also means the enemy, wildness, uncultivated land; they forget to give us a type [1] definition. From a semantic point of view, both in French and in English, the word *jungle* has fared much the same way as *desert* or *forest*. Initially, these words were used in an abstract sense, with a moral, anthropocentric meaning such as "uninhabited, uncultivated region." The physical or geographical use only came later, accompanied by a diversification of images: an arid zone, a place planted with trees, bamboo brakes. We should note clearly the direction taken by the semantic evolution: its passage from the abstract to the concrete, from the concept to the material thing. Legal preceded geographical usage: In the sixteenth century, *forestier* (in French) meant "a foreigner"; *jaṅgal* (in Hindi) meant "an uninhabited, uncultivated land." "Land waste for five years . . . is called Jungle," writes Halhed in the *Code of Gentoo Laws* (1776). This is the relevant time to cite the extremely evocative description left us by the naturalist Victor Jacquemont. It relates to the landscape around Sirhind, fifteen miles north of Patiala, in the part of the Delhi Doab irrigated by wells (see map 2). More important, this description serves as a precious piece of evidence in that it establishes this technical meaning of the word at a relatively recent date in a European language:

> 11 February 1831 at Sirhind
> The countryside is totally flat; there are plenty of jungles along the roadside, in a number of sandy terrains. They consist of wretched bushes of *Butea frondosa*.[3] The leaves, completely withered and desiccated, remain on the tree until the flowers appear in the spring. I know of no more ugly tree. Elsewhere, uncultivated areas show traces of earlier cultivation. All but the very richest of soils are exhausted after two harvests of wheat or wheat and chick peas, every year, with no fertiliser and virtually no ploughing. Eventually, these barely fertile lands become incapable of production. They are abandoned, are invaded by wild bushes and remain *jungles* for an indefinite period.
>
> A number of wells are to be found in the countryside, serving to irrigate the fields where the soil is most sandy.
>
> Babul[4] trees are common; they appear to be allowed to grow wherever they sprout spontaneously. Their very hard wood is the only type which the villagers can use for constructing their carts and ploughs. The horizon seems to end on every side in a forest of these trees. Their light foliage is of the brightest green. They become increasingly common the closer one approaches to Sirhind.[5]

A flat terrain, sandy soil, and acacias: that is the first definition, and a second is superimposed on it: abandoned land which has returned to a wild state. The first definition refers to the climate (aridity), the second to history (abandonment); but history and the climate are both part of the anthropocentric vision of the surrounding landscape—arid lands, hostile to man. In the treasuries of Sanskrit names, *jāṅgala* almost invariably appears accompanied by one of the following two glosses: *nirvārideśa*, a "land without water," and *nirjanasthāna*, an "uninhabited place," with no men, only animals, living there.[6] We can see in what sense, initially, *jāṅgala* both was and was not "the forest," both was and was not "the desert." Let us return to the etymology of those last two words: solitude, wild land, beyond the limits of the inhabited space, a place of exile, and renunciation of the world.

Only later were other images superimposed: the thickets, the tall grasses, the entanglement of lianas, the fevers, and the wild beasts. Such shifts in word meaning are further explained in the excellent rubric of the Oxford English Dictionary.

> The change in Anglo-Indian use may be compared to that in the historical meaning of the word *forest* in its passage from a waste or unenclosed tract to one covered with wild wood. In the transferred sense of *jungle* there is apparently a tendency to associate it with *tangle*.

The modern meaning of the phrase *tangled jungle* might thus appear to result from a simple alliteration or a metonymy within the language.

However, in the nineteenth century, another source of confusion, in the domain of geography, was added to all of this language play. Travelers amalgamated India with the equatorial landscapes of southeastern Asia to such a degree that in the Larousse dictionary, for example, the marshy jungles of Sumatra and Borneo became the model of the genre. Hence, the extravagant substitution of wet landscapes for dry ones: symbolically, the substitution of reeds for bamboos. The jungle "covered with reeds" mentioned by Emile Littré, Pierre Larousse, and the Dictionary of the Académie française (ed. 1879) is the marshy savanna to be found in a few extremely humid zones in the Indian subcontinent, for example, the Terry or Assam. The traditional polarity between *jāṅgala* meaning "dry lands" and *anūpa* meaning "marshy lands" is thus literally reversed: The Hindi name *tarā'ī* ("marshy lands")—the exact semantic equivalent of the Sanskrit *anūpa*—now becomes the aberrant synonym of jungle.[7] The Terry, a proper noun, denotes a discontinuous strip of land, fifteen to thirty kilometers wide. Running west to east parallel to the Ganges along the border of the plain, the Terry forms a natural frontier between Nepal and India. It is sadly notorious for its unhealthy character. This is an area of marshes where waters that had been located higher up and had infiltrated the pebbly beds of the Siwalik foothills now reemerge. In the past, wild buffalo and rhinoceros roamed through the reeds and tall grasses. In the flooded valleys, common reeds *(Phragmites karka)* mingle with plumed reeds *(Arundo donax)* and wild sugarcanes *(Saccharum spontaneum)*.[8] The single-horned rhinoceros is the animal typical of this habitat, although nowadays, threatened with extinction, it has vanished from the Terry and is to be found virtually nowhere other than among the tall grasses *(Imperata cylindrica)* and reeds of the national park of Kaziranga in Assam. The accepted meaning of the word *jungle* as coded in the principal French dictionaries of the second half of the nineteenth century is that of marshes where one catches fevers of a recurring type, and it also applies to a further extensive area: "in the Eastern Indies," which includes Malaysia.

The diversity of lexical forms in classical Hindi—the adjectives include *jaṅgal* (uncultivated), *jaṅglā* (wooded), *jaṅglī* (wild), *jāṅgalī* (picturesque)[9]—and the citations from texts in the Anglo-Indian glossary of Yule and Burnell *(Hobson-Jobson)* allow us to glimpse an evolution, each stage of which is natural and progressive but which finally yields a contradictory conclusion. Consider the evolution of the concept of *jungle*, with its series of characteristics. It may be summarized as follows:

Sanskrit
- dry land (this connotation has disappeared in Hindi)
- uninhabited, uncultivated land (this connotation has been retained in Hindi)

Classical Hindi
- wild land (→ noncivilized)
- forest
- tall grasses (→ weeds)
- picturesque landscape

English
- luxuriance
- insalubrious, malarial land (→ jungle fever, 1808)

As can be seen, there is a total contradiction between the first term and the last:

1. In ancient India: dry lands; healthy and fertile soil. Dominant geographical fact: *an expansion of agriculture in the irrigated plains*. Physiognomy of the *jāṅgala*: the steppe or savanna with thorny shrubs in the northwestern plains.

2. In the nineteenth century: marshy jungles; insalubrious, impenetrable lands. Dominant geographical fact: *endemic malaria*. Physiognomy of the *jāṅgala*: the northeastern flooded savannas.

But now consider the intermediary terms in this evolving series through which it is possible to detect in the collective Indian mentality a veritable mutation, beginning as early as the Middle Ages. This may explain the contradiction finally reached.

To the modern mentality, it seems quite natural that the idea of a "deserted, uninhabited, uncultivated land" should have led to the idea of wildness, noncivilization. Hence, the most common current acceptations of the term: the jungle seen as the territory of wild animals, particularly elephants, as referred to as early as the fourteenth and fifteenth centuries in texts cited by the *Hobson-Jobson*; or the jungle seen as a tribal zone—in particular, the Jungle-Mahals or the Jungle-Terry, the Anglo-Indian names for the region of the Santal (an aboriginal tribe), located on the frontier between Bihar and Bengal in the Rajmahal Hills. This acceptation can be associated with Kipling's "jungle," the land of the Gond tribes on the Seoni plateaus (Madhya Pradesh). Since the naturalists are also anxious to introduce nuances of meaning between the jungle and the forest, jungles have since been defined as forest margins or as secondary formations (such as bamboo brakes) which have invaded the primary forest where it has been destroyed by fire. Conceptual references, such as the idea of "wildness," are indissolubly intermingled with purely physiographic features, such as vegetation cover.

Of course, it is neither the sandy plains of the Punjab nor the marshlands of the Terry that correspond to this constellation of ideas: wildness, wild animals, tribes, forest margins, and bamboo brakes. What does correspond is another type of landscape to be found on the plateaus where monsoon forests predominate. Let us again cite Victor Jacquemont in a letter to his father, written on 24 December 1829, "from the camp at Huinguilisse, on the banks of the Sone" during his travels from Calcutta to Benares; what he is describing, in the main, are the Jungle-Mahals.[10] The word *jungle*, introduced into French by the translations published since 1796 in the *Bibliothèque britannique*, was quite a novelty:

> From Burdwan I marched for seven days north-eastward along the left bank of the Dammhoudoerr . . . , it was there that I came across the Jungles. I confess, I was much disappointed. I had pictured a thick, impenetrable forest presenting all the richness of the forms and colors of the vegetation of the tropics, bristling with thorny shrubs, festooned with creepers, with climbing plants reaching to the tops of even the tallest trees and trailing down gracefully in cascades of flowers: in Rio de Janeiro and San Domingo, I had seen a few isolated features of such a picture. But far from that being

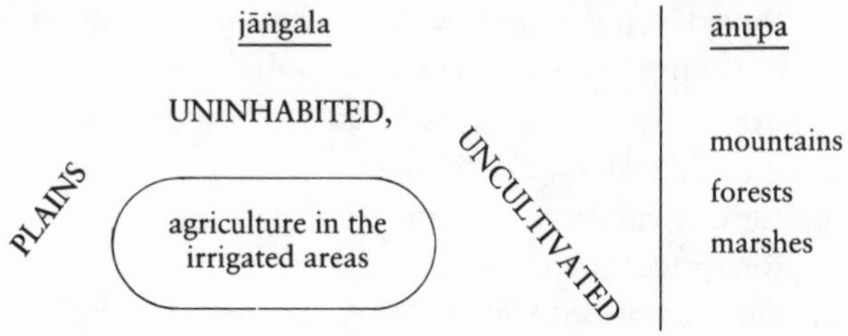

Figure 2. Agriculture encompassed by the jungle

> the case, I here found myself in woods even more monotonous than those of Europe, beneath a few weedy little trees; and instead of the roaring tigers in the distance, only the sound of the woodcutters' axes.
>
> Since then, I have encountered scenes closer to the ones that my imagination had painted for me. I traveled for a hundred leagues along a route traversed by not a single path, bordered, enclosed, walled in to both right and left by the forests and deserted heaths through which it had been cut. I penetrated deeper into these solitudes by walking up a number of dried-up river beds: they were always beautiful. As for tigers, they must be there . . .[11]

Here we find a number of typical features associated together: an uninhabited land ("I penetrated deeper into these solitudes"); a seasonal aridity ("the dried-up river beds"); the closed-in horizon; a combination of forests and heaths (grassy formations). "The forests and deserted heaths": The expression suggests that the jungle appears only on the margins of a great forest, taking over the terrain as soon as the forest opens up or thins out, usually as a result of forest fires. The forests recede, falling back to the water's edge, and meanwhile clearings of savanna develop; the vegetation then passes through every stage of degeneration, from thickets to formations similar to steppe land.

We may thus distinguish schematically between three kinds of landscape, all termed *jungle* at various points in history: [1] dry lands, [2] flooded savannas, and [3] forest margins, the grassy formations adjoining the forest (Jacquemont, Kipling).

The contradiction which is so evident between landscapes [1] and [2] is also present between [1] and [3]: it lies in the very concept of "wildness." In ancient India, *all the values of civilization lay on the side of the jungle*. The *jāṅgala* incorporated land that was cultivated, healthy, and open to Aryan colonization, while the barbarians were pushed back into the *anūpa*, the insalubrious, impenetrable lands (figure 2).

Now we can distinguish a) an opposition between wild land and cultivated land; the aridity of the dry lands is overcome, conquered, colonized by irrigation; b) a second opposition, between the plain and the mountains, the open space (steppes, savannas), and closed-in zones (dense forests, marshlands). At some point as yet impossible to date in the history of ideas, however, those two oppositions flattened out and merged into one: nature and culture, an opposition with which the modern mentality is very familiar. In the times when the *jāṅgala* (uninhabited and uncultivated) contained and included ruralized land, the space was represented as follows:

wild (cultivated)	||	barbarian

Wild space—uncultivated but available—surrounded cultivated land, pushing everything barbarian out toward the margins, but once the *jāṅgala* had become loaded with the values and promises of civilization, the jungle, its modern avatar, passed over to the side of barbarity and the situation was viewed quite differently, as follows:

civilized	||	wild (uncultivated)

Now the uncultivated, uninhabited space was simply one of a number of variants of nature in the wild state. The constellation of ideas traditionally subsumed under the concept of *jāṅgala*—namely, the plain, a dry but salubrious climate, fertile soil, and irrigation, all of which made colonization possible—the whole of this set of physiographic features, together constituting one single mental category, burst apart. Its place was meanwhile taken by a different constellation in which the ideas of luxuriance and violence predominated. The pages that follow will lose all meaning if we fail to recognize this fundamental shift in respect to the categories of collective thought. It is one of the shifts in concepts which have hollowed out a chasm of incomprehension between ancient India and ourselves.

AN ECOLOGICAL DOCTRINE

We have sketched in the setting. Amid the sands of the Delhi Doab, where he has been so good as to venture, the reader is now aware of the reversal of meaning affecting the word *jungle* and has traced its original value. Let us see then what the ancient texts—the medical treatises which first put us on the track of the ancient ecology—say on the subject.

We should at this point remember the context within which the doctor of antiquity practiced his art, in India as in Greece. Anatomy and physiology were quasi-inexistent, and the medical practitioner had no truly biological knowledge on which to base his actions. What pathology depended on, instead, was what the Hippocratics called *prognosis*, the science of the course taken by illnesses and of the signs that herald accidents, crises, and solutions. Without the benefit of a knowledge of anatomy and physiology, the doctor had no means of studying the affected parts of the body or the organic operation of the vital functions—in other words, he could make no local diagnosis of the disease. He was thus obliged to stake his reputation upon his prognostic skill. He was consequently less concerned to recognize the nature of a disease than to foresee its development, taking into consideration the most general conditions of life: climate, seasons, customs, postures. Ecology was an integral part of this practical context. His knowledge of the patient's environment, including the flora and fauna, enabled the doctor to anticipate the course of the disease and to take action on it.

The primary role of this ecological doctrine of the polarity between dry and marshy lands was thus utilitarian: it aided medical prognosis. But for the pundit, the traditional scholar, who was free from the constraints of medical practice and could devote himself to a study of the texts, this ecological doctrine also provided a framework within which to classify the flora and fauna. The series of the three soils (dry, middling, and marshy) thus governed the taxonomy of animals and medicinal plants and also the choice of a particular regimen, be it alimentary, gymnastic, or climatic. My own hypothesis is that one of those functions absorbed the other so that Ayurveda represents two sciences in one: a biogeography absorbed into a therapeutics. The texts invite a double reading, or, to put it another way, one text is enmeshed in the other: a discourse on the world (natural history) is contained within a discourse on man (medicine).

The starting point is a comparison between the animal's *nature* and its pharmaceutical *qualities*. The following discussion turns on a technical term: Sanskrit *cara*, for want of a better term, shall be translated as "environment." Caraka writes as follows: "The environment *(cara)* is a place such as a marshy land, the water, the air, a dry land, etc., in which food can be found. All the beings born in the water or in marshy lands, which live in these environments and whose nourishment is heavy, are themselves heavy. Those which are born in dry lands, which live in dry environments and whose nourishment is light, are themselves light." The quail and the partridge, animals of the dry lands par excellence, give meats light "by nature" *(svabhāvāt)*. The pig and the buffalo are just the opposite: they give meats heavy "by nature."[12] It is as if the animal had no nature other than its therapeutic virtues or defects, in short, its own particular way of being a type of food or remedy. The idea of food incorporates the idea of nature, and living beings are defined in terms of the way they, as individuals, ripen and cook, and the effects of their being cooked, digested, and assimilated.

Cara is a perfect example of a word with a double reference: to nature and to man. The objective or spatial reference—the environment—is incorporated within the subjective or practical reference—the environment regarded as a source of the means of subsistence. Cakrapāṇidatta explains that it is both the place (where one lives) and the food (on which one lives), the double object of a single vital activity. "*Cara*, the environment, is taken to denote both the place where one moves about and the food one consumes. . . . When Caraka mentions a place *as, for example, marshy land, water, ether, dry land, etc.*, it is *cara* by reference to the place where one moves about; when he mentions a place where *one has food at one's disposal*, it is *cara* by reference to food."[13] He is using a language procedure which consists in identifying two different objects by reducing them to one common characteristic: the place and the food are the double object of a single activity denoted by the verb CAR, "to move about" and "to use, to consume." The nature of mobile *(cārin)* living creatures is to eat other things, so the relationship between the animal and its life environment logically takes the form of what the animal eats, which impregnates its body with the qualities of the soil, as Ḍalhaṇa explains in a similar context: "The word *cara* is here taken to mean both food and habitat." This means that, depending upon the place where it lives, on dry or marshy land, in water or in the air, and also depending upon what it eats, whether it is too heavy or too light, cold or hot, unctuous or dry, the meat of a quadruped or a bird will possess such or such a quality, because its tissues will be impregnated with the qualities of such or such a type of food. Using the word in the sense of food, Suśruta refers, for example, to fish *which feed upon* young shoots and *śaivāla* [catalog, line 115]. Using it in the sense of habitat, he refers, for example, to animals *which live very close* to

TABLE 1

VARIOUS LAYERS OF ENVIRONMENT

determination of inhabited space by	man	therapeutics	the regimen, principally dietary, appropriate to such or such a patient in a given environment
		human geography	the customs of different peoples
	the flora and fauna		ecology

villages [catalog, line 92].[14] In zoology, the word means the *territory*, a hunting ground or a place of pasturage, a particular zone that the animal depends on for obtainment of resources.

This concept of the soil or environment, the content of which derives from the polarity between the dry and the marshy, is important whenever a question of taxonomy or regimen arises. Let us leave the flora and fauna aside for the moment. The layering of the various points of view is expressed schematically in table 1.

Human geography is explicitly distinct from therapeutics and is sketched out only in the broadest of terms. Perhaps I may be allowed to provide a brief comparison with Greek medicine at this point. Anthropogeography is extremely rudimentary in India and does not really compare with the famous treatise, *On airs, waters, places*, from the Hippocratic corpus; nevertheless, there is an understanding of its principle, aimed at showing how the physical constitution and mores of the inhabitants are modeled on the nature of the soil and are affected by its climate. On another level, though, we do have the equivalent—this time a very rich one—of another work from the Hippocratic corpus, the treatise *On regimen for health*. This prescription of an appropriate dietary regimen and appropriate physical exercises makes it possible to acclimatize the patient to the ecological conditions or, conversely, to adapt the ecological conditions to the clinical case in question.

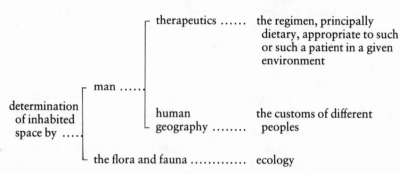

The object of therapeutic intervention is to create a doubly appropriate relationship: to render the environment appropriate to the needs of the patient and, conversely, to render the regimen of the patient appropriate to the ecological conditions. The expressions used to convey this in the Ayurvedic texts are curiously elliptical: "The masters in this science say that the place is of two kinds: the land and the body."[15] Or, similarly: "The place is both the land and the patient."[16] On the one hand, we have the land, the soils: the jungle, and so on; on the other hand, the patient's body, defined as the "receptacle" or the "point of application" of the therapeutic action.[17] This expression is open to misunderstanding; we tend to give it a biological meaning, we take it to be a kind of definition of the couple formed by the organism together with its environment whereas, from the Indian point of view, it refers not to biology but to the philosophy of action. Here again a comparison with ancient Greece is illuminating. Consider Stoicism, with its famous distinction between antecedent causes and immanent causes; of all the things in the world, some depend on us, others do not. What does depend on us? The patient, for example, in all his individuality, in the particular place where his body or part of his body is situated, for here the medical practitioner may intervene by prescribing a particular regimen or medicament for the case in point. What does not depend on us? A landscape determined by the laws of physical geography. A place is of two kinds: it is a subjective localization and also an objective spatial framework.

This dualism, which may be formulated in Stoic terms—man and the world, will and destiny—affects the operation of therapeutic action based on prognosis, the science of the course of diseases. The doctor predicts the next stage and takes the steps necessary to counter or control the foreseen developments. What depends on him is the situation of the patient. What does not depend on him is the objective framework of space and time. This distinction plays an integral part in the very analysis of what is "appropriate" *(sātmya)* or "suits" *(upaśete)* the patient. Notions of suitability, conformity, congruence, opportuneness govern the interventions of the doctor. So we can understand why it is in a chapter on therapeutics that Suśruta introduces his typology of the three soils. He wishes to illustrate a principle of action of general application, the principle of *deśasātmya*, "appropriateness to the place." "What the author calls *sātmya* is what is suitable, what produces well-being. . . . This well-being, which constitutes health, can be obtained in a person who is well by preventing disorders which have not yet occurred, and in a person who is ill by the *sātmya* which cures the illness. And when one defines *sātmya* as *that which is homologous with the nature of the ātman*, that is the strict truth since, if there is conformity with the *ātman*, there is, on that very account, an absence of disorder."[18] One is tempted to use the word *ataraxia*. The *ātman* is the eternal principle which animates the empirical individual in all his successive reincarnations. The dietary regimen and bodily techniques strengthen humors which are too weak, calm those which are overexcited, and preserve those which are even and regular and thus reestablish the harmony between the *ātman*, space and time destroyed by the disease.

This principle of appropriateness carries two different definitions, depending on whether one considers the short-term action or the long-term influence of the climate. In the short term the practitioner intervenes to correct harmful excitation; in emergencies he tries to reverse the situation. "Experts in appropriateness try to oppose a regimen of diet and exercise (literally a *sātmya*) with contrary qualities to those of the places and diseases in question." The qualities peculiar to each place, which are harmful to the patient, must be tempered by compensation through their contraries. In a marshy region, where the excess of unctuosity and heaviness produces disorders of phlegm, the diet indicated is one "with a basis of *jāṅgala* meats and honey, which has both dryness and lightness, qualities which are the opposite of unctuosity and heaviness."[19] In the long term, however, the practitioner seeks to obtain an immunity through habituation: "What is called *sātmya* is what has become beneficial to a person through constant use."[20] Habit produces "habituation" *(aucitya)* or what is also called an "acquired appropriateness" *(okaḥsātmya)*. A clear distinction is drawn between these two kinds of *deśasātmya*, or appropriateness to places.

> There are two kinds of place: the land and the body of the patient. There are two kinds of appropriateness to the patient's body, the one general, the other particular. General: like the sweet *rasa* which fortifies all the elements. Particular: like a local remedy for the eyes, the hair, the throat, etc. There are also two kinds of appropriateness to the land, if one makes a distinction between the land in general and one particular place. General: like those types of foods and customs peculiar to dry lands which are opposites in marshy lands. To particular countries too: as among the Bāhlīka there is appropriateness through the black bean, among the Pallava through wheat, among the Cīna through *mādhvīka* alcohol, etc.[21]

Exotic, from an Indian point of view, are the environments of the Bāhlīka (Bactrians) in northern Afghanistan, the Pallava in Persia, and the Cīna in Tibet, to which particular dietary habits acclimatize these people. In this case the word *sātmya* has a biogeographical sense, meaning the "habituation" that results from a prolonged stay and traditional dietary practices. But the word *sātmya* denotes an intervention made on

TABLE 2

MEANINGS OF DEŚASĀTMYA

	Particular localization	A general principle
Deśasātmya in the therapeutic sense	a local remedy: an eyewash, a lotion, a cataplasm	COMPENSATION using contraries
Deśasātmya in the biogeographical sense	the dietary practices of different peoples	HABITUATION to external conditions

the patient's body; it has the different meaning of a regimen or remedy which "compensates" for some excess or lack: a person wasting away is fed on sweet foods, for example. The information thus provided is summarized in table 2.

Let us now turn to the text in which Suśruta defines the three soils. Here, this distinction between biogeography and therapeutics must be given its full weight. On the one hand, there is the polarity between dry and marshy lands; on the other hand, the series of the three humors: *vāta, pitta, kapha* (wind, bile, phlegm). The therapeutic ideal is a balance between the humors and the *rasa* (the savors of the soil), which may be achieved in two ways. The balance may be simply the product of an "equality" *(samatā)*, the model for which is provided by the temperate countries where the cold and the rain compensate for the heat and the wind, thereby enabling the inhabitants to enjoy an "equality of humors" *(doṣānāṃ samatā)*. The regimen that suits them is thus one which maintains an equality between all the *rasa*. Alternatively, there may be an inequality, an excess on one side or the other, for which the doctor must compensate by means of its opposite. The temperate land is the place of what is "equal" *(sama)*; dry and marshy lands are the places of what is "opposite" *(viparīta)*. But note that although they are set in opposition here, neither one has a lower value set on it than the other.

The place is *ānūpa*, *jāṅgala*, or *sādhāraṇa*:

—*ānūpa*, the place characterized by an abundance of waters, the uneven terrain, rivers, rains and forests, the softness and freshness of the winds, the

> abundance and height of the mountains and trees; the bodies of its men are soft, delicate and fat, disorders of phlegm and wind predominate.
>
> —*jāṅgala*, the free, flat place characterized by sparsely scattered or rare thorny shrubs, a scarcity of water, rains, running water and wells, the heat and harshness of the winds, the sparsely scattered or rare rocks; the bodies of its men are tough and dry, disorders of wind and bile predominate.
>
> —*sādhārana*, the place which presents characteristics of both the others at once.
>
> Because, in a *sādhāraṇa* place, the cold, the rain, the heat and the wind are equal and the people enjoy an equality of humors, for that reason it is conceived as *sādhāraṇa*. The humors are no longer so strong, originating in the water and transplanted into a dry terrain, or else the converse, for they accumulate in their own place but fail to gain in intensity in another. Whoever behaves in a suitable fashion has nothing to fear from the place, his ways of feeding, sleeping and moving his body, etc., have all the qualities of that place.[22]

Marshy land is marked by disorders of phlegm and wind; men from dry lands suffer from disorder of wind and bile. *Sādhāraṇa* denotes a "middle" position: neither too cold nor too hot, neither too wet nor too dry.

The last sentence in Suśruta's text may be understood in two different ways, depending on which of the two Sanskrit commentaries one follows:

1. According to Cakrapāṇidatta, the patient who fears falling victim to an illness peculiar to the region where he lives runs no danger so long as his eating and behavior are *appropriate*—that is, *contrary* to the qualities of the region. His manners, says Suśruta's text, "have the qualities of that place" *(taddeśasya guṇe sati)*; and Cakrapāṇidatta adds a word he takes to be implied: "have the qualities *contrary* to that place" *(taddeśasya viparītaguṇe sati)*. The gloss somewhat distorts the text in order to make it say something which is correct in itself (appropriateness is compensation through opposites) but which the text does not actually say.

2. According to Ḍalhaṇa, in the case of a disease with a known cause, a stay in a place discouraging to the development of that cause, a change of climate, constitutes an excellent therapy. For example, an accumulation of phlegm in an *ānūpa* region is liable to provoke elephantiasis and must be suppressed by dry, hot qualities. The patient thus benefits from a stay in a *jāṅgala* region, but only provided he follows a suitable regimen of eating and exercise, dry and hot being its key qualities. The patient should not, for example, practice the siesta, which

is certainly appropriate to the *jāṅgala* climate but is altogether contraindicated for phlegm disorders. To put it another way: taking A as a marshy climate and B as a dry climate; *a* are manners appropriate to B and *b* are manners appropriate to A. Regimen *a* is homogeneous (similar) to climate A and appropriate (contrary) to B; regimen *b* is homogeneous (similar) to B and appropriate (contrary) to A. The treatment for elephantiasis contracted in A is to go to B and practice *b*.

In other words, Cakrapāṇidatta considers the passage to pronounce a rule useful to the art of medical prognosis on the gravity of an illness: "*Originating in the water*: originating in *ānūpa* country characterized by water. *Transplanted to a dry terrain*: occurring in *jāṅgala* country characterized by a dry terrain. The words or *else* imply the reciprocal *or else originating in dry terrain and transplanted into the water*. For example, elephantiasis usually occurs in *ānūpa* country; if it occurs in *jāṅgala* country it will not be a serious case of elephantiasis because it is repressed by the qualities of *jāṅgala* country, which are contrary to the qualities of *ānūpa*, and by the food and mode of life peculiar to this place, which are the contrary of the *ānūpa*. Not only are diseases benign when they occur in a place which is contrary to them, but disordering of the humors themselves also remains slight when it occurs in a contrary place."[23] Ḍalhaṇa regards the text as setting out a therapeutic method: "He shows that the chances of curing an illness are good when, having been contracted in a place of similar qualities, it is treated in a place of contrary qualities."[24] But in prognosis and therapy alike, the context of the ecological doctrine of the three soils is always that of a projected medical intervention. The practitioner exploits the symmetry of opposites: they balance one another and compensate for one another. The fact that at a deeper level of analysis a higher value is set on one of the poles (the excellence of the dry lands, the insalubrity of the marshes) is not apparent at this point.

Now let us consider the beginning of Suśruta's text. The series of the three definitions is once again to be found, more or less faithfully paraphrased, in all the Ayurvedic treatises and lexicons. Attempting to restore the doctrine to its full coherence, one immediately encounters a difficulty. Wind and bile predominate in the jungle; wind and phlegm in marshy lands: *wind-and-bile* are opposed to *wind-and-phlegm*. On this point Caraka is in complete agreement with Suśruta, as we shall see. But Vāgbhaṭa, whose intention is traditionally held to have been to summarize Ayurveda in a shorter work, for pedagogic purposes, simplifies our definitions. The dry lands and the marshy ones are no longer respectively characterized by an association of two humors, but by one humor alone: "*Jāṅgala* is the region where wind predominates, *ānūpa* where there is a superabundance of phlegm, and the middle region *(sādhāraṇa)* is where the humors are equal." The symmetry is destroyed since bile is no longer mentioned and wind is no longer a common factor in between bile (aridity, dryness) and phlegm (a superabundance of liquids). The difficulty is a typical one. According to the cited texts, an on-the-whole homogeneous tradition (or what, as a working hypothesis, I take to be such) presents a number of variants, some of them complete, others partial or vulgarized. A few of the more perspicacious of Vāgbhaṭa's commentators have drawn attention to this unjustifiable simplification and have restored the definition in its complete form. Parameśvara, one such commentator from Kerala, explains: "*Where wind predominates:* this indicates a predominance of wind over bile; *jāṅgala* is therefore the region where wind and bile predominate. Through the word *tu*, the text indicates that wind also predominates in *ānūpa*, which is therefore the region where phlegm and wind predominate."[25] This is an important commentary, for it introduces a fact that can only be confirmed at a later stage, in chapter 5—namely, that in the wind-and-bile couple, wind predominates over bile.

Caraka enumerates a number of plants and birds, one group characteristic of *jāṅgala*, the other of *ānūpa*; we shall be studying them later on. His description of these two soils is given below; in the margin are indicated the physiognomic features already present in Suśruta, but here the context is different, for it is a matter of determining which regions are propitious for the cultivation and gathering of medicinal plants.

Jāṅgala, free space is abundant, the region is covered in acacia forests . . . many prosopis . . . [list of trees], the young branches dance, swayed by the force of concentrated and drying winds; sand is abundant as are small, sharp, hard pebbles hidden by the mist of the mirages; this is the land inhabited by the quail, the partridge and the cakor; here wind and bile predominate and men are tough and hard;	SUŚRUTA free, flat space hot, harsh winds sparsely scattered rocks wind and bile tough, dry bodies
Ānūpa, the land is covered by forests of marshland date palms . . . [list of palms], usually along the river banks or the seashore where cold winds predominate, alongside rivers whose banks display rushes, and water-willows, adorned by the greenery of the mountains, covered by trees caressed by soft winds, the land	seashore: this feature is absent in Suśruta. cold wind high mountains gentle (soft) winds

is covered by flowering forests and numerous glades. It is hidden by the density of spreading trees, the branches resound to the cry of the wild goose . . . [list of birds]; here men are delicate, wind and phlegm predominate.[26]	soft (gentle), delicate, fat bodies phlegm and wind

Let us attempt a brief comparison. Suśruta emphasizes the contrast between the aridity of the jungle and the humidity of the mountains: thus, the wooded foothills (sal forests in northeastern India) are opposed to the vast flat plains (dry, thorny formations in the northwest). Caraka adds a new connotation to the term *ānūpa* by associating the marshy landscape with, not the mountains, but the sea. The reference to the mountains for example, might be to the Nepalese Terry, while the reference to the sea might be to the delta plain covered with palm trees. Two different landscapes are thus merged in the ideal view that Caraka proposes. Furthermore, he accentuates the luxuriance of the forests, in the interests of symmetry: on one side, dense vegetation, on the other, a denuded terrain.

Concrete examples—places selected from the geographical map of India which might correspond to these definitions—are never named. Thus, if we venture to assign to the category of "marshy lands" on the one hand a delta plain (to wit, the marshy delta of the Ganges or the Mahanadi) and, on the other hand, a humid mountainous region (such as the zones which include outcrops of the Nepalese Terry), that designation is only on the basis of our own working hypotheses and on the strength of all geographical information available to an Indianist of the twentieth century. What we are attempting is to burst through the idealistic traditional view in order to glimpse the empirical sources that lie behind it. To this end, I propose in the following chapters to call in turn on physical geography, botany, and zoology, using them as a series of levers, or filters. But it is important from the outset to recognize the to some extent *literary* nature of the ancient scientific texts. Taken literally, Suśruta and Caraka propose no more than purely conventional definitions where, even in the prose passages, what predominates is a kind of poetic interplay based on parallel formulas: bareness/luxuriance, hot-and-dry/soft-and-fresh, sandy-and-pebbly/flowers-and-glades, and so on. The polarity between dry lands and marshy lands is not descriptive but prescriptive. It is a matter not of physical facts but of brahminic norms.

As is well known, any symmetry offering a pretext for social distinctions is a false symmetry. The most common (Right and Left, West and

East, to mention only a few) are used as a means of passing value judgments. One of the poles (whatever it may be) is given higher value and its opposite is downgraded. Since the jungle and the marshes are, in point of fact, categories of collective thought, not simply geographical facts, they do not escape this false symmetry. *Jāṅgala* and *ānūpa* are the subject of two kinds of discourse: one kind—the texts cited above—opposes them in a symmetrical fashion; the other kind proclaims the primacy of the dry lands. Up to this point, the opposed regions have appeared to be mutually compensatory through both their qualities and their hazards, their harmful excesses being tempered in the middle region. The correct mean is given the highest value and extremes are rejected. The normative character of this ecology is so strong that Cakrapāṇidatta, commenting on the previously translated texts, interprets them as explicitly affirming "the pre-eminence of the *sādhāraṇa* regions."[27] In short, he sees a doctrine of the correct mean. But in reality the "middle regions" are no more than a third term introduced artificially the better to support the symmetry of the first two terms, and they disappear as soon as the preeminence of the *jāṅgala* is affirmed. For example, when Caraka draws up a list of the foodstuffs, remedies, environments, and manners that are most important in their respective categories—the best and the worst, the most beneficial and the most harmful—these are par excellence: "the dry lands among the salubrious places, the marshy lands among the insalubrious."[28] Cakrapāṇidatta, this time quite justifiably, goes on to illustrate the table of categories borrowed by Ayurveda from the *Vaiśeṣika* system of logic: "*Paratva* is superiority, *aparatva* inferiority. With regard to the place, the dry lands are *para* (superior), the marshy lands *apara* (inferior); with regard to time, the period of emission (of vital and nutritive juices) is *para*, the period of [their] capture is *apara*."[29] There could be no clearer indication of the role and logical value of polarities or binary categories, such as the dry and the marshy lands, and the periods of emission (rains, autumn, winter) and of the capture of the nourishing *rasa* (frosts, spring, summer), to which we shall be returning later. These definitions, this division of space and time, these *forms* of Hindu sensibility—in themselves concrete, autochthonous and anchored in the Indian land with all its landscapes and seasons—are broken down into abstract qualities (hot and cold, dry and wet, light and heavy, and so on) and are the basis for countless oppositions, divisions, inversions, displacements, symmetries, homologies, incorporations, decentrations, and other logical configurations, all of which serve as ways to indicate a choice or value judgment. The geopolitical value of *jāṅgala* provides an example, the salubrity and fecundity of the dry lands where, as we shall see in chapter 2, the Hindu king preferred to set up his kingdom.

A few more words are needed to conclude the discussion of this ecological doctrine in which ideas of adaptation, compensation, and equality between contraries play a central role. A brief comparison with Greek thought has suggested how closely medicine is tied to the theory of action. Let us venture a little farther. In India as in Greece, as early as the pre-Socratic period, ideas about justice and political harmony were associated with the idea of health. Health meant equality between the humors. The Greek doctor Alcmæon of Croton was already assimilating the human organism to a State in which *isonomia*, an equality between the forces involved, was the definition of health. And what better way to illuminate the Sanskrit term *samatā* (the "equality" between the humors in the above-mentioned passage) than by a comparison with the Hippocratic treatise *On airs, waters, places* (XII), which conceives of temperate lands in practically identical terms: neither too cold nor too hot, neither too wet nor too dry, where equality predominates in everything *(isomoiria)*.[30] How familiar we, the inheritors of the Greek notion of the correct mean, *isonomia* and compensation for contraries, ought to find these mysterious humors of Hindu medicine: wind, bile, and phlegm! They are fluids circulating underground, in the water, in the air, in our bodies, everywhere all around us and within us, but they are also forces, powers which foment disorders, pathogenic principles between which the doctor must establish justice. Medicine is a form of politics.

Perhaps the reader can by now glimpse the intended manner of progression in this book. Starting from concrete realities, geography, the flora and fauna, we shall be launching ourselves into the scholasticism, classifications, and doctrines for which they provided the material. Having taken the jungle as a starting point, we are here involved in analyzing modes of reasoning and schemas of thought. Soon we shall be returning to geography and the natural sciences rooted on firmer ground, but first we must complete this short account of traditional ecology with a few remarks about the cycle of the seasons.

A DIALECTIC OF SPACE AND TIME

The humors pass through two very distinct phases as they evolve. The first phase is "accumulation" *(sañcaya)*; this process, which is not in itself pathological, results from the climate and the circulation of the nutritive juices throughout the universe. In the second phase, an excess disrupts the "equality" of the humors: this is the "excitation" or "disordering" *(prakopa)*. There are two aspects to this phase: one is a conflict between contrary humors which must be restored to equality (compensation of contraries); the other, an exacerbation of one or two of the humors—or even of all three—which must be tempered (moderation of extremes). The accumulation (phase 1) and the disordering (phase 2) take place at different periods in the year, through the spontaneous evolution of the humors. The seasonal cycle thus provides a conceptual framework within which the etiology of diseases can be explained.

The seasonal cycle, like the typology of soils, may be considered within the framework of a Stoic philosophy and as part of a dialectic between action and destiny. From one point of view, the doctor practices his art, which dominates and corrects the disturbances of pathogenic humors, but from another point of view, the seasons succeed one another inexorably and the medical practitioner can do nothing to make water appear in the bottom of the dried-up watercourses. To prescribe the regimen suitable for the present season means submitting to the inexorable law of time and exercising patience. As evidenced in the Ayurvedic doctrine, a place is of two kinds: the land and the patient, the objective spatial framework and the subjective localization. In the same way, time too is double: "The time is either time as a perpetual flow, or else time as phase; time as a phase relates to an illness, time as a perpetual flow relates to seasonal appropriateness."[31] And further on: "Time means the year, and the phases of an illness."[32] Thus, the spatial and temporal circumstances in which a doctor is led to intervene can always be seen from two points of view. On the one hand, there is time as lived by the patient (the phases of his illness) and the localization of the disorders (the particular parts of his body affected); on the other hand, the seasons and the soils.

At this point another comparison demonstrates the importance of the principle of *sātmya*, the "appropriateness" (of space and time). Let us once again take a look at Greek medicine. "For doctors," Galen says, "there are two different times: the times of diseases and those of remedies . . . the times of diseases means the movements of the causes . . . : beginning, increase, climax, decline. . . . The times of the means of treatment are the opportune times to use them; the opportune times are those when there is a need to employ the means of treatment and when there is nothing preventing it."[33] On the one hand, different phases exist in the evolution of the humors; on the other hand, time serves as the objective framework for our actions, offering us opportunities to be seized, opportune moments that we must know how to use. Galen explained this (Stoic?) distinction in the course of a polemic with the Methodists, a medical sect which flourished among Greek doctors during the Roman Empire. The Methodists held that every disease is either a constriction, a relaxation, or a combination of the two and that the suitable treatment indicated for constriction is relaxation, and vice-versa. "According to them," Galen comments, "neither the part affected nor the cause of the illness nor the age of the patient nor the season nor the country nor any consideration of the forces at work or of the nature or constitution of the patient can be of any use in indicating the correct treatment. They also reject any consideration of the seasons, countries and customs, claiming that all they need do is derive an indication of the suitable treatment from the disorders themselves."[34] The Methodists in effect denied the distinction drawn by Galen between the subjective and the objective, between the two kinds of place and time. They rejected everything associated with the ideas of opportuneness and appropriateness. They also rejected the idea of maintaining or restoring health by remedies appropriate to the particular circumstances. It is, in contrast, these very ideas that predominate in Hindu medicine.

Space and time, soils and seasons form two similar domains in which the principle of appropriateness is applied. Just as it was possible by changing the place to adapt it to the case needing treatment, similarly the medical practitioner took contrary action, if necessary, by creating an artificial environment around the patient.[35] A few observations on the seasonal cycle will clarify an obscure point in the typology of soils.

The year is divided into two series of three seasons: rains-autumn-winter and frosts-spring-summer. The first of these half-year periods is defined by the movement of the sun toward the south. The winds are not too harsh; the moon, whose power is unobstructed, makes all beings grow, watering them with its cold rays and impregnating them with the unctuosity of the *rasa*. This period of "emission" is completed at the winter solstice, which is the moment of man's greatest strength. The sun's movement toward the north defines the second half of the year. The harshness of the heat and the winds destroys all the unctuosity of the world; the sun captures the *rasa*, or juices. This period of "capturing" ends at the summer solstice, which marks the extreme point in the seasonal weakening of men. One of the six *rasa* predominates over each of the seasons, and each *rasa* provokes the accumulation

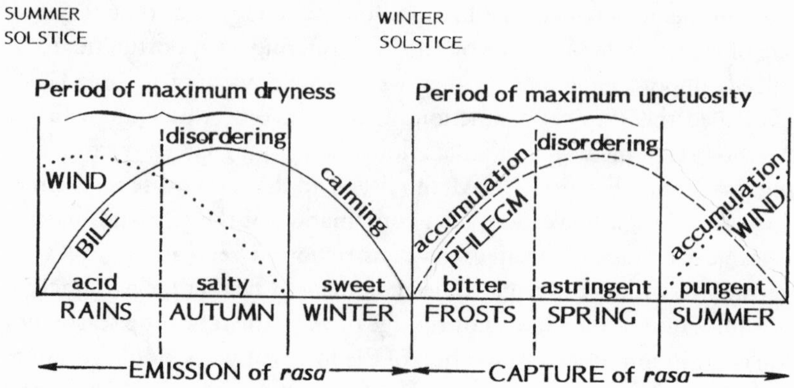

Figure 3. Humors and seasons

and the disordering of one of the three humors, in the order indicated in figure 3. The figure illustrates Vāgbhaṭa's concise formula: "Accumulation, disordering and calming take up three seasons, for wind those which begin with the summer, for bile those which begin with the rains, for phlegm those which begin with the frosts."[36] In this arrangement of the cycle, the most classical one, the alternation between accumulation and disordering, is irregular: winter and frosts play two roles, while the season of rains is overdetermined, being a period of both accumulation for bile and also disordering for wind. Thus it comes as no surprise to find a variant in which the seasonal alternation of the humors is regular: wind (summer-early rains-rains), bile (rains-autumn-winter), phlegm (winter-spring-summer). However, a study of that variant would not be relevant here.[37] It is the first version that is of primary interest, because its lack of symmetry affords it the remarkable property of combining a dyad and a triad. On the one hand, three seasons with clearly distinguished characteristics are noted: heat, rains, and cold, which provoke the accumulation of the three humors, wind, bile, and phlegm. On the other hand, a climatic polarity exists: between the period when "unctuosity" *(sneha)* is at its height and phlegm predominates and the period when, in contrast, "dryness" *(raukṣya)* and disorders of bile predominate.

Note that there is a time lapse between a cause and its effects: the sweet encourages an accumulation of phlegm, the astringent increases wind; and the pungent promotes bile. Unctuosity follows on from the emission of the *rasa*, dryness from their capture: consequences do not follow immediately but rather sometime later, after a whole season.

Hence the gap and the apparent contradiction: emission takes place in a period of dryness, capturing in a period of unctuosity. To account for this apparent contradiction, notions of a "subsidiary force" *(anu-bala)* or "accessory factor" *(anu-bandha)* are introduced; and later we shall encounter other examples of technical terms prefixed by *anu* ("post"- or "para"-), the role of which is to indicate—*in the background* of the given system of relationships—further, additional circumstances and complications. In the present case, phlegm, present in the background, aggravates the disorders of bile in autumn; bile and wind, present in the background, aggravate disorders of phlegm in the spring. Thus autumn and spring are also overdetermined seasons: in the foreground occur disorders of bile (born from the *acidity* of plants and waters in the season of rains, which the sun aggravates in autumn) and disorders of phlegm (born from *sweet* waters and plants, fermented in the spring); in the background are the aggravating factors: phlegm in the autumn (because this is a period of *emission*), bile and wind in the spring (a period of *capturing*).[38]

Now let us return to the three soils. This interplay of combinations around the seasonal cycle make it possible to understand, by analogy, why disorders of phlegm *and wind* are associated in marshy lands dominated by "the unctuous, unctuosity" *(snigdha, sneha)*, while disorders of wind and bile are characteristic of the dry lands dominated by "the dry, dryness" *(rūkṣa,raukṣya)*. It is first and foremost a matter of combining the dyad (dry-marshy) with the triad (wind-bile-phlegm), in texts the speculative and scholastic nature of which is undeniable. The dryness of bile, the unctuosity of phlegm—while wind, the first of the three humors, becomes a common factor: it predominates by reason of its essential astringency in the dry lands but also remains present in the background in the marshy lands where, as we shall see, astringency has a role to play as a "subsidiary *rasa*" *(anu-rasa)*.

The humors and savors are used as tools for an ideal division of the vegetation cover and of the calendar, in accordance with a whole variety of weather conditions ranging from sun to rain. A choice is made between the various seasons and soils, a choice affecting agriculture as well as medicine. For those who know how to decode them, the topography and the calendar indicate which places and moments are propitious and which are harmful, and the means for that decoding is the Ayurvedic theory of the *rasa* emitted during the rains and then captured by the sun.

In this chapter, I have set out the ecological doctrine in its didactic form: three soils, six seasons and their relationships to the three humors, the six savors. Returning now to geography, let us study that doctrine from the point of view of its classificatory function by conducting an inventory of the plains and rivers of northern India, and of the plants and animals which inhabit the *jāṅgala*. The flora and fauna will be distributed in space, and in the process many other things will also come to be mapped.

The jungle is an ecological type: 500 mm of rain per year, a gramineous carpet of vegetation, acacias, and antelopes. More important, within the framework of an anthropocentric division of space, the separation between *jāṅgala* and *ānūpa* serves as a dividing line between health and disease, agriculture and wildness, the Aryan and the Barbarian; it introduces human struggles onto the map, where they dramatize the relief contours, the rainfall divisions, the different types of vegetation, and the distribution of animals, setting a value on them, forming a theory about them.

Let us consider the simple fact that the dividing line, the separation, the dialectic between the jungle and the marshy lands can be noted down on a map of India: this is in India an immense fact of normative ecology. Now, we can look at the map both ways, and see: either an axis with two contrary poles, the west and the east, the polarity of the Indus and the Ganges (chapter 3); or else, a central zone with its periphery. In chapter 2, we shall consider the vast central plain and its margins. Flanked at its two extremities, in the northeast and the southwest, by typically *ānūpa* zones (mountains, dense humid forests, marshes, Bengal, Assam, and Kerala), the India of plains and plateaus with its dry climate stretches from Punjab to Tamilnad: this is *jāṅgala* India, par excellence the territory of *Antilope cervicapra*, the animal species which is unique in that it is coextensive with and exclusive to the *jāṅgala*.

II: Populating the Plains

> And they take refuge in fortified towns, in dry lands, where there is perennial water *(saṃśrayanti ca durgāṇi dhanvānaṃ śāsvatodakam).*
>
> *Vāyu Purāṇa*, VIII, 94

The forest is a deserted place. "*Vānaprastha*: that is to say inhabiting the deserts," wrote Abbé Dubois at the end of the eighteenth century.[1] There are two kinds of men who retire into solitude or, metaphorically speaking, "into the forest": the hermit and the renouncer. The "hermit" *(vānaprastha)* is the father of a family who, "having seen the birth of his son's son," decides to retire into the "forest" *(vana)*, either accompanied by his wife or not but taking the sacrificial fires with him to his hermitage. The "renouncer" *(sannyāsin)* is the wandering ascetic without fire, house, or companion, who begs for his food. The "hermit" and the "renouncer" represent the third and the fourth stages of the ideal life of a brahmin. For both, the forest is the antithesis of the village: a space uninhabited except possibly by wild animals, demons, and barbarians.

As a fine study by Charles Malamoud suggests, in brahminic thought, the forest is an image of emptiness. "When the Renouncer has decided to abandon the village, the world of relationships between men, the world of action, the world of sacrifice, which is consequently a part of *saṃsāra* (the transitory life), he sets off for the forest, stripping himself of all that he possesses, in particular his sacrificial fires: he does so not solely to find solitude but also because the forest, a vast rent in the village fabric, is the image of the void which is the Absolute to which he aspires."[2] Beyond the limits of the world which is, sociologically speaking, full (the built-up area of the village and cultivated land), the forest is an empty space. It is not seen primarily from the point of view of its dense vegetation; rather, it represents life outside-the-world. On this purely normative level, nothing as yet is said of the climate, the character of the waters, the flora or the fauna; the landscape remains to be discovered. That is why the distinction between the village and the forest, the meaning of which is essentially socioreligious, needs to be complemented by another term: the *jāṅgala*. We must restore to the forest its ecological content, its density of vegetation. The *jāṅgala* includes the village world and at the same time constitutes at its margins what Malamoud has called a "rent": an empty space, a wasteland, a gap in the network of human habitation. At the same time, however, the *jāṅgala* introduces openings in the dense, humid forest, clearings which open up the way for human penetration.

The evidence that has been passed down of those distant times when the plains of northern India were colonized is almost exclusively literary, and the texts offer an idealized, nonhistorical image of the period: myths and ritual (the Vedic texts), epic, utopias, legal codes, scientific treatises—but never a truly historical account. We shall try to get around that obstacle in the following pages by dint of constant cross-references between the teaching of the texts and the data provided by archaeology and biogeography. Archaeology provides no direct information on mental representations and social reality, but it does confirm the place of central importance held by the Delhi Doab and gives some indication of the progression of land clearance eastward during the Iron Age. Whenever the texts overlap in a particular domain and geography provides some concrete illustration, it is nevertheless possible to reconstitute a whole vision of the world in question. Starting with the brahminic theme of *dharma* in times of distress, let us first consider a problem constantly present in traditional societies—namely, collective distress in the form of famine and epidemics. This theme, as well as subsequent ones to be considered—the village, the antelope—provide clear evidence of a deep convergence between *Āyurveda* (traditional medicine) and *Dharmaśāstra* (legal codes) and also between *Āyurveda* and *Arthaśāstra* (the science of royal government), which prescribes rules for the defense of the territory and conquest, for the administration of the rural area, hunting, and the forests.

IN TIMES OF DISTRESS

Epidemics constitute the example par excellence of a problem that affects three overlapping areas: medicine, politics (the arrangements made for the people's health), and religion (since an epidemic was traditionally regarded as a penalty for some fault, a consequence of the *adharma*, or failure to respect the norms). The last verse in Caraka's chapter on epidemics shall serve as a starting point:

> Trees and waters are scarce, it is swept by winds, heat abounds: that defines the *jāṅgala*, and diseases there are very few. Trees and waters abound, it is sheltered from winds, heat is hard to find: that is the *ānūpa*, and it is full of troubles. Equal: that is *sādhāraṇa*.[3]

Here, the contrast drawn is not between two different humors—bile in the desert, phlegm in the marshes—but between a scarcity and an abundance of all the humors. The word for "humors" and "troubles" is the same *(doṣa)*; to say that troubles result from a disordering of the humors or from a superabundance of them comes to the same thing. In the dry lands, the sun and winds are harsh; it is a world of scarcity and sobriety; men have dry physiques and no fat: it is here that health can be maintained. In the marshy lands, with their unctuosity and softness, plethora and heavy bodies, disease proliferates.

This last verse in the chapter on epidemics, considered by modern scholars to be an interpolation in the *Carakasaṃhitā*, belongs to what is known as the literature of *nīti*. The theme of *nīti*—the "behavior" to employ in order to attain a determined material "goal" *(artha)*, of a political, economic, or domestic order, for example—gathered around it a vast mass of aphorisms or precepts that have invaded every sector of traditional knowledge, introducing overlaps between them at many points. That is precisely the case here—and all the more so—since one of the original features of Caraka's medical treatise is its incorporation of many borrowings from brahminic philosophy, legal codes, and codes of ritual. One of the prescribed rules in these brahminic codes concerned with the *dharma* of kings is relevant from an ecological perspective. The *Laws of Manu*, the *Yājñavalkyasmṛti*, and others prescribe that the Hindu king should establish himself in the dry lands. "Let him take up residence in a *jāṅgala* place, where cereals are abundant, where the Ārya predominate and which is free from disorders," says Manu; and, glossing the technical term, the Sanskrit commentators of the Middle Ages repeat the expression interpolated in Caraka: "Trees and waters are scarce, it is swept by winds."[4] So here are a concept, a vocabulary, and stereotyped formulas common to both the medical and the legal writings, *Āyurveda* and *Dharmaśāstra* (treatises on the brahminic norms), two domains both separate and complementary within a single overall Hindu tradition. Like all essential elements within the Ayurvedic system, the polarity between the dry lands and the marshy lands is both a consequence and a reflection of the religious polarity between the pure and the impure. According to Manu, the dry lands are "free from troubles" *(anāvila)*, and that means free from both impurities and epidemics. The commentators on the *Laws of Manu* explicitly spell out this double meaning, but Ayurveda itself purveys the doctrine that epidemics are the reflection and sanction of impurities while, conversely, the idea of salubrity incorporates the idea of purity.

Two possible applications of this normative ecology exist: first, a medical application—the protection of salubrious lands; second, an application related to the field of political economy and agronomy and concerned with the choice of fertile terrains. The *jāṅgala* "abounds in cereals" (*sasyasampanna*, Manu). Where the interpolated verse in Caraka ran "diseases there are very few," elsewhere the following variant appears: "it overflows with cereals." Yājñavalkya mentions a complementary feature: "It is suitable for livestock."[5] Remember the extreme diversity of the landscapes in question here. Sometimes the extreme concept is to be considered: the arid margins, the Sahelian zones of Punjab and Rajasthan. Even then the hot "desert" (*maru, dhanvan*), however arid and wild, is never regarded as sterile. Sterile land, the "absolute deserts," as geographers call them, remain outside the field of Ayurvedic medicine for the very reason that they are inhuman, for this is a science prescribed for the well-being of men. In other contexts, the wider meaning predominates: the "dry terrain" *(sthala)*, the arable lands that may be conquered on the savanna.

Analyzing the vast process of the degradation of the forests since antiquity and the drying up of the climate and soils, the Sanskritist E. W. Hopkins concluded that the tiger had for centuries been the most useful animal in India: it protected the forest, the reservoir-forest, the forest sufficiently dense to hold the rainfall that nourished it. If the forest were to thin out as a result of tree felling or fires or the rainfall were to diminish, the rivers would dry up. In this connection, the geographer A. Aubréville has put forward a well-known hypothesis on the origin of the savannas and the "desertification" of Africa: the dried-up gramineous underbrush of the deciduous forest fuel brushfires, which destroy the forest.[6] Agriculture in part profits from this retreat of the forest, but, conversely, increasingly frequent droughts and famines result in the land being abandoned and once more overtaken by wildness. At this point, an inversion of values occurs: the forest becomes a refuge. Thus, among the means of subsistence to which Hindus of caste can have recourse in exceptional circumstances of distress, the *Dharmaśāstra* mention "the forest, marshy land, the mountain" *(vanaṃ anūpaṃ parvataḥ)*;[7] or, to put it more concretely, gathering food and collecting wood.[8] "The *dharma* [for times] of distress" *(āpad-dharma)* is an important concept in brahminic law. Essentially it concerns the whole group (in times of famine and epidemics), but in chapter 7 its equivalent on an individual level shall be addressed: certain constraints are waived (for example, the prohibition against eating meat) when hunger or disease puts lives at risk. A "calamity" *(āpad)* is a progressive accident, a continuous crisis. This idea takes on full significance in the context of a territorial expansion, suggesting a spatial and temporal division between permanence and accident, the endemic and the epidemic. On the one hand, there are permanently dangerous and insalubrious marshy lands: a superabundance of humors, a zone of serious endemic diseases; on the other hand, there are dry lands, where a drama is played out between land clearance and land abandonment. Famines, wars, and epidemics represent so many crises, misfortunes, and momentary setbacks, all of which punctuate the immense historical process of the colonization of the dry lands. It is not the forest that takes repossession of the lands that the peasants abandon at such times but the *savanna*, the all-invading dynamism of gramineous vegetation.

Once aware of the semantic evolution that suppresses all reference to "dryness" in the English word *jungle* and instead emphasizes the luxuriance of the vegetation, and once forewarned of the possible misinterpretation of the word itself, we should be wrong not to take advantage of Kipling's marvelous stories, which have a very real ecological value. The following illustration from Kipling's *Second Jungle Book* gives a gripping description of this return in force on the part of the wild vegetation when disaster has struck. The scene is set in Seeonee district (Madhya Pradesh), to the west of Khanhiwara, on the plateaus escarpments, which dominate the upper stretches of the Waingunga river (see map 3).[9] The Jungle is the dry tropical forest in which teak trees predominate, intermingled with ebony trees, *Terminalia tomentosa, Anogeissus latifolia*, and others. Trees with a wide crown of foliage form a fairly dense stratum, rising no higher than twenty meters. In the underwood, one species of bamboo, *Dendrocalamus strictus*, abounds in the form of impenetrable thickets, some of which incorporate enclaves of purely herbaceous formations (dry bamboo brakes), overlapping with the dry teak forest. H. G. Champion's handbook distinguishes clearly between the two components of this thicket-and-forest

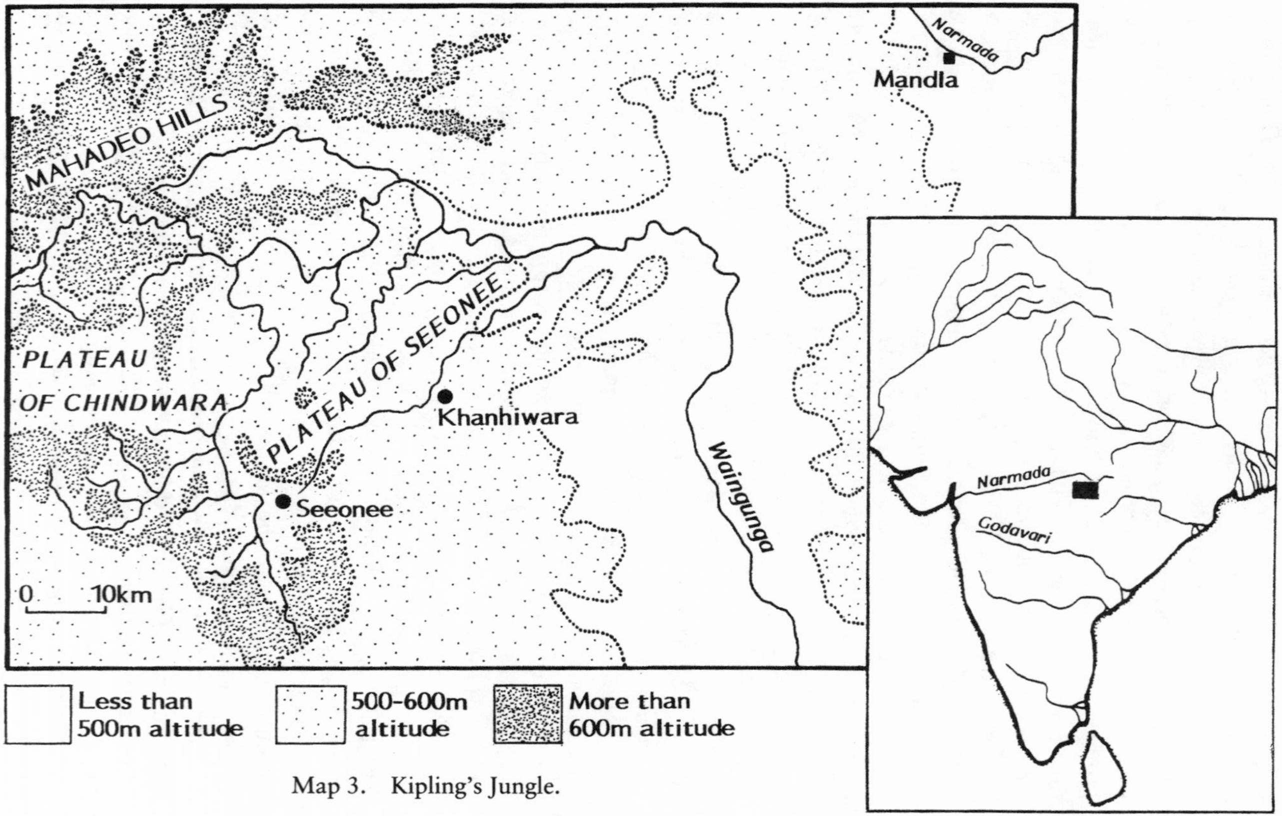

Map 3. Kipling's Jungle.

mosaic.[10] Kipling delights in enumerating distances; he superposes on the collection of stories which make up the Mowgli cycle a kind of idealized topographical model of the relations between a Hindu village, the riverbanks, and the combination of forest-thickets-savanna. Around the Hindu village situated on the banks of the Waingunga, the cultivated plain stretches out over a radius of one or two miles, where the barley and the wheat ripen. Then, on the edge of the plain where the Waingunga comes out of the Jungle, there are the pasturelands, all rocks and scrub and tussocks and little ravines, where the buffaloes wallow in the mud. Up in the Jungle, the charcoal-burners who exploit the wood of the Jungle go off to work, while the potter descends to the plain to sell his pots in the Khanhiwara market. Twenty miles from the Waingunga, in the heart of the forest, is the Council Rock of the Seeonee Wolf-Pack; thirty miles away from the village, in the heart of the plain, is Khanhiwara, the town where Messua (Mowgli's mother) goes to seek protection from an English administrator. The social organization of the space thus emerges clearly: on the one hand, the successive, overlapping zones that surround the village (fields, pasturelands, jungle); on the other hand, a contrast between the forest (the charcoal-burners) and the civilized plain (the potter).

With the scene set, let us now reread the last pages of the story entitled "Letting in the Jungle," in which the Jungle makes its descent. In vengeance, Mowgli unleashes his army of wild animals upon the Indian village where they destroy, one after the other, its pasturelands, its crops, its walls and its grain stores, forcing the peasants to abandon it. They cling to their land up until the end of the dry season. Hoping that he will be able to teach them the proper rites for calming the gods of the Jungle, the villagers send for the chief of the nearest Gond tribes, who live a nomadic life in the forest. By way of reply, he sends them a symbol, a liana, a potent of the assault of the wild herbs at the beginning of the rains: "The Gond said nothing, but picked up a trail of the *karelā*, the vine that bears the bitter wild gourd. . . ."[11] The wild boars complete the destruction of the enclave walls; their violence is matched by that of the vegetation: "The knotty-rooted vines hurried after and threw their elbows over the new-won ground, and the coarse grass bristled behind the vines like the lances of a goblin army following a retreat." By the end of the rainy season, the abandoned land was literally transformed into savanna.

On rereading Kipling, many years later, with the secrets of childhood forgotten, I find that I have not exhausted his treasures. Kipling's works possess a fidelity to the landscapes and the patterns of native sensibility, which enables him to restore to us one of the foremost connotations of the Jungle (in the ancient sense): it results from the battle between man and the forest. The bamboo brakes of the Seeonee district and the marshy savanna of the Terry are, in the last analysis, the results of a similar process that has been continuing for thousands of years, encouraged by the overintensive pasturing of livestock and the excessive exploitation of timber. Brushfires and other phenomena, provoked essentially by the presence of man, bring about the degradation of the dry deciduous forest, the ceiling of vegetation thins out, the *graminaceae* multiply and form thickets. In a similar fashion, on the margins of the Ganges plain, slash-and-burn cultivation brings in its train the destruction of the wet sal forest; once the terrain is abandoned, it is taken over by reeds, becoming a savanna of *Imperata cylindrica*.[12] The various species of the tree-growing stratum progressively disappear; herbaceous species and—in dry regions—thorny shrubs take over. Everywhere, the jungle is the product of the battle between the forest and the cultivated plain. It results from the degradation of the one and the abandonment of the other.

THE IRON AGE

We must now attempt to date the first brushfires to the east of the Delhi Doab, the first gaps made in the dense wet forest, which is believed to have covered the middle stretches of the Ganges at the beginning of the historic period. A few words should be said about the recently discovered archaeological evidence. Less than forty years ago, with B. B. Lal's excavations at Hastinapura in 1950–1952, one link in the chain reemerged: the discovery of a style of pottery characteristic of the Iron Age (Painted Grey Ware Pottery) in the excavation sites along the dried-up riverbed of the Ghaggar and elsewhere in the Doab. Until that time the only sources of evidence pertaining to the history of the Aryans in India during the twelve centuries separating the Indus civilization (fifteenth century B.C.) and the reign of Aśoka (third century B.C.) were literary ones—especially, the Vedic texts and the *Mahābhārata* epic. Now the texts give an entirely ideal, mythological, and ritualistic image of the period. All the same, the most recent Vedic texts (tenth to fifth centuries B.C.) do provide one precious piece of information: that an expansion took place eastward. The center of interest, which was the Punjab in the *Ṛgveda*, moved and became the Delhi Doab (for example, in the *Śatapatha Brāhmaṇa*, under the name of *Kurukṣetra*). These texts mention both iron and the plough. Archaeologists date them to the same period as that of the flowering of the Painted Grey Ware style, associated with the most ancient iron industries. By using radiocarbon techniques to date these pots, Bridget and Raymond Allchin calculated some relatively precise chronological limits: between 900 and 500 B.C., a time span that may cover the Iron Age in this region.[13]

The excavations of the fifties revealed a contrast between the upper and the middle valley of the Ganges (map 4), thus making it possible for archaeologists to infer a progressive clearing of the forest, starting in the Doab and continuing eastward. East of the confluence of the Ganges and the Yamuna (the ancient *Prayāga* and the modern Allahabad), the Painted Grey Ware style is absent. East of this point, the Black and Red Ware style of the Stone Age is replaced with the Northern Black Polished Ware style, found from 500 B.C. everywhere from the Punjab to the lower Ganges valley. According to the hypothesis put forward to account for this contrast between the West, where an iron civilization was flourishing, and the East, where until the sixth century B.C. it appears still unknown, the eastward expansion of agricultural civilization must until that time have been checked by the dense wet forest covering the middle valley of the Ganges.[14]

That is just a hypothesis, however. The literary sources of evidence invoked to support it are enigmatic and impossible to date. When it comes to dating the *Laws of Manu*, the *Arthaśāstra* and the treatises of Suśruta and Caraka, or at least their establishment in the form in which they have come down to us (for some parts of them may be very much more ancient than others), the most erudite discussion results only in an extreme uncertainty, and the same applies to all of these texts. Admittedly, individual events, coincidences, and the evolution of particular social groups—all the things that comprise *history* for us—elude us; but that is not the case with the things that are slowest to change, spatial structures, the almost immobile history of man and his relations with his environment.[15]

One fact certainly does emerge from the texts: The clearing of the land and the retreat of the forest was an ecological process achieved over thousands of years, the very gradualness of which ensured its escape from the uncertainties of history. To cite an excellent historian of medieval India, the retreat of the forest was the "ecological concomitant," the counterpart, on an ecological level, to a major social fact: the displacement and assimilation of the tribal populations.[16] Recent re-

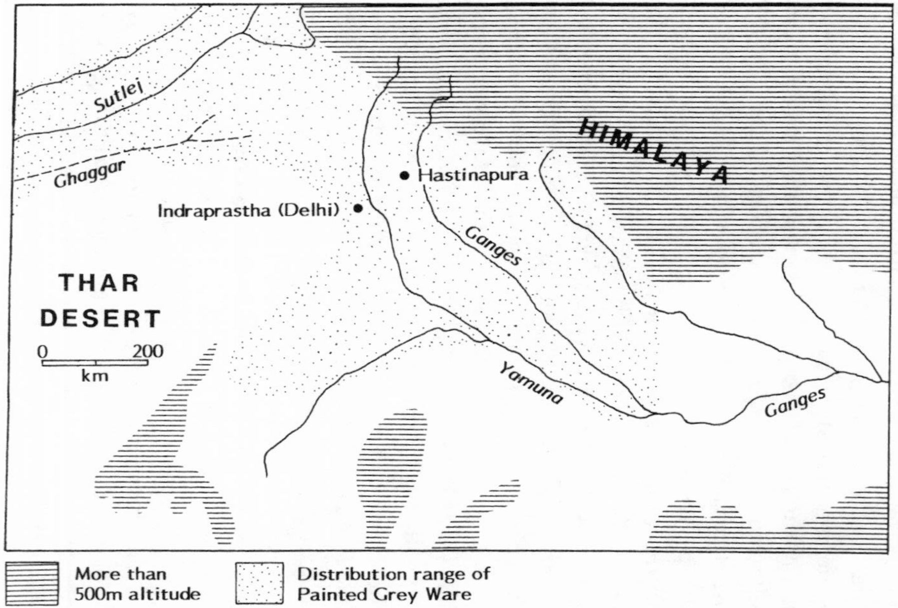

Map 4. Archaeological sites of the Iron Age. Painted Gray Ware (900–500 B.C.) is absent to the east of the Ganges and Yamuna confluence. A contrast between the west (iron civilization) and the east (probably covered with dense wet forest at that time). *Sources*: Bridget Allchin and Raymond Allchin, *The Birth of Indian Civilization* (Harmondsworth, 1968), p. 216, fig. 60 (redrawn); updated by the same authors in *The Rise of Civilization in India and Pakistan* (Cambridge, 1982), pp. 312, 318.

search in effect suggests that peasant cultivation did not expand along a continuous front. It made progress in the great river plains, beaming out from a series of nuclei of civilization, gradually assimilating the non-Aryan tribes into the caste society or else pushing them back into the margins of the arable lands, into inhospitable zones abutting escarpments of high land, arid desert, or dense rain forest. That is also what the Sanskrit texts quite clearly tell us, and what is translated on the level of mythology and ritual into the polarity between the village and the forest.

In traditional literature, the plains of northern India, the Indus and the Ganges, constitute the preferred area of reference. Limited to its central part, this area constitutes the Doab, the "middle country." Conceived in wider terms, it stretches from the Arabian Sea to the gulf of Bengal and is the "Domain of the Aryans." We shall presently be citing a number of more precise, legal definitions. Through their references to this highly valued space—the Hindu space par excellence—the classical Sanskrit texts present a kind of model of villages established in the plain, at the water's edge. The *Arthaśāstra*, a political treatise, is a precious document in this respect, despite the fact that it is impossible to determine to what extent it describes observed facts or to what extent it aims to set up norms and to construct an ideal, Utopian kingdom. In it, ecology plays a role of central importance.

THE VILLAGE AT THE WATER'S EDGE

Kauṭilya's *Arthaśātra* is the only treatise on the art of politics to have come down to us, and it is impossible to determine the date of its composition (the experts' opinions vary between the fourth century B.C. and the third century A.D.). It is not known whether the treatise describes a real political situation or the constitution of an ideal State. The style, referred to as the *sūtra-bhāṣya* style by linguists (aphorisms drowned in commentary: we shall be returning to this topic in chapter 5), is closely related to that of Suśruta and Caraka. It provides a precious complement to our analysis, particularly in its use of technical vocabulary.

The dry lands *(jāṅgala*, or *sthala)* and the marshy lands *(ānūpa)* are defined in terms of rainfall: it rains half as much in the marshy lands as in the dry lands.[17] Such a decisive argument supports the contention that whatever the anthropocentric connotations, the wild, uncultivated, and fallow *jāṅgala* land has first and foremost an ecological reality. Distinctions of rainfall are extremely useful in formulating criteria for a choice among possible types of land to colonize. A small piece of "watered" land *(audaka)*, crossed by a river, is of more value than a vast "dry land" *(sthala)*, where the only source of water is the rainfall. But a small area, even one "favorable to cereals," is of less value than a vast terrain, even if the terrain is infertile "because over a large space one finds both plants of the dry lands and marshy plants"; the variety of climatic conditions to a large extent compensates for the poverty of the soil, since soil deficiency can be remedied.[18] Thus, nuances exist by which to distinguish between a "watered" terrain and a "marshy" terrain, lands where "gathering" is possible (where medicinal plants grow) and lands for "harvesting" (cereals). Furthermore, the interplay of dry lands, marshes, and water margins is relevant to a finer differentiation of space, in the context of the frontiers of a kingdom and its routes of communication. First, it is necessary to distinguish between "pasture lands, dry lands, irrigated fields, vegetable gardens." In this series, *sthala* (dry lands) clearly refers to wasteland; those who undertake to clear and cultivate it are the beneficiaries of a tax exemption.[19] Next, the word *ānūpa* has two very different meanings in the *Arthaśāstra*. First, it may denote "marshy lands, marshes"; that is the case in particular in the description of *forests for elephants* which are planted along the frontiers of the kingdom and where the elephants stand guard "in the mountains, in the water margins [by rivers or ponds], or in the marshes."[20] Second, *ānūpa* also appears in the compound term *ānūpagrāma*, "village at the water's edge," a village set up on the banks to take advantage of the availability of river transport and seasonal irrigation by means of flooding.[21]

The polarity between dry lands and marshy lands may thus be interpreted in two ways: *jāṅgala* or *sthala* may mean either 1) plain, steppe, or savanna, while *ānūpa* by contrast means forests-mountains-marshland or 2) the arid, uncultivated land in between the rivers, while *ānūpa* denotes—within the plain itself—riverside lands, the vegetation of the water's edge. The second interpretation reappears today, used by modern geographers who see a polarity between *bar* lands (the arid lands in between the rivers) and *bet* lands (along the riverbanks).[22] Roaming the *bar* lands are the Jāṅglī—the "nomads," a name given to certain subdivisions of castes or tribes, as opposed to the sedentary peasants. Over a large part of Punjab, the cultivated *bet* lands were traditionally irrigated by flooding; small flood canals were added to the natural network of waterways at a very early date.[23] The villages were situated on the riverbanks bordered with tamarisk trees; in the interior, in contrast, *jāṅgala* took over: acacias, bushes, bare soil;

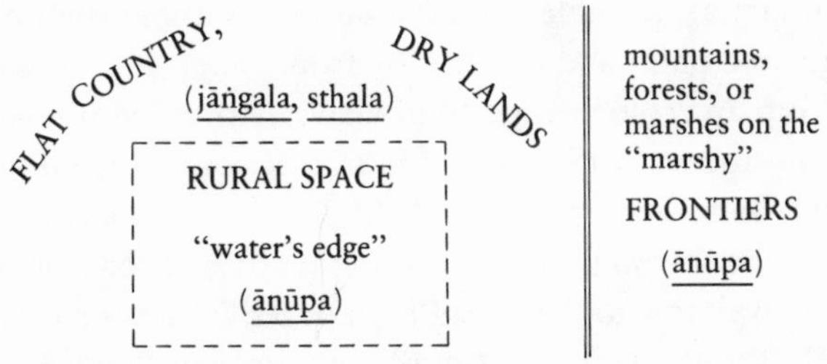

Figure 4. Water's edge encompassed by the jungle

snakes, lizards, a few gazelles. Here the Jāṅglī lived with their camels and their meager herds of livestock and patiently searched for food.[24] One single pair of vernacular terms (of Arabic origin?) conveys a whole constellation of biogeographical oppositions: the dry and the wet, uncultivated land and irrigated land, the nomad world and the peasant world.

Water thus appears twice in the ideal representation of the territory. It predominates at the frontiers of the kingdom, in wet forests and marshes possessing the insalubrity and impenetrability necessary both to protect the arable lands from possible invasion from outside and to limit their expansion. Water appears a second time at the heart of the rural space: flooded fields *(kedāra)*, villages on the riverbanks *(ānūpa-grāma)*, and water holes *(pānīya)* for the livestock, a complementary feature that Suśruta was to mention later. This double distribution of the space—not simply dry/marshy but also uncultivated/irrigated—and the double positioning of *ānūpa* regions both on the frontiers and on the water's edge, detectable at every point in the prescriptions concerning enclosures, ditches, conservancy, and tolls—may be expressed figuratively as in figure 4.

The ecological picture should be completed by another series of terms bearing sociopolitical significance: the "country" *(janapada)*, the "fortified town" *(durga)*, and, above all, the "forest" *(aṭavī)*, a technical term whose essential role has been underlined by Charles Malamoud: *Janapada*—the "country," the rural space or even the "soil," and the "people of that soil," the space under administration, together with its population, *aṭavī*—"primitive, barbarian tribe in the forest," and, by metonymy, the "forest," inhabited essentially by barbarian tribes who pose a threat to the kingdom along its frontiers.[25] The opposition as here revealed between the flat country *(jāṅgala)* and the impracticable frontiers *(ānūpa)* does not contradict the opposition between the country *(janapada)* and the forest *(aṭavī)*, the one most familiar to Indianists.

The two in fact are complementary and overlapping: the forest is both the uncultivated plain and the marshy frontiers.

Thus, from an ecological point of view, there are a number of different kinds of "forests": the term used in this context is no longer *aṭavī* (barbarians), but *vana* or *araṇya* (land covered with trees). The dense, wet forest is the starting point for a whole series of forms ranging from the most inhospitable to the most "humanized": "forests for elephants" *(hastivana)*, "timberlands" *(dravyavana)*, royal "hunting grounds" *(mṛgavana)*, "paradises" *(abhayavana)* for tame animals, "hermitages" for studying the Veda and for sacrifices to Soma *(brahmasomāraṇya)*.[26] Except for the wet forests, all these types of vegetation fall into the category of dry lands, in which respect they elsewhere stand in contrast to the rural space: fields, vegetable patches, tamarisk trees, and reeds along the riverbanks, and so on.

One of the most burning questions in biogeography is that of forest limits. Through what transitions and for what reasons did the great, dense, wet forest disappear, gradually eaten into by various forms of savanna? In the extraordinary ecological fresco produced by Kauṭilya, two types of answers to this question clearly emerge. First, there is a climatic division between the dry milieu, where the forest is no longer able to resist the encroachments of man, and the marshy milieu, where the forest maintains itself through its very density, through its self-nourishing humidity, through its self-protecting wildness. Then, man introduces a second division within the dry lands: between the village and the forest already "humanized," between the country and the wasteland.

One of Kauṭilya's pronouncements cited above made the point that a sufficiently vast terrain is an ecologically complete territory since it contains both dry and marshy regions. In the *Arthaśāstra*, a geographical web of interconnections determines how royal power should be exerted over the space in question, a space conceived right from the start to be ecologically complete, with its double interplay of expansion in the direction of distant lands and enclosure around the established nuclei of civilization. Its immense central plain is bounded in the distance by mountains, dense forests, or marshes, and within the plain there is the jungle (wasteland), also distant from the village centers. It is fascinating to note how all of these types of spatial organization—with their divisions and decentralizations—appear in exactly the same forms in the *Suśrutasaṃhitā*. Their role there, however, is more discrete since it is no longer a matter of administrating the space itself but of distributing the animals within it. Such a convergence should come as no surprise. From a different and homogeneous points of view, *Arthaśāstra* and *Āyurveda* develop the very same traditional norms, one and the same brahminic science of environments, orientations, and positions within the given space found elsewhere in ritual, astrology, and so on. It is true that this unity of knowledge in classical India is not immediately apparent, even if we are gradually accumulating evidence for it. It is because, despite the great abundance of scientific Sanskrit texts, when one comes to tackle a particular instance of detailed conceptual organization—in this case, the double polarity between jungle-and-village and jungle-and-forest—few documents formulate it precisely enough for it to be analyzed; at every turn it is assumed to be known, at every turn it is mentioned—which testifies to its traditional character—but always merely as an allusion. The interpreter feels confronted with an enigma—that is, until the day when a precise text provides him with the key. Thus, in the entire corpus of the medical *saṃhitā* of the Great Triad (several thousand pages in all), only one very short text clearly expresses the following, generally implied—albeit fundamental—fact: to wit, that the village, the countryside, the rural space is both *inside* the jungle and *different* from it. It lies within the jungle but is something else: spatially it is included but ecologically it is separate from it.

Figure 5 summarizes Suśruta's catalog of meats, omitting the aquatic fauna—crabs, turtles, shellfish, and fish—to be studied later in chapter 4. The figure thus shows all the groups in the *jāṅgala* category but shows only those of the water's edge, the forests, and the marshes in the *ānūpa* category. One feature is immediately noticeable, namely, the quadruped/bird couples: the antelope and the quail, the lion and the crow, the elephant and the wild goose. One nuance of language or thought is worth noting here. In Sanskrit, as in many other languages, a bird is not a *bête*. In French, the word denotes all animals except man, while the English word *beast*, like the Sansrit *mṛga*, denotes a quadruped as opposed to a bird or a fish. Hence the classical expression *mṛgapakṣin*, "beasts and birds." If we concentrate on the major animal in each group, the catalog thus presents three couples:

Two *JĀṄGALA* animals of the savannas	Two PREDATORS (see chapter 6)	Two *ĀNŪPA* animals of the forests and marshes
the quail and the antelope	the crow and the lion	the wild goose and the elephant

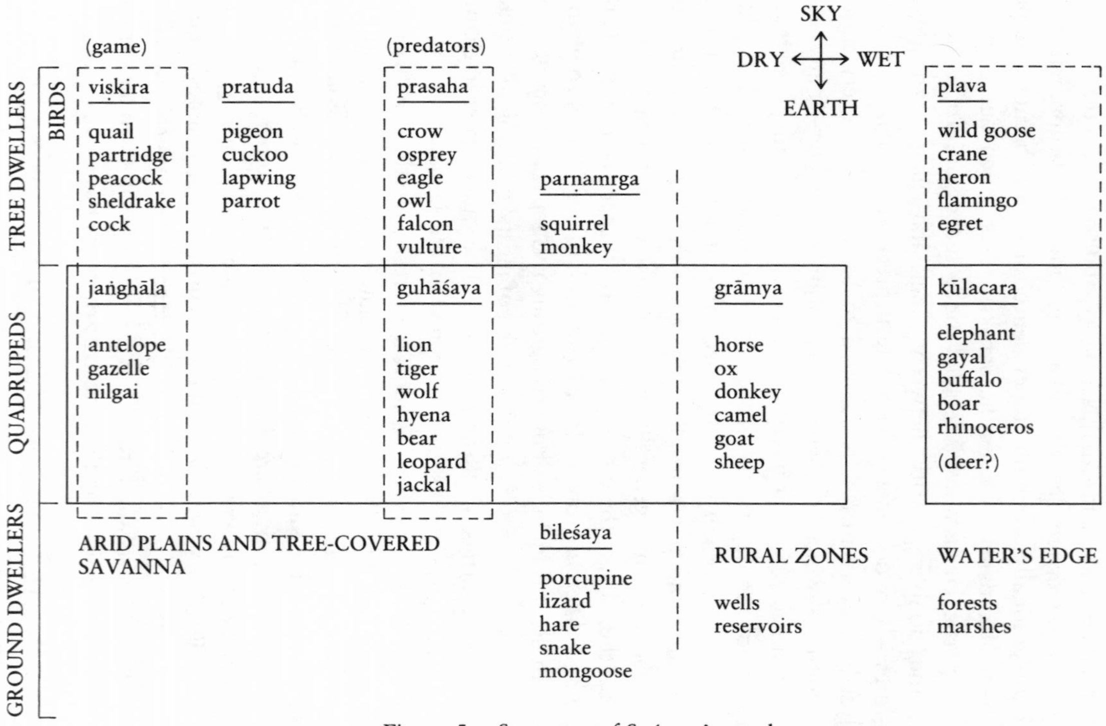

Figure 5. Structure of Suśruta's catalog

The figure also accommodates another important group: the *grāmya* animals, "those of the village," the domesticated animals, included in the *jāṅgala* category, where they are the last cited. In the interests of simplicity, this discussion is limited to the quadrupeds. The reader will easily be able to associate any particular quadruped with its winged counterpart. Each group is defined by its greater or lesser distance from the antelope; in this way, the catalog reveals three fundamental contrasts (as can be seen below):

antelope	polarity between dry and marshy lands	elephant
antelope	polarity between wild and domesticated animals	horse
antelope	couple prey and predator	lion

In the corresponding catalogs found in Caraka and Vāgbhaṭa, the *grāmya* category does not appear, as is shown in the schematic comparison between the classificatory categories in table 3. Predatory and domesticated animals are included in the same group.[27] *Prasaha* denotes "those which eat by pulling": this label applies both to *herbivores* that graze and to *carnivores* that tear. From that point on, the animal catalogs in Caraka and Vāgbhaṭa lose most of their meaning since certain fundamental contrasts are disregarded. As can be imagined, the position of the *prasaha*—grass croppers, carnivores, or monkeys—is ambiguous: they are now defined as *sādhāraṇa* "(animals) of the middle lands," now grouped with the *ānūpa* "(animals) of the marshy lands."[28]

One fundamental lexicological feature should be noted. The word *grāmya*, "domesticated (animals)" (literally, "those of the village"), which by metonymy qualifies meats produced by the raising of stock, very often appears in therapeutic prescriptions in each of the large *saṃhitā*, in association with *ānūpa*, "marshy (meats)," and *audaka*, "aquatic (meats)." The compound word *grāmyānūpaudaka*, "domesticated marshy and aquatic (meats)," is expressly set in opposition to *jāṅgala*, "(meats) of the dry lands," and occurs as such in so many instances that it is not necessary to give the references until later in the discussion. *Grāmya* and *jāṅgala* animals are thus classed together,

TABLE 3
ZOOLOGICAL CATEGORIES

Suśruta	Vāgbhaṭa	Caraka
jaṅghāla have legs	*mṛga* quadruped game	*jāṅgala*
viṣkira scatter their food	*viṣkira*	*viṣkira*
pratuda peck	*pratuda*	*pratuda*
guhāśaya have a lair	(included in *prasaha*)	(included in *prasaha*)
prasaha pull at their food	*prasaha*	*prasaha*
parṇamṛga tree dwellers	(included in *prasaha*)	(included in *prasaha*)
bileśaya have a burrow	*bileśaya*	*bhūmiśaya* have a burrow
grāmya domesticated	(included in *prasaha*)	(included in *prasaha*)
kūlacara inhabit riverbanks	*mahāmṛga* large *mṛga*	*ānūpa*
plava float	*matsya* fish	*vāricara* go on water
(aquatic fauna)		*vāriśaya* go in water

although *grāmya* meat possesses pharmaceutical or dietetic qualities which associate it with *ānūpa*. Two brief lines from the *Suśrutasaṃhitā* provide the beginnings of an explanation:

> This category [the one just mentioned] which produces little discharge is called *jāṅgala*. The beasts and birds which live far away, on the margins of lands inhabited by man and far from water, produce few discharges, as is well known. On the other hand, the beasts and birds whose habitat is very close by and which live very near to the water, produce large discharges.[29]

Chapter 5 will expose the humoral physiology underlying this pharmaceutical property of *ānūpa* meats, namely, their ability to produce abundant discharges from all the humors and all the tissues, through all the channels and openings of the body. In principle, *jāṅgala* meats do not possess this dangerous property, but even here it is a matter of degree: they are more or less *abhiṣyandin*, "productive of discharges, out-flowings, fluxes," according to their position in the hierarchy of meats. That is the meaning of the passage in Suśruta. For the moment, simply note the most propitious place for the *jāṅgala* meats: the arid plain extending into the distance as far as the margins of the inhabited regions, far from villages and watering places. The sweeping nature of the formula engenders skepticism and requires us to consult Ḍalhaṇa's commentary for a more detailed explanation: "The property of producing only a few discharges does not apply to all *jāṅgala* meats, says the text. The word *jana* (men) here means *grāma* (village), so that the sense is: animals which live far from a village. Others, reading *dūre janātta* (a variant), interpret as follows: the beasts and birds which occupy a habitat *far away and cut off from men* are etc. *Dūre pānīyagocara*: the animals whose territory is far away from water, which live far away from water, that is the meaning."[30] In the immensity of the Plain, far from the Villages, far from the Forests.

THE TERRITORY OF THE ANTELOPE

The gazelle and the antelope are two distinct genera. There is only one species of each in India. *Gazella bennetti*, the Indian gazelle, is par excellence native to the steppes and uncultivated lands intersected by ravines and nullahs (dried-up watercourses). Its specific area is restricted to the northwest: Baluchistan, Punjab, Sind, Rajasthan. In contrast, the Indian antelope, *Antilope cervicapra*, is to be found in all the plains of the Indian subcontinent, with the exception of the rainy or mountainous regions of Bengal, Assam, or Kerala. The antelope is the foremost animal in the Ayurvedic catalog: the *jāṅgala* animal par excellence, named before any other and prized more than any other for its flesh. The justification for its preeminence, however, stretches far beyond merely medical matters.

Handbooks of animal ecology relate its "Ethiopian origin."[31] To appreciate the full significance of the matter, we must compare the zone of distribution of *Antilope cervicapra* (map 5a) with others of the exact converse distribution. A case in point is the zone of the gaur *(Bos gaurus)*, which belongs to the Indochinese fauna (map 5b). The antelope is found in the plains, expanding along a northwest/southeast axis; the gaur is found in the forests or mountains, expanding along a northeast/southwest axis, with an essential discontinuity in its distribution as it disappears to the south of the Madhya Pradesh and reappears on the Western Ghats. (A discussion of this immense biogeographical polarity taken as a whole will be presented later.) At this point, only two words are necessary: here is *jāṅgala*, and there is *ānūpa*. Here, brahminic India, the flat country "where the black antelope lives in a natural state"; and there, barbarian India, the mountains-forests-marshes, from where the antelope is excluded.

Antilope cervicapra lives on flat terrain with sparsely wooded formations. It is particularly adapted to long treks across the tree-dotted savanna, which is characterized by a combination of tall grasses, thorny shrubs, and trees of the dry forest type—the teak, the jujube tree, the

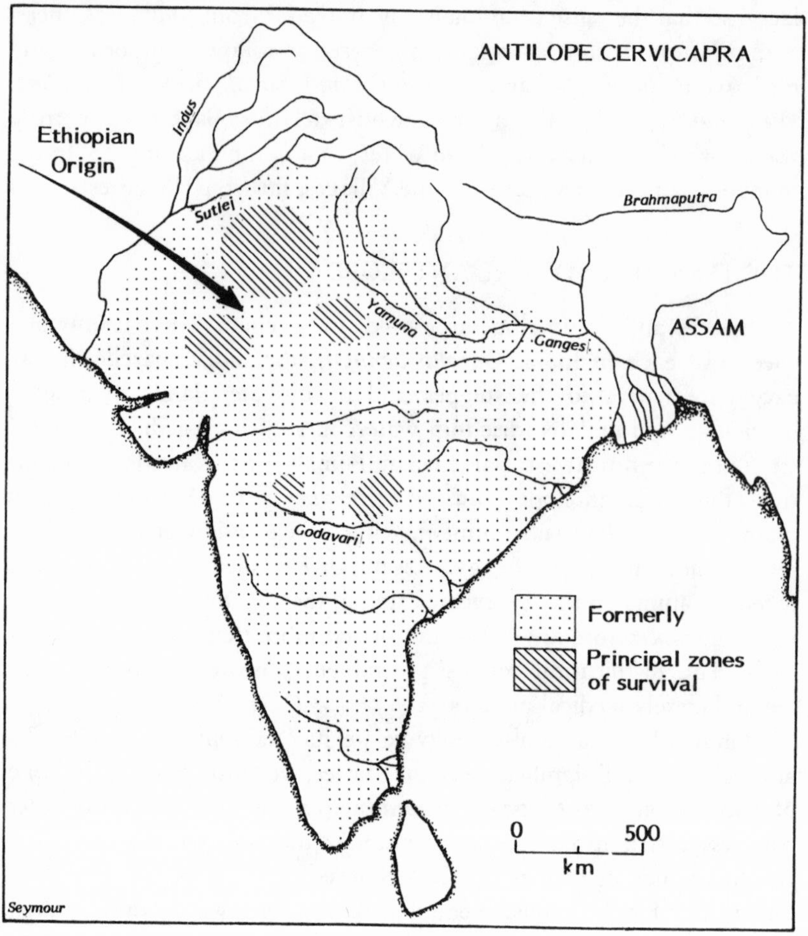

Map 5a. Distribution of the antelope.

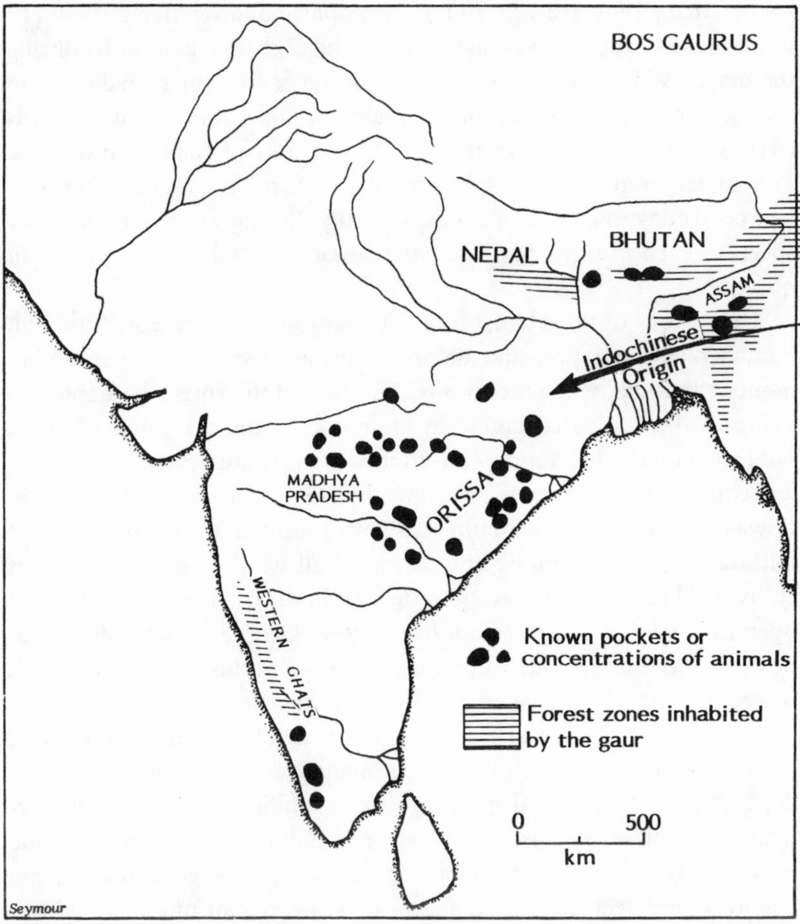

Map 5b. Distribution of the gaur. *Sources*: G. B. Schaller, *The Deer and the Tiger: A Study of Wildlife in India* (Chicago, 1967), chaps. 6 and 7; F. J. Simoons, *A Ceremonial Ox of India* (Madison, 1968).

rubber tree *(Anogeissus latifolia)*. Very sparse and relatively small (12 to 18 meters), these trees denude of foliage over several months during the dry season. In the thickets there are tigers and other predators. In the past the antelope lived in the plains in great abundance, in herds twenty or thirty strong. In the very dry regions of Rajasthan and the Punjab, larger groups sometimes comprised as many as several hundred beasts. Today the antelope has virtually disappeared, and its very survival, even in one or two sanctuaries or national reservations, is in question.

The history of this almost total elimination is very recent. Although human overpopulation and deforestation are extremely ancient phenomena in India, when the forests disappeared the antelope adapted to living in the cultivated lands. In his book on the mammals of India published in 1874, Thomas C. Jerdon was marveling even then at having come across herds of antelope thousands strong in the Punjab. It was the construction of the railways (needing wood for sleepers) followed by the systematic liquidation of all wildlife in the vicinity of cultivated land that defeated the antelope. In the tragic and impassioned opening pages of *The Deer and the Tiger*, George B. Schaller relates how, at the time of independence in 1947, a veritable massacre took place, comparable to that of the 1880s on the American prairie. Considered a form of colonialist oppression, the regulations limiting hunting with rifles were abolished. Prevailing hunger served as a pretext for the destruction of all the wild species guilty of spoiling the harvests, in particular the antelope whose preference for a habitat in open terrain made it extremely vulnerable. A new breed of hunters emerged, roaming the countryside in jeeps, at night, and firing at every pair of eyes caught in the headlights. It was 1951 before the first measures of conservation of the fauna were taken, by which time the antelope had been virtually exterminated. Just a few years had quite simply wiped it out and, as it were, erased it from the landscape. Texts and monuments survive from the India of classical times; for the fauna, there are a few national parks. Together they constitute the only evidence to help us imagine the landscape as it used to be. On that basis, let us now undertake a kind of *archaeology of representations*. Our aim will, in part, be the following: in default of observing the landscape and fauna as they were in reality, I shall at least hope to represent them as the tradition conveys them. I must begin with a few remarks concerning the antelope *cervicapra*, for its abundance, distribution, beauty, and a number of unusual features of color and form made this animal a symbol in classical India, an emblem, a cultural factor of great importance, as the texts still show, even if it has disappeared from the terrain.

Let us return to the series of the four zones of vegetation cover schematically outlined in the Introduction (see also map 1). The antelope was distributed over the first three zones: [1] the steppe covered with thorny shrubs, [2] the dry forest or tree-covered savanna and [3] the monsoon forest—three zones which together account for practically the entire Indian subcontinent. It was absent only from Assam, Kerala, and Ceylon and, of course, within its own specific areas wherever the forest became too dense or the terrain too steep. But these limitations are of minimal significance when compared with one fundamental taxonomic feature: *Antilope cervicapra* is a species unknown anywhere except in India. It is exclusively Indian, and its distribution defines the zone of brahminic civilization. I should immediately point out that this is not a simple fact, a fact of nature; on the contrary, it is a situation that has developed over the course of history. Let us assume the antelope to have been naturally adapted to the steppes and the savanna; but the thorn forest and tree-covered savanna are themselves the product of an evolution in India, an evolution that depended in particular on the presence of man and, more generally, on what ecologists call "biotic factors." And even if we take the antelope to have been indigenous to zones [1] and [2], it was only as a result of the clearance of the forest, brushfires, and the action of man that it penetrated zone [3], following the paths opened up by slash-and-burn cultivation.[32] We have, on the one hand, a fact of natural history: the specific area of the antelope is coextensive with brahminic India; on the other hand, what is taught by the texts: ever since the Vedic period, the antelope has been a symbol. These are two aspects of a single overall fact: to a certain degree, the antelope followed rather than preceded the paths of diffusion of the brahminic society and in this fashion came to occupy the entire area of the plains of India. History was responsible for completing the very remarkable taxonomic relationship originally introduced by nature between the specific zone of the antelope and that of the brahminic civilization.

In Vedic ritual, the skin of the black antelope is an instrument of sacrifice and a symbol of the brahminic land, land propitious to sacrifice, land where sacrifices can be made; the same definition is used in treatises on Dharma. The "skin (of the) black (antelope)" (*kṛṣṇājina*) can be used at different moments for different actions: the officiating brahmin wraps himself in it, or spreads it over the sacrificer's seat, or arranges it on the altar. "The skin of the black antelope is the sacrifice, and the skin of the black antelope is this land, for on this land the sacrifice is spilled."[33] Why this association of images? We do not know, although we may suppose that an exceptional physical characteristic, such as its black color, may have been regarded as amazing and may have stimulated the imagination. The fact is that the color of the coat of the antelope *cervicapra* signals a sexual dimorphism that is relatively rare and accounts for the duality of the animal's Sanskrit names. The coat is a fawn color in the case of the female, which is called *hariṇa*, but a very dark brown along the spine and flanks of the adult male, known in Sanskrit as *eṇa*. This almost black coat is exceptional; gazelles and antelopes usually have a light-colored coat, which does not get overheated and is adapted to the strong sun. But whatever the material details that stimulated men's imaginations—and the black coat was not the only one, there was also the spiraled design of the horns—they would not have constituted the basis for a whole set of symbolical representations had they not thereby provided religious ideas with a language. The antelope is the sign that presides over a whole group of religious and mythical values constantly present in the background of our enquiry. Let us simply note that the object chosen to symbolize the land of sacrifice is precisely the pelt of an animal that is never used as a *victim*, but is, on the contrary, the very epitome of *game*: there are many links, little recognized, between hunting and sacrifice.[34]

Hunting and sacrifice are two complementary methods of producing meat: the one provides game (wild animals); the other sanctions the consumption of livestock, since the slaughtering and consumption of meats not ritually consecrated constitute a defilement and are practiced only by the untouchables. On the level of religious representations, sacrifice—even blood sacrifice which presupposes the raising of livestock among which victims are chosen—is indissociable from cultivated land. Hunting, in contrast, defines the relations between weapon-bearing man and wild nature. Working on the land implies stock raising (for the purposes of ploughing, at least) and the possession of fire for cooking: sacrifice is a culinary action.[35] While sacrificial activities are concentrated no farther than the outskirts of the village, if not always within the inhabited space, the pursuit of game leads the hunter out into the distant space of the forest. Game means, par excellence, the antelope. We shall return later to the word *mṛga* which, at different degrees of logical extension, denotes "game," "quadrupeds," "antilopinae-and-cervidae," or, simply, "antelope."

Intimately associated with the plain, the antelope does not penetrate into rain forests or mountains. It does not lead the hunter just anywhere, making him lose his way; the paths it follows in uncultivated land trace out ways for agricultural civilization to penetrate there. Using a distinction proposed in the Sanskrit texts, one might say that over the as-yet "wild" regions of the plain, the free movements of the antelope delimit a particular domain—the India of the plains and castes, brahminic India—beyond which stretches "barbarian" space. This is the "Domain of the Aryans" *(Āryāvarta)*, also delimited by geographical frontiers, lying as it does between two mountain chains and two seacoasts: the Himalaya and the Vindhya mountains, the Arabian Sea and the Gulf of Bengal. Viewed, however, from a wider perspective and a different frame of definition based on ecological criteria, the area of brahminic diffusion is associated with the plain *in general*, where the antelope roams freely. "Country where the black antelope roams in its natural state *(svabhāvatas)* should be recognized as suitable for sacrifice," say the *Laws of Manu*, "any other than that is barbarian country." "It is in the country of the black antelope that you must receive the instruction of the *dharma* [the duties of caste]," Yājñavalkya tells his disciples; and the *Mitākṣarā* specifies: "the country where the black antelope roams at will," freely.[36] A social exclusion is involved: those excluded are the barbarians, the non-Aryans, literally the *mleccha*, those who stutter, those who do not know Sanskrit. But it is formulated in the language of ecology: push them out! Beyond the borders, out of the *jāṅgala*, out of the plain, to the margins of the fertile soil, into the *ānūpa* forest where there are mountains, dense forests, and marshes, which make access impracticable and dangerous. In the plain the antelope runs free in its "wild" *(āraṇya)* state. Now we shall no longer confuse wildness (in the dry plain) and barbarity (on the marshy borderlands).

The *Arthaśāstra* describes an institution comparable to one mentioned by Xenophon among the Persians: the "paradise," the reservation for wild animals kept in various zones of the royal domain, surrounded by moats, where the *abhaya*, the law of "safety," is decreed. "Tamed antelopes and cervidae" *(dānta-mṛga)* live there at peace with "beasts of prey" *(vyāla)*, whose claws and teeth have been removed to render them harmless.[37] Both poetry and painting have exploited this image of the tame antelope in an attempt to illustrate the theme of separation and absence. Although close and virtually tame, the antelope comes from the far horizons. To the young woman in the park, beneath a weeping willow, playing the tambura as she sings of the sadness of her lover's absence, awaiting his return, the black antelope which attentively draws near is like a messenger from the distant plains where the one she loves is voyaging (see photograph). The paintings of the Kangra school which illustrate this theme accentuate the importance of the physiographical details: the black and white coat, the spiraling horns of the adult male, the weeping willow (cultivated in the valleys of Punjab), and the immense plain stretching as far as the eye can see.[38] That is why the antelope is ranked first of all among the animals known as *jāṅgala*, "those of the jungle," or sometimes *jaṅghāla*, "those which have legs," running free over the wide expanses of the plain.

Let us pause to take an overall view over the ground we have covered by stressing the following two points: First, underneath the confusion of images introduced by one language borrowing vernacular terms from another and the ambiguities of exoticism, the jungle is rediscovered in the true sense of the word: the land without water, the land without men. We shall call the jungle a category of collective thought, since it summarizes or incorporates a whole body of traditional ideas, at once legal and medical, geographical and political, biological and religious. Second, the recent developments of phytogeography provide precious arguments and analytical schemata to help prize from the ancient texts evidence of a fundamental biographical problem: that of the frontier zones on the margins of dense, wet forests and of the savannaization of the dry forests. Whatever the illustrations considered, be they classical or modern—the semiarid plains of Punjab, the bamboo brakes of Madhya Pradesh, or the flooded savannas of Assam—the jungle establishes itself by encroaching on the forest (which opens up, decays, recedes), while peasants, in their turn, encroach on the jungle (the land yet uncultivated). But again, at times defeated by disastrous floods, fire, or other calamities, and unable to maintain the land they have planted, men also retreat, giving up to the wild grasses this land—a land they may one day reconquer, but which the forest, for its part, will never recover. Who could forget in India the forests that have died out, and the dramatic expanse of wastelands, the lands once abandoned, the lands then desertified?

"The Lady and the Buck," Miniature from Garhwal, c. 1780, Victoria and Albert Museum, London. *Source*: W. G. Archer, *Indian Paintings from the Punjab Hills* (London, 1973), Garhwal no. 27, Victoria and Albert Museum

III: The Indus and the Ganges

The Ayurvedic catalogs of rivers, flora, and fauna provide a unique illustration of one *total fact*, one of those bedrock cleavages that condition a society's history together with the development of its mythology. The waters that rise in the Himalayas and bathe northern India flow eastward into the Gulf of Bengal, and westward into the Arabian Sea. "The rivers of the foothills are thus carried toward two centers of subsidence: that of Bengal and that of the Indus. Between these two formations the alluvial deposits thin out, at the tip of the northern spur of the Dekkan which, situated in between the Sutlej and the Yamuna, constitutes a veritable watershed between surface and subterranean waters. It is also a climatic frontier."[1] To the west (Punjab, Sind) less than 200 mm of rain falls annually and only over a very short season of one month; but the farther eastward one proceeds, from Delhi to Bengal (that is, from 500 mm to 2 m of annual rainfall), the longer the rainy season becomes (increasing from two months to six months or more). This division, with the Delhi Doab as its axis, is evident in every domain: geology, hydrography, ecology, and, most of all, agriculture and eating practices. *In the west the people of wheat, in the east the people of rice.* This coarse formulation shall be refined and completed at the end of the chapter.

The map of India and the catalogs that provide information on the flora and fauna display an ideal system of lines and surfaces, axes and compartments by which the space is divided up in accordance with the traditional values. The Delhi Doab lies at the center of this spiritual geography, but instead of the polarity between the center (dry) and the margins (wet) as developed in the preceding chapter, a west/east axis shall now be considered: the polarity between the Indus (dry) and the Ganges (wet). To illustrate this ideal pattern of South Asian space and soil, I shall sketch in on the map the main lines of the traditional classification of rivers, plants, animals, and diets.

Still starting from the same sources—the medical treatises of the Great Triad and the commentaries on them—I shall again try to splinter and penetrate the ritualistic, or scholastic, surface of the Sanskrit text by systematically mapping out the nomenclature of concrete things to allow the underlying ecology to emerge clearly. Working from this at once ethnological and epistemological perspective, I see nothing more illuminating than collecting and comparing the various geographical maps on which experts in the various disciplines have inscribed their own specialized typologies: distribution of different series of vegetation (Pierre Legris), types of fauna (William Blanford), types of agricultural regions, and in medical geography, the dividing line between the zones of epidemic and endemic malaria. Graphic illustrations will later be provided. It is one single design—the Indus/Ganges polarity—broken down and reduplicated into all of its facets on every different level.

THE RIVERS

Whereas the Ganges plain forms a water catchment system—the Yamuna and the Ganges being joined by a continuous series of confluences and flowing in the direction of regions of increasingly heavy rainfall—the Indus, in contrast, once swollen by the Sutlej, is joined by no other rivers and crosses a desert, thus forming a surface not of water-catchment but of losement.[2] In the west, rivers vanish into the sands; in the east, affluence of waters. On the basis of these hydrographical facts, prehistorical "events" have been imagined: the "disappearance" of the Sarasvati River, the "capture" of the Yamuna by the hydrographic system of the Ganges. Their reality is doubtful, but their lasting impact on Hindu spiritual geography is immense. The point where the Sarasvati is lost in the sands of the Hissar (see map 2) and the point where it is supposed to "reappear," at the confluence of the Ganges and the Yamuna, are the symbolical eastern and western limits of the *Madhyadeśa*, the "Middle Country" (see map 6).

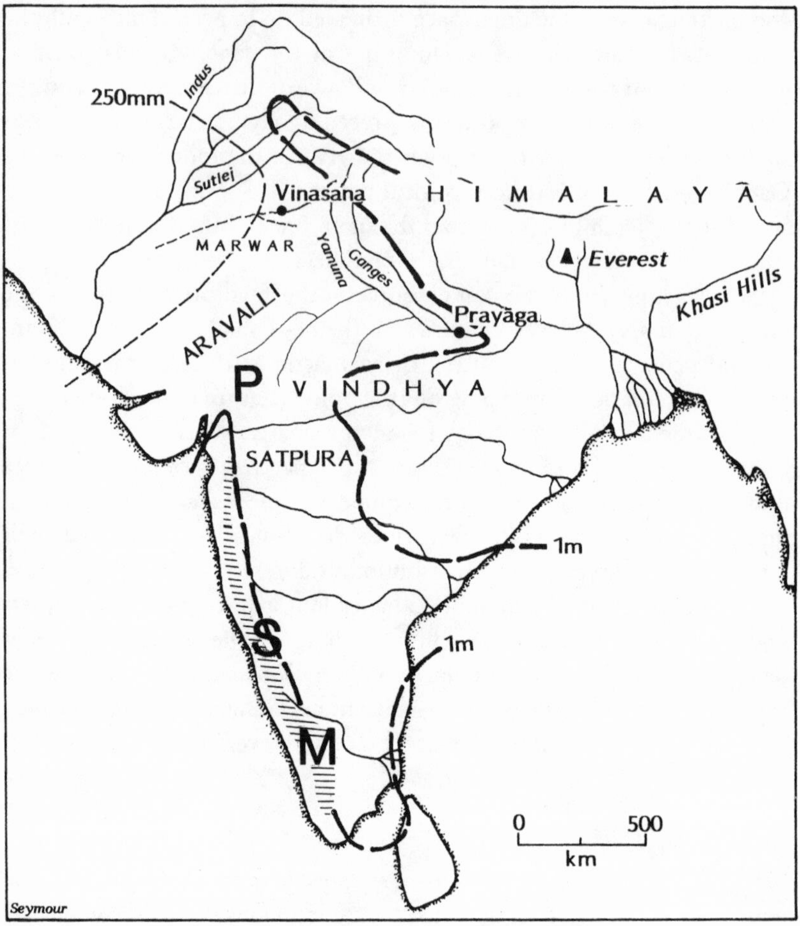

Map 6. Traditional toponymy. *Vinaśana* (where the *Sarasvatī* is lost in the sands) and *Prayāga* (the modern Allahabad) are the western and eastern limits of the *Madhyadeśa*, the "Middle Country." P, *Pāriyātra* (Aravalli range and western part of the Vindhya range); S, *Sahya* (northern part of the Western Ghats); and M, *Malaya* (southern part of the Western Ghats) are some of the seven "principal mountain ranges" *(kulaparvata)*. Hachured: the Western Ghats; Dotted: the isohyets of 250 mm and 1 m, which represent the natural boundaries of the *Madhyadeśa*.

I will attempt to seize on the overall configuration, one of those spatial structures within which we use to live and move about but which cannot be reduced to the empirical facts in which they are realized. Geology, biology, geography, agriculture, nosography—this is a scattered mass of particular facts onto which an ideal configuration projects its trail, its lines of force. We have to show how empirical facts are subordinated to the schemata of classical thought, and for that reason we must proceed from words to perception, moving on from what is taught in the texts to what is projected onto space.

We must keep a grip on both ends of the chain and consider in conjunction two phenomena intimately linked in Hindu mentality, although the link has not hitherto been generally perceived: one is connected with the structures of space, the other with the structures of language. The first is a phenomenon of what is *inscribed in the space*: The polarity between fire and water, dryness and unctuosity, is literally inscribed on the map of India, as is clearly spelled out in the Ayurvedic catalog of running waters, the list of *jāṅgala* plants, and the zones over which *jaṅghāla* and *kūlacara* animals are respectively distributed. The second phenomenon to consider is the process of *poetic composition*, through which traditional knowledge is expressed in the versified texts: On the level of language, a whole gamut of stereotyped formulas give expression to underlying structures that the eye is incapable of perceiving in space. They are beyond the limited powers of visual perception but are the objects of words, the words of the Rishis, transmitted by the classical texts.

The first thing to strike the listener (for these texts are usually recited aloud) is a pattern of octosyllabic hemistiches grouped in fours to form a distich:

(37c) Full of troubles, *ānūpa* water,
(d) Causing fluxes, to be condemned.
(38a) Free from those troubles,
(b) irreproachable, *jāṅgala* (water),
(c) not acid after digestion, it kills thirst,
(d) recommended, it increases joy.
(39a) Eupeptic, sweet and cold,
(b) *sādhāraṇa* water, light.[3]

A familiar theme: in dry lands, an absence of disorders, all the humors calm; in marshy lands, in contrast, plethora, discharges, and fluxes. There are many versions of this same theme. In the *Bhāvaprakāśa* (a sixteenth-century compilation), for example, Suśruta's two distiches cited above are expanded by new formulas:

Little water and few trees,
a typical disease: bile-blood,
that is what defines the *jāṅgala* place;
from it comes *jāṅgala* water.
Much water and many trees,
typical diseases those of wind and phlegm,
it is called the *ānūpa* place;
from it comes *ānūpa* water.
The place of mixed characteristics,
that is *sādhāraṇa*;
the water of this region
is *sādhāraṇa* water.
The *jāṅgala* water is dry,
salty, light, eliminates bile,
gives fire, eliminates phlegm, beneficial,
it cures many disorders.
Ānūpa water provokes fluxes,
sweet, unctuous, dense, heavy,
eliminates fire, gives phlegm, cordial,
it provokes many disorders.
Sādhāraṇa water is sweet,
eupeptic, cold, light,
thirst-quenching, appetising, (calms) thirst,
calms inflammation and the three humors.[4]

Compare two equivalent hemistiches, even if they come from different texts, such as Caraka:
anūpo bahudoṣaś ca
"[It is] *anūpa*, and it is full of disorders" (cited in chapter 2)
and Suśruta:
anekadoṣam ānūpam
"Full of disorders, *ānūpa* [water]" (37c)
and Suśruta again:
vāry abhiṣyandi garhitam
"[*ānūpa*] water, the cause of fluxes, to be condemned" (37d)
and the *Bhāvaprakāśa*:
ānūpaṃ vāry abhiṣyandi
"*Ānūpa* water, the cause of fluxes"
Such a comparison clearly identifies these hemistiches as a series of interchangeable variants; the same idea slips through, propagating itself in text after text in countless lexical, grammatical, or prosodic modifications, which, however, in no way alter the meaning. It furthermore becomes evident how a whole host of indications, prescriptions, and evaluations may adhere to a single word of polar significance, invariably constituting octosyllabic hemistiches.

Before considering the concrete applications to various types of running and still waters, let us consult the catalog of waters in the version given by Caraka and Vāgbhaṭa. There is one striking difference: the third term is no longer *sādhāraṇa*, the correct mean, compensation for the two contraries, an abstract term. Here, the third term is *mountain*. The waters are divided up from the point of view of their ecological qualities and defects, between *jāṅgala, ānūpa*, and *śaila* (the mountain). This results in a new set of formulas:

ānūpa-śaila-dhanvānām	(Caraka, *sūtra* XXVII, 214c)
jāṅgalā'nūpa-śailataḥ	(Vāgbhaṭa, *sūtra* V, 13b)
dhanvā'nūpa-mahīdhrāṇāṃ	(*Aṣṭāṅgasaṅgraha, sūtra* VI, 16a)

Words are inverted, synonyms exchanged (*dhanvan = jāṅgala, śaila = mahīdhra*), and the flexional endings vary, but the sense remains identical: the qualities of the waters vary according to whether their source or container is ecologically dependent on "dry lands, marshy lands, or the mountain." It might well be objected, however, that of the two terms, *ānūpa* and *śaila*, one is redundant. Have we not seen in our earlier chapters how the mountain is contained within the extension of the term *ānūpa*? How can this redundancy be explained?

Running and still waters produce a series of technical terms: *nādeya*, "river (water)," *sārasa*, "lake (water)," *tāḍāga*, "reservoir (water)," and so on.[5] The *jāṅgala/ānūpa* polarity is rounded off by the sequence (set of formulas) devoted to the contents of a lake, a reservoir and, by metonymy, to the varying type of source or receptacle: lake, reservoir, pool, well, fountain, or waterfall. The rivers are included in this series, so they too are classified.[6]

At the same time, the rivers are the subject of a geographical classification set out in a distinct sequence. It is at this point that the triad *jāṅgala-ānūpa-śaila* is quite literally mapped: a contrast is established between the rivers flowing westward and those flowing eastward; at their source is the Himalaya range whose streams provide the purest and most beneficent water. A three-term pattern appears, as presented in figure 6. The water of the mountains is light because it bounces and breaks on the rocks:

> The rivers with churned, shaken waters breaking on the rocks, which rise in the Himalayas, are beneficent, pure *(puṇya)*, used by the Rishis. The rivers with pure *(vimala)* waters in which rocks and gravel are carried along, which rise in the *Malaya* have water similar to nectar. The rivers which turn westward are beneficent, their water is pure. Those which flow slowly and pour into the eastern sea are generally heavy. Those which rise in the *Pāriyātra*,

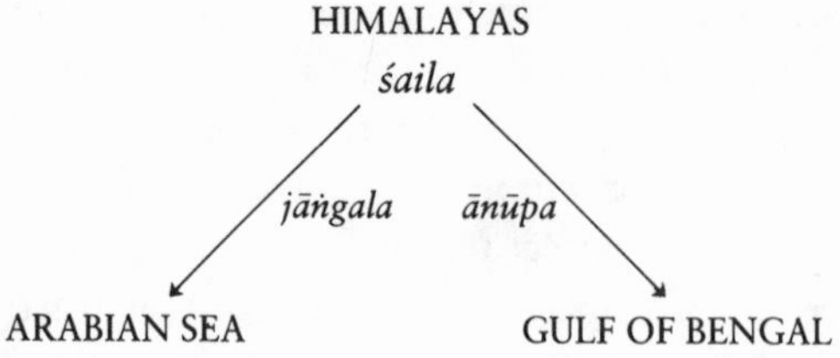

Figure 6. The three types of running waters: *jāṅgala* (flowing westward), *ānūpa* (flowing eastward), and *śaila* (Himalayan streams)

> the *Vindhya* and the *Sahya* produce diseases of the head and heart, diseases of the skin and elephantiasis.[7]

It is remarkable, in a medical work, to come across this pious homage to the Himalayas, where the Rishis live. Substantialism of an extremely obvious nature—water will be light if the river rushes along swiftly, heavy if it flows slowly—combines with religiosity to suggest a particularly ambiguous idea: that of the water's purity. In the Himalayas, the waters are "holy, pure" *(puṇya)* and are also "diaphanous, free from impurities" *(vimala)*; transparency is the material sign of the water's auspicious nature. Note the association (repeated in Vāgbhaṭa) of the Himalayas, par excellence the land for the gathering of medicinal plants, and the *Malaya*, a mountain range identified by its location in the southern part of the Western Ghats: Cardamon Hills, Travancore Hills, which even today still produce a great variety of medicinal plants.[8] The Ayurvedic medical practitioners of Kerala use this ecological association between *their* mountains and *the* mountain range par excellence, the Himalayas, to explain the exceptional vitality of their own regional tradition.

The third term—*śaila*, "mountain"—is absent from the *Suśruta-saṃhitā*'s presentation of this polarity. It offers a similar topographical framework: the contrast between the rivers flowing eastward and those flowing westward, and the series of the main mountain ranges. But far from being pure and beneficent, the Himalayan waters are a source of parasites and the Malayan waters a source of elephantiasis, and other abnormalities. A consideration of this contradiction and the manner in which the commentators manage to resolve it—without rejecting either Suśruta or Caraka—will be presented later in the text. First, note how Suśruta arranges the running waters in his ideally centered space:

> [People praise the excellence] of rivers flowing westward *(paścimābhimukha)* because the water is light; but those which flow eastward *(pūrvābhi-*

> *mukha)* are decried because the water is heavy; those which flow southward *(dakṣiṇābhimukha)* are not too bad because [the country they cross is] of a temperate *(sādhāraṇatvāt)* character.[9]

The "temperate" or "middle" region is none other than the *Madhyadeśa*, the "Middle Country," as emerges clearly from Dalhaṇa's commentary:

> Now [the text] specifies the qualities of the rivers [depending on whether they are:] situated in the dry lands in the west *(jāṅgala-paścima-deśa)*, situated in the marshy lands in the east *(ānūpa-pūrva-deśa)* or situated in the temperate lands in the middle *(sādhāraṇa-madhya-deśa)*. "Flowing westward": situated in dry land in the west and flowing into the western sea; "flowing eastward": situated in marshy land and flowing into the eastern sea; "flowing southward": situated in the middle country.[10]

Obviously northern India, the Indus-Ganges plain, provides the space of reference: the "Domain of the Aryans" *(Āryāvarta)* delimited by the Himalaya range in the north, the Vindhya range in the south, the Gulf of Bengal in the east, and the Arabian Sea in the west. Within this framework, the various ecological types, waters, plants, and animals are distributed and oriented. The localizations are not merely empirical—that is, the names of the regions mentioned in the texts are not given as though they denoted simple, observed facts. They are not neutral but evoke a whole complex of sentiments and religious traditions. The names of the different regions are keys for the memory and represent signs, values, and poles.

There is a mythical, epic, and juridical background to the traditional toponymy (map 6) which merits a brief discussion.[11] At the heart of the Aryan domain an ideal center is fixed, the "Middle Country" *(Madhyadeśa)*, between *Vinaśana* and *Prayāga*. *Vinaśana* is the place where there is a "disappearance," the spot where the Sarasvati River is lost in the sands. *Prayāga* is situated at the confluence of the Yamuna and the Ganges. Let us push a little farther in our attempt to concentrate the space and provide it with a center. The western part of the *Madhyadeśa* is the setting for the epic drama of the *Mahābhārata*. It is the battlefield, the land of high deeds par excellence: the *Kurukṣetra* or *Kurujāṅgala*, the "Jungle of the Kuru." Curiously enough, at the end of the last century, scholars who opposed *kṣetra* ("battlefield, cultivated territory") to *jāṅgala* ("uncultivated land") situated the former to the west and the latter to the east of the Yamuna.[12] Yet, as evidenced in the preceding chapters, in epic the *jāṅgala* is also the theater of epic drama, a stake to be fought over, a highly valued land. Thus, from west to east, the "Aryan Domain" is composed of three zones: Indus-Middle-Ganges; in other words, *jāṅgala-sādhāraṇa-ānūpa*. Inside the Middle Country and in its western part, the *Kurujāṅgala* represents both a center and a positive pole.

There is, to be sure, a huge discrepancy between what the texts say and what the biogeographical reality reveals. The literary documents used in this book purvey a normative discourse; they idealize landscapes, making the broad dividing lines of ecological distribution more rigid. Their details are by no means free of contradictions and equivocalities. The interpretation of the series of catalogs (of rivers, plants, quadrupeds, and so on) that will be examined here raises a methodological difficulty which dogs us at every step. Our aim is to reveal an overall structure. Here, for example, beneficent waters flow westward, unhealthy ones eastward. But how much importance should be attached to discrepancies of detail in the catalog? Is it a matter of perspective each time? Allowance must be made for the scholastic aspects of the tradition, which incorporates a number of levels and must reconcile different needs. The classification of rivers involves one such discrepancy, and it is a serious one: as everyone knows, the waters of the Ganges are sacred and endowed with healing virtues. Yet here it is taught that the rivers which flow eastward convey unhealthy waters. The terms of this contradiction need to be specified.

We read that in the Middle Country the rivers flow "southward": that might well apply to the upper course of the Yamuna and the Ganges. But we definitely sense that what is essential is the idea of a contrast between west and east within an ideally centered space, that the "south" here represents a "middle" and that the concrete identity of the rivers "flowing southward" is of little importance. A norm is being put forward: beneficent waters flow toward the arid west; unhealthy waters flow toward the marshy east. A number of complementary features are then added: the excellence of the Himalayan waters (Caraka, Vāgbhaṭa) or the lightness of the waters of the Marwar rivers (Suśruta),[13] features which confirm the overall structure.

Let us now consider the counterexamples, the features which contradict the overall picture. There are at least two of these, two difficulties which the commentators resolve by means of some cunning distinctions. The first is that the Ganges has to be classed among the unhealthy waters; the second that the Himalayas are the object of contradictory evaluations. How can one forget that the Ganges is sacred and that its water cleanses the pilgrim of all defilement? And how can the Himalayan waters, also pure and auspicious according to Caraka, provoke diseases of the heart and head, swellings, elephantiasis, and goiter, as Suśruta claims?[14]

The task of the commentators is to reconcile apparently contradictory texts and, more generally, to reconcile the Ayurvedic doctrine with the Hindu religion as a whole, by introducing a number of opportune distinctions. Although as a rule medicine and religion are mutually supportive and, as we have seen in chapter 2 in connection with epidemics, regions and things (physically) unhealthy are generally also (morally) impure, in the present case Cakrapāṇidatta, who was the first to note the difficulty, gets out of it by making a few distinctions. The purity of the waters of the Ganges (a religious notion) is not of the same order as the insalubrity of the waters which flow eastward (a notion of medical geography). Caraka said that the waters which flow into the Gulf of Bengal are "*generally* heavy" precisely because the Ganges is an exception. The commentator does not say that the water of the Ganges is purifying (a religious notion), although that idea is implicit in the objection that he raises, only that it is "beneficent," *pathya* (a medical notion). He justifies this by an indirect reference: he reminds us that the Ganges rises in the Himalayas. Two verses earlier Caraka has declared rivers rising in the Himalayas to be "beneficent, pure, used by the Rishis" (a religious notion). Hence, the Ganges is pure! The extent to which this *scientific* discourse is impregnated with the *religious* tradition is evident. What if the two are in contradiction? Both will nevertheless be retained, each on its own level. Thus the commentator will confirm both the bioclimatic and medical polarity between the arid Indus and the marshy Ganges and also the purity of the waters of the Ganges.[15] Similarly, that Suśruta and Caraka, the mythical authors of canonical texts, should be in contradiction is quite unthinkable. So, in the medieval commentaries, they are brought into agreement at the cost of introducing yet another distinction between the "heights" or "plateaus" *(adhityakā)* and the "valleys" or "foothills" *(upatyakā)*. The gushing water of the Himalayan heights is pure and beneficent; and, the commentator claims, Suśruta's condemnation of the Himalayan waters refers exclusively to those of the valleys or foothills, which are stagnant and therefore "unhealthy."[16] Perhaps this is a purely scholastic distinction, yet it may bear some relevance. Consider the unhealthy zones in the Nepalese Terry where waters which have gone underground upstream make their reappearance. This is a whole system of divisions within the space as represented in figure 7.

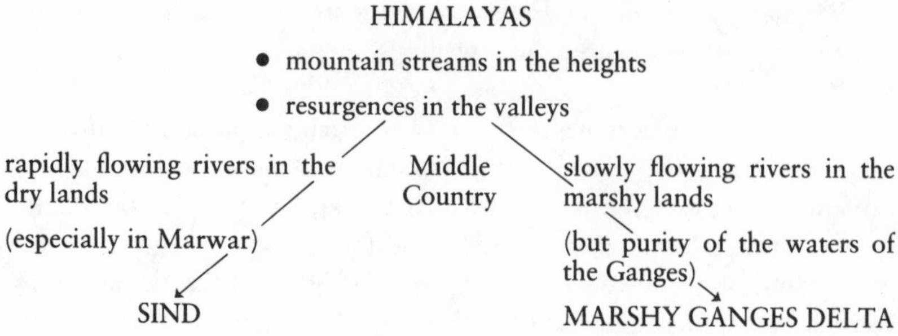

Figure 7. The hydrographic system

Are these principles of distribution and the same overall structure to be found in the flora and the fauna?

THE VEGETATION SERIES

When we turn to plant taxonomy, we are confronted by the new difficulty of ascertaining a method for identifying plant species for which we possess only the old Sanskrit name. It is possible, of course, to use oral traditions that link the Sanskrit name with the vulgar names of such and such a vernacular language, but identification then remains no more than plausible. Uncertainty affects the identity of each plant species taken individually. We shall try to circumvent this problem by studying groups, or series, whose biogeographical coherence reinforces the probability of the identifications proposed for each of the individual terms.

This is a risky method of proceeding, for there is a danger of introducing into the traditional lists an order that may be adventitious and illusory. Let us nevertheless consider the evidence. When Caraka describes the *ānūpa* landscape as "covered by forests of *hintāla, tamāla, nārikela*, and *kadalī*,"[17] should we assume the choice of those four terms to be purely contingent? Why were those particular four selected, out of the seven hundred plants composing the Ayurvedic flora? Each of the four terms may be considered exemplary:

hintāla	marshland date palm	(*Phoenix paludosa*)
tamāla	gamboge tree	(*Garcinia* sp.)
nārikela	coconut palm	(*Cocos nucifera*)
kadalī	banana tree	(*Musa paradisiaca*)

The marshland date palm is typical of the mangroves, especially in the Sundarbans (Bengal delta). The identity of the *tamāla* may be disputed: Is it *Garcinia xanthochymus* or *Garcinia morella*?[18] Whichever its identity, it is a typical "Indo-Malaysian" element in the flora,[19] a tree permanently in leaf, distributed over zones that are par excellence *ānūpa* (the wet forests): in the northeast, Assam (Khasi Hills) and eastern Bengal; in the southwest, the western Ghats; and in Ceylon. The coconut palm is a palm tree of the coastal regions, again primarily in the Gulf of Bengal and Kerala. Finally, the banana tree is cultivated throughout India except in the northwest and is indigenous to the eastern Himalayas, Assam, and Burma. Would it be too rash to consider this as a coherent group and conclude that the series refers primarily to the marshy northeast of India?

True, other plants might well be chosen to characterize *ānūpa* and we know of other such lists the content of which is different. For example, the *Bṛhatsaṃhitā*, a sixth-century encyclopedia and astrological treatise, in a chapter devoted to "the *Āyurveda* of trees" enumerates "sixteen native to *ānūpa*."[20] Sixteen is a stereotyped number indicating the completeness of the list, which mentions species growing, for preference, along the banks of watercourses, such as the *jambū* (*Eugenia jambolana*) and the willow (*Salix* sp.), also mentioned by Caraka: *vetasa, vānīra, vañjula*, all long identified with the rattan but considered today to be different species of the *Salix* genus.[21] One day it will be possible to check by computer not only the terms themselves but also their co-occurrences, their groups, the associations between the various plants, the features that in each case are typical and structural in these traditional lists of plant names in which the Ayurvedic texts abound.

The series of *jāṅgala* plants appearing in the same passage of the *Carakasaṃhitā* is worth studying by using a similar method. It does seem possible to distinguish in a convincing fashion between the several different kinds of plant formations which appear here, apparently intermingled:

kadara	a variety of acacia
khadira	*Acacia catechu*
asana	*Terminalia tomentosa* or *Pterocarpus marsupium*
aśvakarṇa	sal tree *(Shorea robusta?)*
dhava	*Anogeissus latifolia*
tiniśa	*Ougeinia dalbergioides*
śallakī	*Boswellia serrata* (produces incense)

sāla	*Shorea robusta*
somavalka	a variety of acacia *(A. arabica?)*
badarī	jujube tree *(Zizyphus jujuba)*
tindukā	ebony tree *(Diospyros* sp.*)*
aśvattha	*pīpal* fig tree *(Ficus religiosa)*
vaṭa	banyan tree *(Ficus bengalensis)*
āmalakī	emblic myrobalan *(Phyllanthus emblica)*
śamī	*Prosopis spicigera*
kakubha	*Terminalia arjuna*
śiṃśapā	*sīsū* tree *(Dalbergia sissoo)*

In this list, we notice first a number of trees that are among the most commonly cultivated in the vicinity of villages all over India: the jujube, the ebony, the *pīpal*, and the banyan, all traditionally associated with either gardening (the jujube) or ritual activities (the *pīpal* fig tree). Here, as in the catalog of meats, the *grāmya* space (the village) is included within the *jāṅgala* space (the dry lands).

Now consider the trees at the top of the list. Thorny trees, understandably enough, the acacia genus: *Khadira* denotes in particular *Acacia catechu*, but according to the Sanskrit commentaries and herbals, *kadara* and *somavalka* are "species of *khadira*," in which occurrences *khadira* would then denote the genus *(Acacia)*, not the species (*catechu*). *Somavalka* is generally identified as *Acacia arabica*. Next comes a group comprising *Terminalia-Shorea-Anogeissus*, which it is important to consider as a whole. Here, however, we are confronted by some difficulties of identification. The ambiguity of *asana*, which may denote either *Terminalia tomentosa* (the classical interpretation) or *Pterocarpus marsupium* (a recent revision), does not present too many problems: both species belong to the same plant formations.[22] Now, although proposed by eminent experts (Sri Yadavji Trikamji, Thakur Balwant Singh),[23] the identification of *aśvakarṇa* with a species of the (typically *ānūpa*) *Dipterocarpus* genus is to my mind unacceptable. Let us not forget that the Sanskrit herbals and commentaries on many occasions mention the synonymy between *aśvakarṇa* and *sāla (Shorea robusta)*, and let us adhere to this classical interpretation to prevent the present list from appearing incoherent. The repetition—the sal being mentioned almost immediately afterward by its other name—is really not exceptional in lists of this type, which pad out the Sanskrit treatises with redundancies in an almost systematic fashion. Thus the series of plants just considered belong essentially to what Pierre Legris, in *La végétation de l'Inde*, calls "deciduous dry formations," intermingled with others characteristic of "thorny dry formations" (table 4).

TABLE 4

THORNY DRY VS. DECIDUOUS DRY FORMATIONS

Thorny dry formations	Deciduous dry formations with sal
Acacia catechu	
	Terminalia tomentosa (?)
	sal (?)
	Anogeissus latifolia
	Ougeinia dalbergioides
	Boswellia serrata
	sal
Acacia arabica (?)	
Zizyphus jujuba	
	Diospyros melanoxylon
	Phyllanthus emblica
Prosopis spicigera	

The presence of fig trees, the pipal and banyan that come in between, is virtually insignificant from a geographical point of view; these species are distributed throughout India, sometimes cultivated, sometimes *ruderal* (growing in rubbish).[24] At the bottom of the list are two tree species which are deciduous but are associated with a proximity to water: *Terminalia arjuna* in the liana forests, and *Dalbergia sissoo* (rosewood), which grows with *Acacia catechu* in the pre-Himalayan depressions and valleys of the Terry.[25]

The trees listed in the right column in table 4 are sometimes associated with those in the left column, sometimes opposed to them. For example, *Phyllanthus emblica* (producer of one of the myrobalans) is associated with, among others, *Acacia catechu* and *Zizyphus jujuba* in the undulating regions of the Aravalli. A traditional division opposes country where the *babūl (Acacia arabica)* predominates to country where the *āonlā* (*Phyllanthus emblica*) flourishes: "Aonla, aonla, Mewar; babul, babul, Marwar," runs an old couplet of Rajasthan.[26] To the northwest is the sandy plain of the Marwar, scattered with occasional *babūl* trees; to the southeast lies the Mewar, more hilly and better watered. But there are some transitions between the thorny shrubs of the Marwar (zone a, map 7) and the dry forest, which includes teak trees on the plateaus of Madhya Pradesh (white zone, map 7). *All* the deciduous tree species mentioned in the right column of table 4, with the sole exception of the sal, come into contact with the

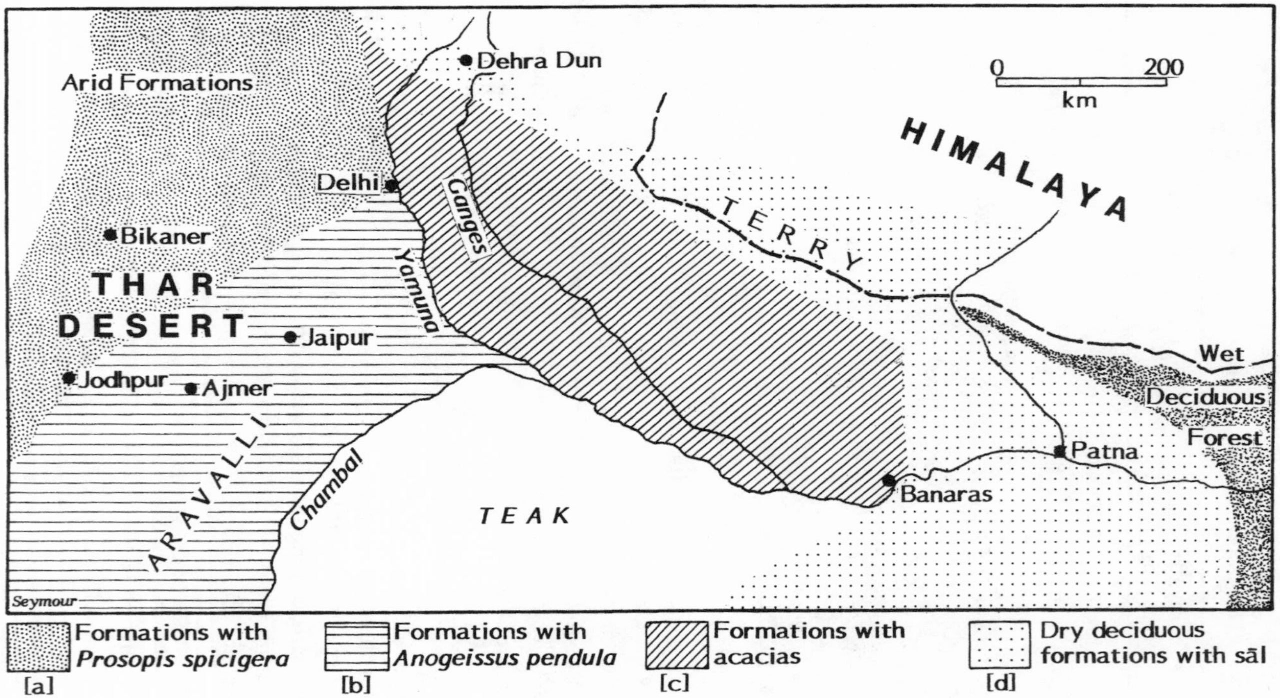

Map 7. Space of reference (in northern India) for the series of *jāṅgala* plants: types of plant formations. *Source*: Pierre Legris, *La Végétation de l'Inde: Ecologie et Flore* (Pondicherry, 1963). Redrawn for this work.

series of thorny trees or are even associated with *Acacia catechu, Zizyphus jujuba*, and so on. Within a vast region dominated overall by a series of vegetation comprising *Anogeissus pendula* (zone b, map 7), they thus form a number of transitional series comprising *Anogeissus latifolia* and *Terminalia tomentosa*, the location of which may be found on the "Rajasthan" sheet of the International Vegetation Map.[27]

If we may adopt the major categories of plant formations determined by Pierre Legris (map 7) as the typological and topographical framework for our analysis, the list of *jāṅgala* plants appears to refer to three types of thorny shrub formations:

1. *Prosopis spicigera, Acacia arabica . . .*
2. *(Anogeissus pendula), Acacia catechu, Zizyphus jujuba, Diospyros melanoxylon, Anogeissus latifolia . . .*
3. *Acacia arabica, Acacia catechu . . .*

as well as to the dry deciduous sal forest.

We could multiply uncertainties; the polysemy of the Sanskrit names renders virtually any identification ambiguous. Today, for example, the experts are unanimous in translating *śamī* as *Prosopis spicigera* (one of the *Mimoseae*, which has the same name in Hindi); yet it is impossible to forget the other, classical identification, *Acacia suma*.[28] But these uncertainties do not affect our argument. The method that we are attempting to follow is different. By distinguishing groups of terms, I hope to surmount two difficulties that remain insoluble so long as one continues to consider each term in isolation: first, there is the difficulty of translating the Sanskrit name, and second, the difficulty of locating the plant in question within a formation of which it would appear to be characteristic. These problems disappear as soon as one concentrates on groups, for a group can be meaningful even when some of its elements remain indeterminate. The overall structure of the list serves as a guide in the translation of one term or another: it indicates the most *likely* identification, the one that is most reasonable in the given context.

Biogeographical research in India reached its maturity in the 1900s when, each in his own domain, the botanist Joseph Dalton Hooker and the zoologist William Thomas Blanford defined a typology for the space of India divided into regions and subregions by reference to both the flora and the fauna, each region localizing a particular type of vegetation or fauna. A concluding remark on the vegetation is in order before turning to the fauna. Hooker's *Sketch* (1903) divides the area into three zones and hence into three types of vegetation that take over one from another as one moves from west to east: the Indus (thorny shrubs), the upper valley of the Ganges "from the east of Rajasthan to the Kosi River" (dry forest), and Bengal (wet forest).[29] Is this not the very same division that governs the nomenclature of plants in the previously analyzed passage from Caraka?

THE QUADRUPEDS

In 1901 in an article on "The Distribution of Vertebrate Animals," Blanford introduced a polarity between the India of the plains and plateaus (the cis-Gangetic subregion) where, among other characteristic families, the *Antilopinae* group lives; and wet, mountainous India (affinities here between the trans-Gangetic subregion and the Malabar coast tract), where the bovine group is distributed.[30] Hooker, the botanist, and Blanford, the zoologist, provide our enquiry with arguments of a similar nature, for the same difficulties are encountered when we turn to the Ayurvedic catalog of animals. Can we proceed as before, by taking two opposed lists of *jāṅgala* and *ānūpa* animals and interpreting each of their respective elements through the biogeographical polarity between the two groups they constitute? The difficulty of identifying and translating each of the terms on our lists is connected with the difficulty of *distributing* the lists in coherent groupings over the map of India.

We shall limit our analysis to two short lists that set in opposition two great fauna regions of the respectively "cis-" and "trans-gangetic" regions. On the one hand, over the great, flat, open expanses, we find antelope *cervicapra*, the nilgai, and the four-horned antelope. On the other hand, in the underwoods or wallowing in the water and mud, we find elephants, water buffaloes, the single-horned rhinoceros and, to a certain extent, great deer such as the *barāsiṅgha*. However, we run into obscurities when it comes to the distribution of the deer and more generally a confusion between what we would nowadays call the *Cervidae* and the *Antilopinae*.

The following list of the *jaṅghāla* animals given by Suśruta includes only the identifications deemed justifiable on the basis of Ḍalhaṇa's commentary. The word *jaṅghāla* means "those that have splendid legs *(jaṅghā)*."[31] They are essentially large, fleet-footed herbivores:

eṇa	antelope *cervicapra* (adult male)
hariṇa	antelope *cervicapra* (female, young)
ṛkṣa (ṛṣya)	nilgai (*Boselaphus tragocamelus*)
kuraṅga	chowsingha (*Tetracerus quadricornis*)
karāla	musk-deer (*Moschus moschiferus*)
kṛtamāla	?
śarabha	?
śvadaṃṣṭrā	?
pṛṣata	chital, or spotted deer (*Axis axis*)
cāruṣkara	?
mṛgamātṛkā	?

First, a word of warning: There are many uncertainties, and the translations proposed rest on the authority of Ḍalhaṇa who, coming as he did, ten centuries after the text on which he comments, was certainly not free from retrospective illusions. However, the little that we know is enough to convince us that this series *overall* is composed of "antelopes"—in the wider sense, *hariṇa*—and deer.

Cakrapāṇidatta and Ḍalhaṇa use the word *hariṇa* (adj.) "fawn-colored" and (noun) "antelope," as a generic term: *eṇa, ṛṣya, kuraṅga, pṛṣata, cāruṣkara*, and *mṛgamātṛkā* are each in turn referred to as "species of *hariṇa*" *(hariṇa-bheda, hariṇa-jāti)*.[32] The antelope with a fawn coat thus appears as the model or paradigm of the group. With the further connotation of the "reddish-brown" color of the coat, *hariṇa* denotes a whole group of "fawn" animals; *bête fauve* was used, similarly, in Old French for deer, buck, or roebuck. This term, however, is in competition with another. Vāgbhaṭa's commentators refer instead to "species of *mṛga*" *(mṛga-bheda)*, as do the traditional lexicons. We shall be returning later to the ambiguity of *mṛga*, which can cover the whole collection of "*Antilopinae*-and-*Cervidae*."[33] I should repeat that the species antelope *cervicapra* is unique within the *Antilope* genus. The sexual dimorphism (fawn coat for the females and the young; brownish-black for the adult males) explains the duality of the black *eṇa* (the Anglo-Indian black buck) and the fawn *hariṇa*: the two names apply to a single species, although *hariṇa* may also be used to refer to other, closely related species. Some eminent Sanskritists have translated *hariṇa* as "gazelle"; but that identification is either too narrow (if they are limiting themselves to the *Gazella bennetti* species, which is the only one present in India) or too ambiguous (if they are confusing antelope and gazelle). Let us agree to translate *hariṇa* henceforth: a) in the strict sense of "antelope," a species taken as the model for a group, and b) as the group of "antelopes (and assimilated species)," which includes the gazelle, the horse-antelope *(nilgai)*, the four-horned antelope *(chowsingha)*, the spotted deer *(chital)*, and so on.

The Sanskrit word *ṛkṣa* ("antelope") is not recorded in the dictionaries—obscured as it is by its homonym *ṛkṣa*, meaning "bear"—but nevertheless there can be no doubt of its existence. A precious gloss by Ḍalhaṇa both indicates the equivalence between *ṛkṣa* and *ṛṣya* and at the same time gives one of the Hindi names for the nilgai: *rojh*.[34] There is one gloss on the subject of this animal that appears repeatedly in the Sanskrit commentaries and lexicons: *nīlāṇḍo hariṇaḥ*, literally an "antelope with blue-black testicles."[35] This was perplexing until, one day, while reading the *Bhāvaprakāśa*, I noticed at a few lines distance a very curious shift from *ṛṣyo nīlāṇḍakaḥ to ṛṣyo nīlāṅgakaḥ*, "the antelope with the blue-black body."[36] From there, a single step leads us to the Hindi name *nīl-gā'e*, the "bovine with the blue-black [coat]" (the Anglo-Indian blue bull). The *nīlāṇḍa→nīlāṅga* variant provides a remarkable example of how Ayurvedic scholasticism operated: the most suggestive classical connotation (of black testicles) is eliminated, to be replaced by a vulgarized, less exceptional version (a black body); and on this is grafted the confusion between the nilgai and the bovines—a confusion so common that in several regions of India the nilgai is considered sacred on the same grounds as the cow, and its meat is prohibited.

Our linguistic hypotheses concerning the other terms in the list of *jaṅghāla* animals are more conveniently collected in table 5, where the vernacular names appearing in Ḍalhaṇa's commentary are compared with their Hindi equivalent: Skt. *catuḥśṛṅga* = H. *causiṅgā, causiṅghā*; or more generally with the corresponding rubric (in boldface type) in R. L. Turner's comparative dictionary of Indo-Aryan languages.[37] Thus, *karkaṭaka* (Ḍalhaṇa) = * **karkuṭaka** (Turner). The table also takes account of the descriptive notations.[38]

It is very difficult to understand why the list includes the *karāla*, a deer native to Kashmir, Nepal, and Sikkim. The presence of the *śarabha* is also puzzling: a fabulous animal with eight legs, the size of a camel, and with large horns, reputed to live in the mountains of Kashmir; perhaps a fantastical idealization of the large goats of the Himalayan forests.

Within the framework defined by Blanford in his famous article, let us attempt to distribute the terms of the series over the map of India (map 8). A clear ecological frontier separates the antelopes (and similar

TABLE 5
JAṄGHĀLA ANIMALS, FROM THE SANSKRIT TO THE VERNACULAR NAMES

	Ḍalhaṇa's commentary	Hypotheses	
• ṛkṣa	"*roru*"	H. *rojh*	< ***rōhya**
• kuraṅga	"*caturaṅga*" may be explained by comparing Ḍalhaṇa ad *sūtra* XX, 5 and *uttara* XXXIX, 153: "*catuḥśṛṅga*," "*bhedulī*" in the vernacular	H. *causiṅgā* "four-horned" = *bheṛī* "ewe"?	< **catuḥśṛṅga** < **bhēḍra**

The four-horned antelope is currently called "wild sheep," *bakrī* (< **barkara**) in the Dekkan (Raghu Vira, *Mammals*, p. 98). Hence my hypothesis: *bhedulī* = *bheṛī*.

• karāla	"its teeth protude underneath; it lives in mountains such as the Himalayas; called "*kastūrīmṛga*" in the vernacular" (ad *sūtra* XX, 5)	Cf. **kaḍāra** "whose teeth protude" **kastūrī** "musk deer"	
• kṛtamāla		?	
• śarabha	"eight feet, the size of a camel, large horns, with four feet on its back; it lives in Kashmir" (Ḍalhaṇa ad *sūtra* XX, 5, and Cakra. ad Caraka, *sūtra* XXVII, 45)	**śarabha**	from which are derived the names of the markhor in Dardic and Kafir speech, and the Sindhi *sarahu* "mountain goat" (markhor, ibex)
• śvadaṃṣṭrā	(variant: –*ă*) "four teeth, very vicious"; in Kārttikapura (?) it is called "*karkaṭaka*" (Ḍalhaṇa ad *sūtra* XX, 5, and Cakra. ad Suśruta, *sūtra* XLVI, 54: "*karkaṭa*")	= muntjak, barking-deer? = ***karkuṭaka**?	 Cf. **kurkura**

There may be a confusion between H. *kākar* "muntjak" (< **kakkaṭa**) and *kūkar* "dog" (< **kurkura**)

• pṛṣata	"*cittala*"	H. *cītal*	< **citrala**
• cāruṣkara		?	

TABLE 5 (cont)

• mṛgamātṛkā	"very small, large belly"; *caturaṅga* female, "*bhedalī*" in the vernacular." Cf. Hemādri ad Vāgbhaṭa, *sūtra* VI, 43: "resembles a hare."	= the musk deer *Tragulus meminna*? Cf. *bheṛī*

H. = hindi,
< = etymology
Boldface type = entries in Turner's dictionary
Rhagu Vira = Rhagu Vira, K. N. Dave, and Lokesh Chandra, *Indian Scientific Nomenclature of the Mammals of India, Burma and Ceylon* (Nagpur, 1953).

creatures) from species such as the *karāla* and the *śarabha*, which live in the "trans-Gangetic" or even "Tibetan" zones. The distribution of the *nilgai* is identical to that of antelope *cervicapra*: throughout "cis-Gangetic" India, including the Punjab (which Blanford classifies separately) but avoiding the dense forest, the mountainous zones, and the Ganges delta. The gazelle *(Gazella bennetti)* is present to the west of the Indus and in the northwest of the peninsula; the eastern limit of its specific zone is in Madhya Pradesh and may be symbolized by a line passing from Seoni to Chanda,[39] as schematically indicated on map 8. Favorite habitat: jungles (wastelands) intersected by ravines and nullahs (dried-up watercourses). Admittedly, it might be objected that there is no case for considering the gazelle, since it does not even appear on the list of *jaṅghāla* animals or at any rate is not identified there. My justification would be that if the Ayurvedic catalog is coherent (as our working hypothesis assumes), the gazelle *rightfully* belongs to the antelope group (in the wider sense) and is an integral part of this group, even if half the creatures in the group remain unidentified. Furthermore, *jaṅghāla* and *jāṅghika* are also proper names specifically attributed to the gazelle, as is attested by a number of traditional lexicons that at the same time mention some others: *śrī-kārin, sīt-kāra, chiṅ-kāra*, all constructed on the onomatopoeic *tchhrrss*, an allusion to the hissing sound that the gazelle emits when alarmed.[40] I would, indeed, be inclined to go further and suggest that the word *cāruṣ-kara* is formed in the same fashion, to name the gazelle.[41]

The area of distribution of the four-horned antelope *(chowsingha)* and the spotted deer *(chital)* is to some extent identical (see the dashed zone in map 8, which Blanford calls "cis-gangetic"). Both favor an un-

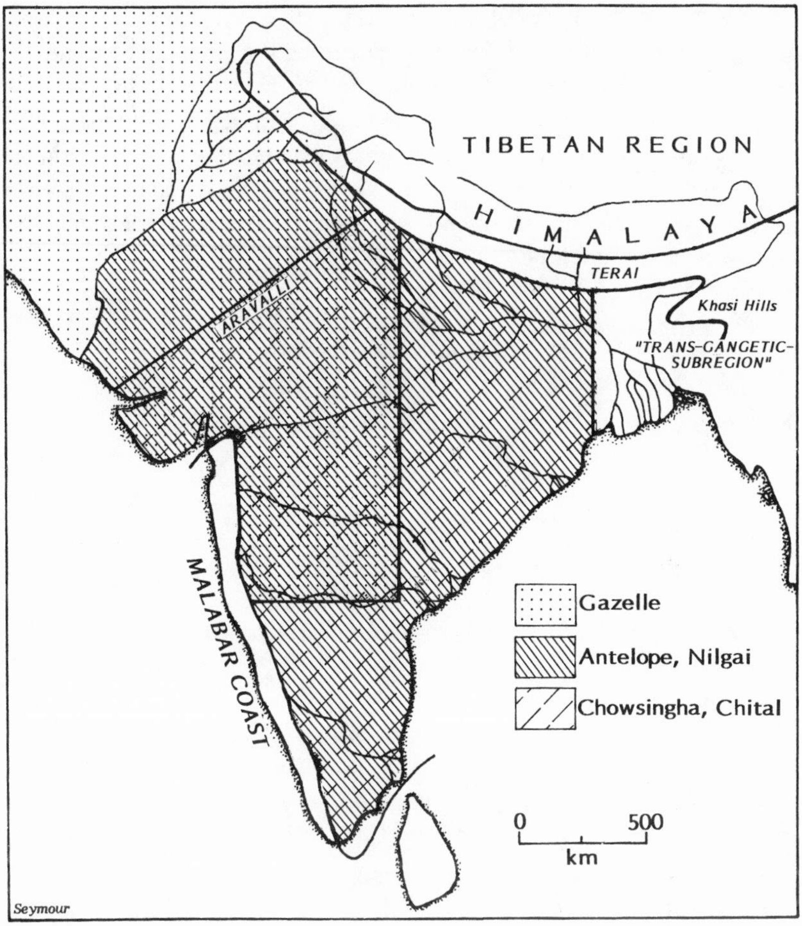

Map 8. Distribution of *jaṅghāla* animals very free of foot over wide expanses.

dulating terrain with nearby water and are unknown on the arid plains of the Punjab and Sind. However, the chital spills over considerably from this zone and can be found as far north as the valleys of Bhutan and Assam, in Bengal (Sundarbans), and in the south (Ceylon), in grassy clearings of the sal and teak forests at altitudes of up to 1,200 m. According to George B. Schaller, its distribution corresponds to that of the deciduous forest (both wet and dry), except in hilly or mountainous regions.[42] Like all the deer family, the chital must be near water but, in contrast to the sambar, which lives in the heart of the dense forest, and the barasingha, which lurks in the tall grasslands, the chital flourishes in open terrain at the edges of woods.[43] From an ecological point of view, one can understand why it is classified among the *jaṅghāla* animals.

There remains the perplexing presence of the "musk-deer" and the *śarabha*; the same difficulty, in a converse form, occurs in the series of the *kūlacara* animals, the large mammals which come to disport themselves and drink at the water's edge, since here the unidentified names *gokarṇa* and *nyaṅku* are mentioned, names generally translated by Sanskritists as "antelope."

Here is the list of *kūlacara* animals, "those that live on the banks":

gaja	elephant *(Elephas maximus)*
gavaya	gaur *(Bos gaurus)*, gayal *(Bos frontalis)*
mahiṣa	water buffalo *(Bubalus bubalis)*
ruru	barasingha *(Cervus duvauceli)*
camara	yak *(Bos grunniens)*
sṛmara	?
rohita	?
varāha	boar *(Sus scrofa)*
khaḍgin	rhinoceros *(Rhinoceros unicornis)*
gokarṇa	?
kālapucchaka	?
udra	otter *(Lutra lutra)*
nyaṅku	?
araṇyagavaya	gaur ("wild," *araṇya-)*

The presence of elephant, buffalo, boar, and rhinoceros raises no problem of either a philological or a biological nature (the Sanskrit names are the habitual ones, and these are par excellence animals of the waterside). "Herds of wild boar, emerging from the pools (where they were wallowing)" is a classic literary theme.[44] The first difficulty arises, however, from the intermingling of two fauna that are in reality quite distinct: the fauna of the fluvial regions (essentially, the water buffalo, the rhinoceros) and the Himalayan fauna (the yak, the otter, and, to some extent, the gaur). Remember the definition of the *ānūpa* place, which Suśruta associates with mountains, even high mountains. It is with this perspective that Suśruta mentions the otter, which assuredly lives at the water's edge but only that of mountain streams or lakes, in the Himalayan regions.[45] By dint of distorting his perspective, Suśruta even includes the *camara*, or yak, despite the fact that its area of distribution is quite marginal in relation to the space of reference defined at the outset (northern India).[46] One possible justification for the presence of the yak is its relationship to the *Bovinae*: The gaur and the yak, Ḍalhaṇa tells us, are "like the bovines" *(go-sadṛśa)*. The puzzle continues when we learn that the *sṛmara* is "a large boar" and that the *rohita* is of "the class of the *mṛga*" or, according to others, a boar. Finally, there appear three unidentified names, which might refer to antelopes:

gokarṇa	Hindi form *gokarṇ*, can indisputably denote the nilgai. But is that the meaning here? Ḍalhaṇa: "it has the ears of a bovine; it is called *gona*." Turner: < **goṇa** "bull"? Cf. Cakra. on Suśruta, *sūtra* XLVI, 94: "*gola-hariṇa*"; Caraka, *sūtra* XXVII, 45, ed. Bombay: "*gālgu-hariṇa.*" Compare with the Sindhi *goinu* "elk," the Sinhalese *gōnā* "deer" (Turner's Dictionary: < **gokarṇa**).
kālapuccha	(variant: *–ka*) "(animal) with a black tail." Cf. Hindi *kāl-pūñch* "gazelle."
nyaṅku	(?) For some, "antelope," for others (*Vaidyakaśabdasindhu*, the editors of the *Bhāvaprakāśa*, etc.) "barasingha." The vernacular names given by Ḍalhaṇa remain obscure: "*nyaṅguṇa*," and Cakra, on Suśruta: "*nākula-hariṇa*," on Caraka: "*nyaṅkuśa*." Note that: "Elk" in Anglo-Indian refers to the sambar or barasingha.

Biologists distinguish a number of subfamilies among the *Bovidae*, such as:

1. *Tragelaphinae*: four-horned antelope, nilgai;
2. *Bovinae*: gaur, yak, buffalo;
3. *Antilopinae*: antelope, gazelle;

etc. (*Ovinae, Caprinae*. . .).[47]

Here they are divided into *jaṅghāla* and *kūlacara*, as represented in figure 8.

In principle the distinction is a clear one but it is blurred by a number of additions or equivocations: a) the elephant, boar, and others are included in the *Bovinae* class; b) the *Cervidae* are arbitrarily divided into two groups; and c) a number of terms refer indistinguishably to both antelopes and deer.

Before embarking on a biogeographical comparison, some clarification is needed on the translation of *mṛga* and the conventions to be adopted:

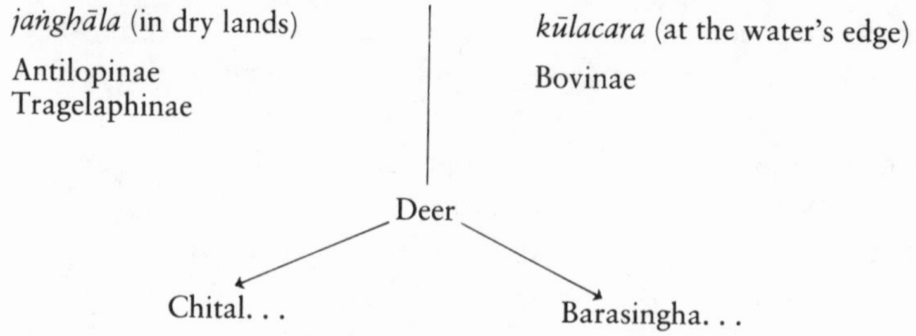

Figure 8. The *Bovidae* divided into those living in dry lands (*jaṅghāla*) and those living at the water's edge (*kūlacara*)

• *mṛga* I. Mental category

1. "Quadruped" (*mṛga-pakṣin* "q. and birds").

2. "(Quadruped) game"; the opposite of both *paśu* "livestock" and *vyāla* "beast of prey."

3. "Wild animal"; including predators and wild *Bovinae.*

II. Biological reality

1. "Antelope"; among quadrupeds, game par excellence. "Gazelle" may be accepted in a poetic context (*mṛgadṛś*, a woman with the "eyes of a gazelle").

2. The antelope considered as the model of a class, *mṛga-jāti*, the "class of *mṛga*" which includes *Antilopinae, Tragelaphinae*, and *Cervidae*. In these circumstances, of course, a "deer" is a *mṛga*, but this meaning is only arrived at by extension. As a convention, we shall use the translation "*Antilopinae*-and-*Cervidae*."

Thus, when Suśruta opposes *jaṅghālā mṛgāḥ* to *kūlacarāḥ paśavaḥ*, we should interpret the former as the fleet of foot *Antilopinae*-and-*Cervidae*, and the latter, the *Bovinae* and assimilated species that live at the water's edge.[48]

The reader may find the importance given to linguistic comparisons surprising: compounds, synonyms, vernacular equivalents to the Sanskrit names. It should be remembered, however, that the flora and fauna never prompt descriptions in the classical texts, as they do in the Greek tradition. They are simply mentioned as series of terms on which the lexicons and commentaries superimpose others. Description is achieved through synonymy and compound substantives—that is, through a vast interplay of equivalences on the following model, one repeatedly used in texts of logic: "*aśvakarṇa*, the *horse-ear* plant, is *sāla*, the sal"; the compound describes the long spatula-shaped sepals enclosing the flower of the sal tree. There is no end to such wordplay: *kuraṅga* is "tetracere" or "four-horned" *(catuḥśṛṅga)*; the nilgai is "cow-ear" *(gokarṇa)*;

and so on. Presently we shall recognize the importance to be allotted to stylistic and poetic features. It is only in the commentaries—and rarely even there—that one finds a description utilizing anything other than nouns, an account or sentence which uses personal verb forms. One rare case is given below. It comes from Ḍalhaṇa's commentary on the *ruru*, in all likelihood a name for the barasingha, or swamp deer:

> The *ruru* loses its horns in autumn. It is described as follows: extraordinarily large horns, a body shaped like a sambar, but it is distinguishable from the sambars by the fact that it lives at the water's edge; it loses its horns in autumn, it bellows (RU-root), hence, perhaps, this name *ruru*; a variety of the great *mṛga* which lives principally in the country of the Cedi.[49]

In contrast to the *Bovidae* and *Antilopinae* whose horns are permanent, the *Cervidae* shed their antlers yearly. So the animal in question is a deer. The comparison with the sambar is significant. Whereas the sambar *(Cervus unicolor)* lives in the forest in the shelter of the trees, the barasingha *(Cervus duvauceli)* flourishes in clearings or swamps. According to S. H. Prater, the existence of two different species of barasingha can be explained by two different biocenoses: one species with small, hard hooves, still to be found on dry terrain, once lived in the clearings of the sal forests of Madhya Pradesh and in Orissa (but very few have survived); the other, with wider, more flexible hooves, still inhabits the marshes of Uttar Pradesh (on the eastern bank of the Ganges, at the foot of the Siwalik Mountains), the Terry and Assam (although its numbers, too, have been decimated). They spend most of the time in the water.[50] "In the country of the Cedi," Ḍalhaṇa adds, at the end of his description. Without seeking to identify this country too precisely (for precision would be misleading here), I am inclined to understand: "to the south of the Ganges." The *ruru* is neither a deer of Kashmir nor a sambar. It can only be the barasingha, whose specific area of distribution (map 9a) calls to mind the diffusion of Sino-Indian elements of fauna in the interior of the peninsula, in cis-Gangetic India.

The series of *kūlacara* animals, which is of scant coherence from the point of view of etymology or synonymy, acquires a unity at the biogeographical level. These animals are found in the northeast (trans-Gangetic region) and the southwest (Western Ghats). Map 5b in chapter 2 provides the model: the distribution of the gaur. In the cases of elephant, gaur, buffalo, boar, and rhinoceros, however, the area of distribution spreads farther into Burma, the Indo-Chinese peninsula, and Malaysia, where identical or related species are to be found. They repre-

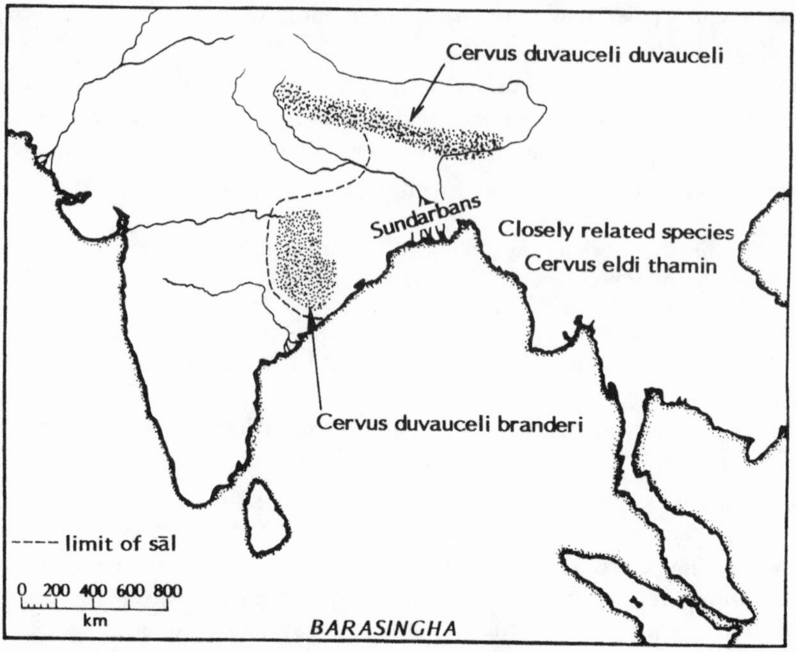

Map 9a. Distribution of the barasingha. The *duvauceli* species was formerly present in the Sundarbans (the Bengal delta).
The importance of the southern frontier of sal forest as a dividing line can be clearly seen.

sent the great Indian fauna of "eastern" origin. Maps 5a and 5b (the antelope and the gaur) and map 8 of cis-Gangetic India, flanked to the northeast and southwest by marshy and mountainous regions, clearly show the distribution of two different faunas along two opposite and intersecting axes: the antelope, and others from northwest to southeast; the gaur and others from northeast to southwest.

The specific range of the barasingha is revealing, as is that of the water buffalo: though present in Madhya Pradesh and Orissa, they do not extend farther south. (Of course, we are here concerned only with the wild species.) The frontier between the sal and the teak domains plays a decisive role; these are two facies—the one wetter (sal), the other dryer (teak)—of the same type of vegetation. The frontier of the barasingha specific range coincides in the south with that of the sal domain.[51] When compared with the elephant and the gaur, which crossed the whole peninsula to reach the wet forests of the southwest, the expansion of the barasingha might be described as incomplete. The

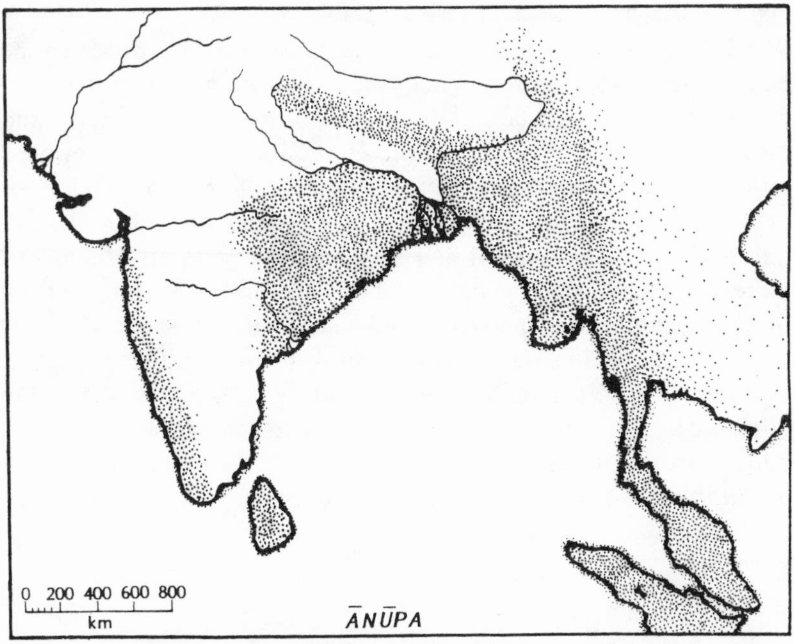

Map 9b. Distribution of the *ānūpa* animals. It shows a schematic representation of the distribution of *ānūpa* animals and the extent to which they belong to the "eastern" domain: species identical or related to those present in India inhabit Burma, Malaysia, and elsewhere.
The discontinuity between the northeast (as far as Orissa) and the southwest (Malabar coast and Ceylon) is interpreted by ecologists as an apparent break in an underlying continuity. From the Indus to Tamilnad (white): the dry lands; from Bengal to Kerala (dotted): the axis of expansion for the "eastern" fauna.

same reason accounts both for the absence of the barasingha and the buffalo in the south and for the discontinuity in the distribution of the gaur and the elephant. The gaur and the elephant are present in Orissa, disappear in Maharashtra and Andhra Pradesh (*jāṅgala* regions), and reappear in the forests of Mysore (see map 9b). This group (elephant, gaur) crossed the ecological obstacle that the dry lands of the plateaus of the Dekkan constituted for them, as *ānūpa* animals; the former group (barasingha, buffalo) were deterred by that barrier and stopped short at the limit of the wet surface area of the dry forest, namely the limit of the sal.

Nuances could be introduced into this schema by distinguishing between species which prefer the mountain forest (gaur) and those which, in contrast, are adapted to low-lying marshy lands (rhinoceros, buffalo); the elephant, which is very adaptable, flourishes in either habitat. We should remember, furthermore, that domesticated species of the buffalo are widespread throughout India. Finally, *gavaya* in the *kūlacara* series may denote both the gaur *(Bos gaurus)*, a wild species, and the gayal *(Bos frontalis)*, a domesticated species of the gaur. They need to live in forest land. Essentially, they inhabit mountainous regions of between 600 and 2,000 meters but are also present at higher altitudes (reaching the yak's domain) and at much lower ones. F. J. Simoons writes that in the pre-Himalayan valleys "the mithan (gayal) overlaps the distribution of common cattle and water buffalo."[52]

Although precise modifications might further enrich this enquiry, it does enable us to determine our classificatory categories spatially. Let us glance at the map of India: in the center, extending from the Indus to Tamil country, lies the *jāṅgala*, the territory of the *jaṅghāla*; at the northeastern and southwestern extremities lie the *ānūpa* territories of the *kūlacara*.

WHEAT AND RICE

Dry lands in the Indus valley, marshy lands in the Ganges basin: this is both a physical fact, inscribed on the map, and a cultural pattern acknowledged in the Sanskrit texts. I feel no compunction in merging these two levels of approach. When agriculture, stock raising, health and food ways are concerned, mental representations definitely become indissociable from physical facts: together they comprise a single, total, social fact. The Indus/Ganges axis heralds a still more fundamental division that runs from north to south across monsoon Asia. Is it not a frontier between two civilizations?

Let us try and tackle the most obvious contrast and the most difficult to explain: the production and consumption of milk. "The Middle East, India and Tibet practice the milking of cows, female buffaloes, goats and sheep. This area, within which milk is consumed, stands in contrast to another where it is not: Ceylon, the mountains of Assam" and the whole of eastern Asia.[53] What bearing does this contrast have on our analysis? From the point of view of the *consumption* of milk (food ways), the whole of India falls to one side of this frontier; but from the point of view of agro-pastoral *production*, the frontier between two types of traditional economies passes right through the heart of India. On one side lies western Asia, with the raising of cows, horses, sheep, and goats; on the other side, the low-lying lands of eastern Asia (including the rice-growing regions of India), with the raising of pigs, buffaloes, and ducks. In the west, the major crops are grown by direct seeding; in the east they are established primarily by the transplanting of cuttings and seedlings.[54] In the west: milk-cows, millet and wheat; in the east, the consumption of pork and the planting-out of rice shoots, with buffaloes used essentially as draught animals.

I admit that this is a simplification. Nowadays, rice is cultivated and planted out along the whole of the Indian western seaboard. All the same, the contrast remains quite evident. Just a telling incident: I was on the train between Madras and Trivandrum. Dinner was served. Sharing my compartment was a Punjabi traveling in the South on business of some kind. As soon as his fingers touched the rice, he was overcome with nausea: "Ahhh, this rice . . . I loathe their rice!"

Geographers can qualify the partitioning of the space of India with countless nuances. Admirable maps thus make it possible to appreciate at a glance the succession of types of agriculture in the Indogangetic plain: in the west millets; then wheat (Punjab); in the middle reaches of the Ganges valley, a combination of rice (in autumn) and wheat (in spring); and finally, in Bengal and the valleys of Assam, rice (together with pulses, vegetables, jute). A map of agricultural production over the peninsula as a whole clearly reveals how the "India of millets" extends southward from the northwest along the axis of the dry lands, "the dry central axis" as François Durand-Dastès calls it.[55] The geography of feeding customs is more subtle but corresponds in the main with that of agricultural production.

Such methods might be used to interpret the rare passages devoted to human geography in the Ayurvedic treatises. While maps could be used to locate the facts spatially, the interpreter should be on guard: the teaching purveyed in these texts both idealizes the facts and refers to now-vanished customs:

> The Bactrians, Persians, Tibetans, Sogdians, Greeks and Scythians include among their habits: meat, wheat, *mādhvīka* alcohol, fire and the sword. The Easterners have a regimen with a basis of fish; the people of the Sind have a regimen with a basis of milk. But for the *Aśmaka* and the *Avantika* [on the plateaus of the Dekkan?], it is a regimen with a basis of oil associated with acid substances. Tubers, roots and fruits: that is the habitual regimen of the people of the *Malaya*. The habitual regimen in the south: *peyā*, and in the north-west: *mantha*. The habitual regimen in the *Madhyadeśa*: barley, wheat, cow's milk.[56]

A simplification of this quote helps to draw out the contrasts. First, *vegetarian* India is here distinguished from the warlike regions of the north and the northwest, with their eaters of meat and drinkers of alcohol. It is an idealized, normative contrast: Ayurveda is a brahminic science. Next, within India itself, a polarity is expressed between the people of the northwest and those of the south: the former eat *mantha*, or barley gruel, the latter *peyā*, or rice gruel.[57] Finally, a polarity is expressed between milk and fish in connection with the people of Sind—the *Saindhava*—and those of the east—the *Prācya*, that is, the Biharis and the Bengalis. It is a polarity duplicated by another, as Caraka explains: the Bactrians, the peoples of *Saurāṣṭra* (Surate), Sind, and the delta of the Indus "habitually put salt in their milk," whereas the Easterners and Tibetans *(Prācya* and *Cīna)* in contrast make an excessive use of alkaline substances.[58] In the west, there is a predilection for the salt series, in the east, for the alkaline series.

The interest of the text lies not in the information it provides but in the perspective in which that information is viewed. Did these dichotomies ever really correspond to the ethnographical reality? The significance in antiquity of putting salt in one's milk is unknown. But the essential purpose of the oppositions set up between barley gruel and rice gruel, milk and fish, salt and alkali, was to mark out contrasts within the space of reference. The inventory of different customs and the nomenclature of different peoples were unimportant: what was set up was a system of orientations (figure 9):

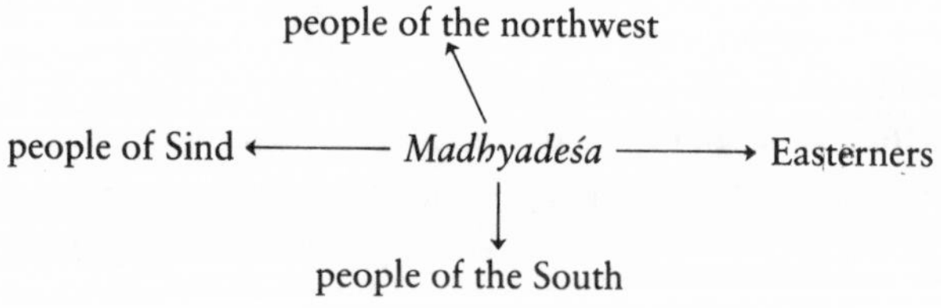

Figure 9. The broad lines of a human geography

A few words lost in a welter of therapeutic prescriptions convey the broad lines of a human geography in the Ayurvedic treatises. They record at least two fundamental facts: a) that the growing and consumption of millet, barley, and wheat extend along the axis of the dry lands, from the northwest to the south (the axis of expansion for the *jāṅgala* fauna), and b) that the consumption of milk is a western custom.

This completes the first part of our study. It has attempted to situate the jungle and its limits on the map of India, to establish the central position of the Delhi Doab and of the plains and plateaus that form the central dry axis oriented from the northwest toward the south of the peninsula, and to reveal the total social fact constituted by the polarity between the Indus and the Ganges, using toponymy, the study of flora, the taxonomy of quadrupeds, and the geography of feeding habits as keys for interpreting the ancient texts. That is the first aspect of the classical tradition: all that falls within the order of perception, everything that can be situated within the space, within the landscape, on the map, a collection of doctrines and nomenclatures which can be confirmed, specified, and visualized through geography.

Now we must turn to the other aspect of this tradition: all that pertains to the order of words. Our first task will be to study the phraseology which enables the doctor to assess, compose, and prescribe remedies. A lengthy process of cooking imbues these remedies with the savors and beneficent virtues of the jungle.

IV: Zoology in Pharmacy

Modern works devoted to Indian medicine generally classify the doctrine under traditional Greek and Latin headings: anatomy, physiology, pathology, and so on. Interpreters consequently suppose the ordering of the material to have been similar to that adopted in our own ancient medicine. This analogy, however, should not be taken for granted. One difference of capital importance which does not emerge from that mode of presentation affects the very nature of the *reasoning* in ancient India, the style of the Sanskrit texts and the rules of literary composition. Once a field or subject of study has been determined, we, as the heirs of Greco-Latin logic, proceed by way of description and argument; each heading announces the account of a particular line of research. Osteology, physio-logy, path-ology: the suffix itself indicates an objective approach, a distinction drawn on principle between the researcher and his field of study. The situation in the Ayurvedic treatises, however, is quite different. In ancient India, the primary material of knowledge was constituted by the *recitation of series of words* of a more or less stereotyped nature. Presently I am concerned only with the fauna and *materia medica* of animal origin; and I would suggest it erroneous to give the name of zoology to what, in Sanskrit literature, is at most a bestiary. The word *zoology* is used in this chapter heading simply by way of an *antiphrasis*. There could have been no zoology in the minds of the Indian scholars, no osteology or physiology. Instead, based on a Sanskrit image, there are endless "garlands of names" (*nāmamālā*). Onto these name lists are grafted an amazing combinative system of "savors" (*rasa*) and "qualities" (*guṇa*).

Balwant Singh and Chunekar have counted more than fifteen hundred names of plants and about three hundred names of animals in the Ayurvedic Great Triad. To take accurate account of all the synonyms mentioned in the treasuries of Sanskrit names and in the commentaries, these figures should be multiplied by at least three. It is potential material for a huge network of semantic coordinations. Such a study is at present beyond the scope of this book, for it would presuppose a very lengthy work of indexing and totally new methods of linguistic comparison. Furthermore, two logical and linguistic problems would be involved: the problem of synonymy and that of reference. Take the example already cited: *aśvakarṇa*, "horse-ear," is a synonym for *sāla*, the sal tree. It is a way of describing it: "horse-ear" refers to the elongated, spatulalike shape of the sepals. *Sāla* is also known by another name—*sarja*, or "resinous." These descriptive names are what logicians call "cognitive" synonyms, in that they denote one and the same referent, the sal, although their meanings or connotations are different. A single plant or animal may thus possess a dozen or more names. Through the particular connotations of each cognitive synonym each name adds to our knowledge. To describe is thus to name. The cuckoo provided another such example. In his *Historia animalium*, Aristotle, describing the behavior of these birds, mentions a well-known fact: "The cuckoo makes no nest but lays its egg in the nests of other birds. It lays only one egg but does not itself hatch it. It is the bird in whose nest the egg has been laid that breaks it to hatch it out and that feeds the young bird."[1] The Ayurvedic treatises contain no such account or story but rather provide only an equivalence between two synonyms. One of the names of the *kokila*, the Indian cuckoo, is in effect *parabhṛta*, "the-one-which-was-fed-by-another." This is the name to be found in the catalog of animals in the *Suśrutasaṃhitā* (see the appendix, the Nomenclature of Animals). While the Greek and Latin naturalists observed and registered curious details and invented the model of knowledge called *natural history*, the Indian scholars, following a quite different path of reasoning, forged and created a thesaurus of names and their semantic equivalents.

We must defer the study of these onomastics to some later date and instead focus our analysis on the manner in which therapeutic savors and qualities are grafted on this animal nomenclature by means of *logical* and *poetic* rules that determine the use of several hundred adjectives and nominal forms of verbs for descriptive purposes.

THE CATALOG OF MEATS

The catalog of meats in the *Suśrutasaṃhitā* is the most complete and orderly of any catalog I have come across in the classical literature of Ayurveda. It will therefore constitute the catalog of reference to which we will compare the other catalogs to indicate differences, note variants, and complete the network of synonyms. In a dozen or so pages of a chapter devoted to *materia medica*, where the list of meats is inserted between those of the cereals and fruits (the order is traditional), Suśruta names one hundred and sixty-eight meats, further classifying them into two categories: *jāṅgala* and *ānūpa* (including fishes). The listing of the animal kingdom is complete except for the insects, which are studied elsewhere, in texts concerned with poisons and venoms.

All meats, even the most fabulous, are endowed with pharmaceutical properties. We must, from the outset, recognize the ideal and symbolical nature of this nomenclature, which includes so many rare or even imaginary species. Were the therapeutical prescriptions contained in this catalog ever really applied? Are they even formulated to that end? Probably not. When Caraka lists the items necessary to ensure the correct functioning of an Ayurvedic hospital, he enumerates the animals to be kept available within its precinct: the quail, the partridge, the hare, the antelope.[2] Even if we assume—with no independent evidence—that the flesh of these (eight) species of animals together with a few other products of stock raising or hunting may have been used, the number of species likely to have supplied truly *materia medica* is very tiny (no more than a few dozen) compared with the total number included in the catalog (one hundred and sixty-eight). What then was the purpose of an inventory that had so little practical application? Seeking to interpret this text at a distance of twenty centuries, I believe it may be seen as a kind of "zoology." Thus, my hypothesis maintains that this text represents a corpus of knowledge about the fauna, knowledge not set out as such but slipped into the mold of discourse intended for the use of medical practitioners.

Among the Sanskrit texts of a scientific character, none is truly zoological. The *Mṛgapakṣiśāstra* by Haṃsadeva (thirteenth century), the "Treatise on quadrupeds and birds," is unique in this field and offers only a series of poetic tableaus tinged with eroticism. The treatises on horses and elephants (royal animals), bordering on veterinary medicine and warcraft, must be set apart. All that remains is a traditional bestiary—images (as, for example, those on the seals discovered at Mohenjo-daro),[3] myths and fables, and nomenclatures—the richest examples of which are to be found in the texts of *materia medica.*

A few remarks on the style and chronology of the Ayurvedic texts may be useful. They can be divided into two types: the "corpus" (*saṃhitā*) or treatises on medicine, and the "dictionaries" (*nighaṇṭu*) of *materia medica.* The treatises and the dictionaries belong to two different literary genres which flourished at different periods. Some indication of the date of the treatises of the classical Great Triad is available: the most recent (Vāgbhaṭa) goes back to the seventh century. The dictionaries, in contrast, seem to have appeared later, sometime between the twelfth and the fourteenth centuries, although serious doubt remains about the *Dhanvantarinighaṇṭu*, formerly considered to be the most ancient (fourth century) but now dated to the twelfth century by the most eminent specialist in this literature.[4] It is possible that at some ancient date the dictionaries formed part of the treatises, becoming detached from them later. If that is the case, the classical period (which produced the treatises) was followed, in the Middle Ages, by a scholastic period (when the double labor of glossing and compilation produced commentaries and dictionaries based on the most ancient of the texts).

There are many dictionaries and they take various forms. The *Dhanvantarinighaṇṭu* considers each remedy separately, enumerating the series of synonyms, followed by the series of pharmaceutical qualities. In contrast, the *Madanapālanighaṇṭu* (fourteenth century) consists of a sequence of concise catalogs in verse form, the arrangement and style of which resemble those of a chapter in a *saṃhitā*. At a later date, there appeared works of a hybrid style, such as the *Bhāvaprakāśa* (sixteenth century), incorporating the lexical substance of the *nighaṇṭu* and at the same time vulgarizing the classical treatises. Such works constitute a veritable literary genre and one not limited to the specialized domain of Ayurveda. These "treasuries of names" (*abhidhānakośa*) occupy a place of importance in Sanskrit literature in general. The dictionary's role in the expression of knowledge cannot be overemphasized. Its style of thought might be called the "Codex style," whereby "knowing" is collecting names and formulas. Anything pertaining to the natural sciences of zoology and botany is cast in this intellectual mold and then taught in the form of a pharmacopoeia. To limit ourselves to the particular theme of the present enquiry, we are constantly obliged to read "animals" where the texts say "meats." Is it a question of fauna, then, or of dietary prescriptions? This ambiguity deserves further explanation.

All the texts, treatises, and dictionaries contain a catalog of meats, more or less clearly based on the polarity between *jāṅgala* and *ānūpa*. Suśruta's catalog begins as follows:

> And now we shall enumerate the different kinds of meats, namely: aquatic, *ānūpa*, domesticated, carnivorous, whole-hoofed and *jāṅgala*. That makes six kinds of meats, which are listed in order of increasing excellence.

A hierarchy is thus immediately established, although it is not yet explained why aquatic meats should be the worst and *jāṅgala* ones the best. The principle on which the hierarchy rests is not indicated until the end of the catalog. The corresponding schema is admirably rigorous; Suśruta literally incorporates two orders of considerations, one within the other. Inside, circumscribed and contained, is a *distribution of animals* according to biogeographical criteria:

Those of the dry lands
- which have legs
- which scatter grain (quail, partridge . . .)
  etc.

Those of a wet habitat
- which live on the river banks (elephant, buffalo)
- which float (goose, crane . . .)
  etc.

In its introduction and conclusion, however, framing the distributive schema and encompassing the biogeographical considerations, a *hierarchy of meats* is found, for which the criteria are medical:

> Aquatic, *ānūpa*, domesticated, carnivorous and whole-hoofed, and those which tear at their food, those which have a burrow, those called *jaṅghāla* (which have legs), those which peck and scatter grain (in that order) precisely—these are (meats), each one of which is lighter (*laghu*) than the one before and produces far fewer fluxes (*alpābhiṣyandin*) than the one which precedes it (in the list), and vice versa.[5]

The two passages by Suśruta cited above—the one a catalog introduction, the other a catalog conclusion—correspond name for name in describing the different kinds of meat: aquatic, marshy (*ānūpa*), domesticated, carnivorous, whole-hoofed. These passages differ, however, in that one proceeds to add *jāṅgala* to the series while the other gives a detailed list of subdivisions of the *jāṅgala* category. Nevertheless, both passages formulate one and the same hierarchy of the medical

TABLE 6
THE SCALE OF VALUES

the best	
the lightest *(laghu)* and astringent meats	**jāṅgala** of the dry lands
	ekaśapha whole-hoofed
	kravyāda *(kravyabhuj)* carnivorous
the heaviest meats, the ones which produce the most fluxes *(abhiṣyandin)*	**grāmya** domesticated
	ānūpa *(anūpaja)* marshy
	jaleśaya *(jalaja)* aquatic
the worst	

qualities of meats. This scale of values is set out schematically in table 6.

First, let us consider the classificatory terms shown on the right in this table. A problem arises in the middle of the list, where it is immediately apparent that of the two terms *ekaśapha* and *grāmya*, one is redundant: the "whole-hoofed" or solidungulates, are also "domesticated" animals; the whole-hoofed animal par excellence, the horse, is even the first named of the domesticated animals. How should this redundancy be interpreted?

Throughout Sanskrit literature, *grāmya* ("domesticated") is opposed to *āraṇya* ("wild"). It is this contrast, this classical polarity between the village *(grāma)* and the forest *(araṇya)* that here produces an interference in the purely medical ideas. While *jāṅgala* and *ānūpa* are specialized words stemming strictly from the technical vocabulary of medicine, *ekaśapha, kravyāda*, and *grāmya* appear in many varied contexts and belong to the overall Hindu tradition. Words such as "whole-hoofed" *(ekaśapha)* and "carnivorous" *(kravyāda)* certainly have a zoological meaning. They affirm a quite specific taxonomical fact, namely that members of the horse family (horse, donkey, to name a few) are whole-hoofed, while carnivores (of the dog or cat family) have divided toes. It would be reasonable to assume that here the words are used for that particular, technical reason. Within the framework of the Hindu tradition, however, we should recognize that these words also have another meaning: they refer to a feature of classical culture; they denote the contrast between domesticated livestock (whole-hoofed) and wild animals (carnivores); in short, between the village and the forest.[6] The classical polarity between the village and the forest is thus superimposed on a specifically medical hierarchy.

We will encounter other such contextual interferences in later examples. Suffice it to say that a scientific document such as this catalog of meats refers one to multiple schemata of thought between which there is a measure of interference yet each of which is perfectly coherent at its own particular level. These examples of overdetermination within a traditional science may be subjected to an ethnoepistemological analysis.

Ekaśapha and *kravyāda* apart, there remains an opposition between the top and the bottom of the scale, which plays an important role in Ayurveda. In effect, when the therapeutic properties of the *grāmya* meats are under consideration, they are systematically grouped with the marshy and aquatic meats. For example, the prescription for the patient suffering from flux or plethora is to consume only *jāṅgala* meats, which are light and astringent, and above all to avoid meats that are "domesticated-marshy-and-aquatic" *(grāmyānūpaudaka)*, which are heavy and produce too many secretions and discharges. Or, conversely the consumptive patient must consume the most nourishing meats—the *grāmyānūpaudaka*. This is a specifically medical polarity.

To understand such medical polarities, we must reflect on the pharmaceutical or dietetic properties indicated in the left-hand column of table 6. The meaning of such properties as light, astringent, heavy, and so on is strictly determined by their inclusion within a series of technical terms. The series of savors, the six *rasa*, comprise sweet, acid, salty, acrid, bitter, and astringent. The series of qualities, the twenty *guṇa*, include light, heavy, cold, hot, dry, unctuous, and so on. Each series functions like a logical machine. As soon as we use one of these apparently anodine words—for example, if we say that a meat is *light*—we are caught up in the machinery. Hundreds of adjectives are involved and a table of concordance must be drawn up between them. Their technical meaning may be defined either through the gloss of a commentator or by making cross-references from one text to another. This technical language then gave rise to a whole scholastic system. "Light" is what is "drying," "cicatrizing," the "opposite of that which produces heaviness and obstruction."[7] In this context, *laghu* ("lightness") qualifies not the perceivable appearance of things but a type of physiological action. Its contrary is *abhiṣyandin*, "that which produces abundant discharges" or "that which produces obstructions."[8] The two

This gift is worth a
thousand words.
POWELL'S
BOOKS
portland, oregon
800-878-7323
powells.com
Powell's Books
gift cards.
Available in any denomination.

adjectives *laghu* and *abhiṣyandin* thus constitute the two poles of the scale of meats, and the antithesis between them is absolutely clear-cut. As we shall see, the host of other adjectives used to qualify each animal species is logically subordinated to this antithesis.

Provided below, by way of a sample, is Suśruta's catalog. What interests me is what might be called the rhapsody of adjectives. The breaks in each section of the catalog (as represented by Arabic numbers in parentheses) correspond to each new series of animal names; the nomenclature, as such, is to be found in the appendix at the back of this book. Some of the animal species mentioned in the catalog are extremely rare, some even fabulous, but that does not prevent them from having savors and properties (also of a fabulous nature) attributed to them. What is at stake is not science in the sense in which we understand it, that is, observational and experimental science, but a particular vision handed down from time immemorial. That explains the inclusion in this inventory of such fabulous animals as the *śarabha*, an eight-legged monster which haunts Indian literature from the Vedic period right down to the poems of Kālidāsa, or the *makara* and other dragons of the sea. Their presence testifies to the fact that no basic differentiation is drawn between science and myth, between the real world and the world of the seers.

How magical the meat of the *śarabha* must be! Perhaps the very action of listing it is in some way tantamount to eating it and so, figuratively speaking, a way of appropriating its fabulous power.

Suśruta's Catalog[9]

(53) And now we shall enumerate the kinds of meat, to wit: aquatic, marshy *(ānūpa)*, domesticated, carnivorous, whole-hoofed and animals of the dry land *(jāṅgala)*, which makes six kinds of meats, which are listed in order of increasing excellence. But they are further classified into two categories: *jāṅgala* and *ānūpa*. The *jāṅgala* category is then sub-divided into eight, to wit: those which have legs *(jaṅghāla)*, those which scatter grain *(viṣkira)*, those which peck *(pratuda)*, those which have a lair *(guhāśaya)*, those which pull at their food *(prasaha)*, those which live in trees *(parṇamṛga)*, those which have a burrow *(bileśaya)*, and domesticated animals *(grāmya)*. The *jaṅghāla* and *viṣkira* categories are the best two.

(54) Here are these two. The *jaṅghāla* quadrupeds: antelope . . . , etc. are astringent, sweet, light, calm wind and bile, are pungent, cordial and purify the bladder.

(55) [Among them, 55d] astringent, sweet, cordial,
calming bile-blood and disorders of phlegm,
constrictive, appetising, fortifying,
the *eṇa* (black antelope), febrifuge.
(56) Sweet, of sweet digestion,
it calms (all) humors, stimulates the (digestive) fire,
cold, it retains urines and stools,
the *hariṇa*, fragrant, light.
(57) Of the two, *eṇa* is the black one,
hariṇa is the name of the red one,
the one neither black nor red
is called the *kuraṅga* (four-horned antelope).
(58) Cold, it calms bile-blood,
the *mṛgamātṛkā* [and eliminates, 58d]
conjunction of the three humors, consumption, dyspnoea,
cough, hiccup, loss of appetite.

(59) The *viṣkira*, which have three claws,[10] are the quail, the partridge . . . , etc.

(60) Light, cold, sweet,
astringent, they calm all the humors.
Constrictive, stimulating the fire,
astringent, sweet, light,
the *lāva* (quail), and of acrid digestion,
but recommended in cases of a conjunction of the three humors.
(61) Rather heavy, hot, sweet,
virilifying, it increases intellect and fire,
the *tittiri* (partridge), it calms all the humors,
constrictive, it clears the complexion.
(62) Cold, it calms bile-blood,
light too, the *kapiñjala* (grey partridge),
both in disorders stemming from phlegm
and in cases of sluggish wind it is appreciated.
(63) It calms hiccup, dyspnoea, wind,
especially the *gauratittiri* (= *kapiñjala*).
Virilifying, they calm wind and bile,
they increase intellect, fire, strength,
(64) the *krakara*, light, cordial,
and similarly the *upacakra*.
Astringent, sweet, salty,
good for the skin, hair and loss of appetite,
(65) the *mayūra* (peacock) [strengthens, 65b] voice, intellect, fire,
the senses of sight and hearing.
Unctuous, hot, it calms wind, virilifying,
diaphoretic, it strengthens the voice,

(66) and it is nourishing, the wild *kukkuṭa* (cock);
similar to it, the domestic (cock), but heavy,
[it calms, 66d] disorders of wind, consumption, vomiting,
and irregular fever.

(67) The *pratuda* are: the pigeon . . ., etc.

(68) Astringent, sweet, dry,
they feed on fruits, they excite wind,
cold, they calm bile and phlegm,
retain urine, give few stools.
(69) Among them, it excites all the humors,
the *bhedāśin*, it deranges excretions.
Astringent, sweet, salty,
heavy, the *kāṇakapotaka*.[11]
(70) It calms bile-blood,
astringent, desiccant,
of sweet digestion,
heavy, the *pārāvata*.
(71) The *kuliṅga* is sweet, unctuous,
it increases phlegm and semen,
it calms bile-blood; the domesticated [*kuliṅga*, 71d]
is, however, excessively spermatogenic.

(72) The *guhāśaya* are: the lion, the tiger . . ., etc.

(73) Sweet, heavy, unctuous,
fortifying, they calm wind,
of hot energy, good for
those who suffer [constantly, 73c] from the eyes and private parts.

(74) The *prasaha* are: the crow . . ., etc.

(75) They are [similar, 75b] to the *lion*, etc. series,
[all, 75a] these meats in the *crow*, etc. series,
for savor, energy, digestion,
especially good for consumption.

(76) The *parṇamṛga* are: the squirrel . . ., etc.

(77) Sweet, heavy, virilifying,
good for the eyes, good for consumption,
they evacuate urines and stools,
they calm cough, haemorroids, dyspnoea.

(78) The *bileśaya* are: the porcupine, the lizard . . ., etc.

(79) They can give consistency to urines and stools,
are, like the preceding group, of hot energy, sweet digestion,
they can calm wind, excite phlegm and bile,
unctuous, they calm cough, dyspnoea, cachexia.[12]

(80) Among them, astringent, sweet,
the *śaśa* (hare) calms bile and phlegm;
by reason of its not too cold energy,
it is moderate (in its action) on wind.

(81) The *godhā* (varan lizard) is of sweet digestion,
astringent, acrid,
it calms wind and bile,
nourishing, fortifying.

(82) The *śalyaka* (porcupine), sweet, calms bile,
light, cold, anti-toxic.
The *priyaka* (snake) is good in disorders of wind,
and the *ajagara* (snake) good for haemorroids.

(83) [The *sarpa* (snakes), 83d]
calm haemorroids, wind, the humors,
vermifuge and anti-toxic,[13]
good for the eyes, of sweet digestion,
they increase intellect and fire.

(84) The *darvīkara* and the *dīpaka*,[14]
among (the snakes) are of acrid digestion,
sweet, very good for the eyes,
they evacuate urines, stools and wind.

(85) The *grāmya* are: the horse . . . , etc.

(86) All the *grāmya* calm wind,
nourishing, they excite phlegm and bile,
of sweet savor and digestion,
they stimulate (the fire), fortify.

(87) [Among them, 87d]
not too cold, [nor too] heavy, [nor too] unctuous,
provoking sluggish bile and phlegm,
the *chagala* (goat) does not produce discharges,
it calms catarrh.

(88) Nourishing, the meat of the *urabhra* (sheep),
heavy, it produces phlegm and bile;
that of the *medaḥpuccha* is virilifying
and has qualities similar to that of the *urabhra*.

(89) [The *gavya* (the meat of the ox), 89c]
calms dyspnoea, cough, catarrh
and irregular fever,
good for fatigue and an excess of fire,
purifying, it calms wind.

(90) Rather salty, like that of the *urabhra*,
is the meat given by whole-hoofed animals (*ekaśapha*).
This category which produces few discharges
is called *jāṅgala*.

(91) [c] The beasts and birds
[a] which live far away from inhabited (lands),
[b] which live far from water,
[d] produce few discharges.
(92) [c] The beasts and birds
[a] whose habitat is very close,
[b] which live very near to water,
[d] in contrast produce large discharges.

(93) The *ānūpa* category is subdivided into five, namely, those which live on the banks (*kūlacara*), those which float (*plava*), those which have a shell (*koṣastha*), those which have feet (*pādin*), and fish (*matsya*).

(94) The *kūlacara* quadrupeds are: the elephant . . . , etc.
(95) Virilifying, they calm wind and bile,
sweet of savor and digestion,
cold, strong, unctuous,
diuretic, they increase phlegm.
(96) [Among them, 96c] very dry and desiccant,
of hot energy and corrupting to bile,
sweet, acid, salty,
the *gaja* (elephant) calms phlegm and wind.
(97) As for the meat of *gavaya* (gayal),
unctuous, sweet, it dispells cough,
of sweet digestion too,
it is aphrodisiac.
(98) Unctuous, hot, sweet, virilifying
the *mahiṣa* (buffalo) is satisfying, heavy,
[it increases, 98d] sleep, virility, strength, and milk,
it makes flesh firm.
(99) The meat of *ruru*, truly sweet,
has a secondary astringent savor,
it calms wind and bile,
it is heavy, very spermatogenic.
(100) Similarly, the meat of *camara* (yak),
unctuous, sweet, dispells cough,
also of sweet digestion,
it calms wind and bile.
(101) The meat of *sṛmara* too,
with a secondary astringent savor,
calms wind and bile.

(102) Diaphoretic, nourishing, virilifying,
cold, satisfying, heavy,
unctuous, calms fatigue and wind,
the meat of *varāha* (pig) fortifies.
(103) The meat of *khaḍgin* (rhinoceros) calms phlegm,
astringent, it calms wind,
propitious to the ancestors, purifying, good for longevity,
very dry, it retains urine.
(104) The meat of *gokarṇa* is sweet,
unctuous, tender, it provokes phlegm,
also sweet of digestion,
it calms bile-blood.

(105) The *plava*, which go in flocks, are: the goose . . . , etc.

(106) Cold, they calm bile-blood,
unctuous, virilifying, they calm wind,
they evacuate urines and stools,
are sweet of savor and digestion.
(107) [Among them, 107c] heavy, hot, sweet, unctuous,
fortifying voice and complexion,
nourishing, spermatogenic,
the *haṃsa* (goose) eliminates disorders of wind.

(108) The *kośastha*[15] are: the conch . . . , etc.

(109) The *pādin* are: the tortoise . . . , etc.

(110) *Śaṅkha* (conch), *kūrma* (tortoise), etc. are sweet
of savor and digestion, they calm wind,
cold, unctuous, good for (an excess of) bile,
they produce stools, increase phlegm.
(111) Among them, the black *karkaṭaka* (crab),
fortifying, moderately hot, calms wind;
the white one is cicatrizing, it evacuates
urines and stools, calms wind and bile.

(112) The *matsya* are subdivided into two: *nādeya* (those of the rivers[16]) and *sāmudra* (those of the oceans).

(113) The *nādeya* are: the carp . . . , etc.

(114) *Nādeya* fish are sweet,
heavy, they calm wind,
hot, they provoke bile-blood,
virilifying, unctuous, they produce few stools.

(115) Among them, with a secondary astringent savor,
feeding on young shoots and *śaivāla*,[17]
the *rohita* (carp) calms wind,
does not over-excite bile.
(116) The *pāṭhīna* produces phlegm, virilifying,
it is somnolent, carnivorous,
can corrupt blood and bile,
provokes dermatoses.
The *murala* is nourishing, virilifying
produces milk and phlegm.
(117) Those which come from lakes or reservoirs
are unctuous, of sweet savor;
the deeper they go, the stronger they are,
the less water there is, the less strong they are.

(118) The *sāmudra* are: the shark . . . , etc.

(119) The *sāmudra* are heavy, unctuous,
sweet, do not produce too much bile,
hot, calm wind, virilifying
they increase stools and phlegm.
(120) [The *sāmudra*, 120b] are fortifying, especially
because they are carnivorous.
The *nādeya* [are superior, 120d] to the *sāmudra*
in quality because they are fortifying.
(121) But among them, because they calm wind,
the two which come from wells and cisterns are superior in quality;
[of these two, 121d]
because they are unctuous, of sweet digestion,
those of stone-built reservoirs are superior in quality.
(122) The *nādeya* are heavy in the middle,
because they move with the head and the tail;
but those which come from reservoirs or lakes
have particularly light heads.
(123) Because they do not travel over large distances,
the fish of springs and fountains,
moving a little away from the region of the head,
are excessively heavy.
(124) Heavy in their lower parts
are the fish of the ocean;[18]
(125) because they move with their chests,
in their case the front part of the body is light.
[b] That concludes the category of *ānūpa*
[a] meats which produce large discharges.

(126) Next, one should not consume the meat of animals that are dried up or putrid or killed by disease, poison, snakes or infected, wounded,

decrepit, emaciated, too young, nor of animals living off inappropriate foods[19] because, since its energy has disappeared, is vitiated, killed, damaged, minimal or immature, it becomes a source of humors. The meat to be taken is that of animals other than these.

(127) [b] Dried meat is heavy,
[a] and produces loss of appetite, catarrh.
[c] That which has been killed by poison or disease is fatal,
[d] and that which is (too) young excites vomiting.
(128) That which is [too] old provokes cough and dyspnoea,
that which is corrupted by disease excites the three humors,
that which is putrid is a source of nausea,
that which is emaciated excites wind.

(129) The best meats are, among the quadrupeds, the females, among birds the males, among extremely corpulent animals the smaller ones, among non corpulent animals the fat ones; similarly, within a given species, the thin are better than the fat.

(130) We shall specify the heaviness or lightness of a meat according to its location, etc. in the following manner: with the series of tissues, from blood to semen, the list is composed in order of increasing heaviness; similarly for thigh, shoulder, chest, head, foot, hand, rump, back, skin, kidneys, liver, intestines.

(131) Head, shoulder, rump, back
and the thighs of both sides,
it should be understood: from the most heavy to the least heavy,
but for the tissues: from the least heavy to the most heavy.[20]
(132) In the body of every living being
the middle is heavy;
the upper part is heavy in males,
and the lower part in females.
(133) The chest and neck in birds
are especially heavy.
[d] The middle part in birds
[c] seems equal, on account of the movement of the wings.[21]
(134) Excessively dry is the meat
given by birds which feed on fruits.
Meat that is excessively nourishing,
that given by carnivorous birds.
(135) The birds which feed on fish produce a meat which excites bile;
those which feed on grain, a meat which calms wind.
Aquatics, *ānūpa, grāmya,*
carnivores and whole-hoofed animals,
(136) *prasaha* and *bileśaya*
and those called *jaṅghāla,*

pratuda and *viṣkira*, precisely,
are progressively (more) light
and less prone to produce fluxes
and vice versa.

(137) Animals whose size is excessively large for their own particular species are meats without strength and heavy. Among all living beings, of all the body, the best pieces that one can consume are those around the region of the liver. In default of the best pieces, an animal of middling age, a fresh, intact meat is what one should take. And in this connection:

(138) The life environment,[22] parts of the body,
specific nature, elements, actions,
sex, size, preparation,
and quantity are what should be examined in meat.

(*end of the catalog of meats*)

What interests me is the combinative system of adjectives, therapeutic actions, and stereotyped hemistiches. This translation is valid only to the extent that the reader accepts a number of conventions which make it possible *to reduce the verbal inflation to a logical uniformity*. On the one hand, if the full verbosity of the original text is retained, it becomes overwhelming. If, on the other hand, the diversity of synonyms is reduced to a single, identical translation and if the vast amount of literary "padding," which facilitates the production of units of prosody of eight syllables but has no useful function in the expression of the thought, is disregarded, then the structure emerges, liberated from its constraints. My translation accordingly leaves out many of the particles (used as padding) and also words such as *jñeya*, "it should be known that," or *smṛta*, "it is taught that."

A more serious manipulation is my consistent and indiscriminate practice of translating as "calm" or "eliminate" a whole series of verbs or verbal nouns with different roots: *°hara*, *°han*, *°ghna*, *°nāśana*, *°śamana*, *°praśamana*, *°pranāśana*, and so on ("to kill, destroy, eliminate, chase away, calm"). The nuances would be misleading here. The choice made between the various expressions is primarily determined by meter requirements and the number of syllables necessary to make up the oracular number: octosyllabic quarter stanzas. Besides, all these words constitute what might be called logical operators. The essential is to indicate the positive or negative role of a particular medicinal substance. A particular meat calms or excites, eliminates or provokes, diminishes or increases the designated humor (wind, bile, phlegm), or a designated disorder or syndrome (bile-blood, dyspnoea, haemorroids). It is a logic of "more" and "less," of the favorable and the unfavorable. The compounds appearing in such numbers, essentially in the parts of the catalog written in verse, are made up of two types, or groups, of elements: *objects* or object-terms and *operators*. The object-terms name the humors, disorders, syndromes, or vital functions (e.g., the digestive fire); the operators mark those objects with either a plus or a minus sign:

—*māruta-nāśana*, "calms wind"

—*marut-kara*, "excites wind."

Substitute for *māruta* or *marut*, meaning "wind," any of the possible synonyms: *vāyu, vāta, anila*, and so on; and substitute for °*nāśana*, "which calms . . ." any of the verbal nouns already cited. The invariable result is that one of the three humors, wind, is marked as *minus*; the same applies in the case of °*kara*, "which excites. . . ." But, after all, plenty of French and English words are composed in the same way: "antitoxic" *(viṣāpaha)* or "febrifuge" *(jvarāpaha)* are "poison" *(viṣa)* and "fever" *(jvara)* with a minus sign added (°*apaha*, "which eliminates").

The same result is obtained by using a different series of operators which specify that a particular remedy is "good for" a particular disease: "indicated" *(hita)*, "salutary" *(pathya)*, "recommended" *(pūjita)*, "praised," "appreciated" *(śasta)*, and so on.

Suppose the translator-decoder decides no longer to respect the verbal diversity of the operators, and instead simply records the object terms by marking them with the positive or negative sign applicable each time they appear. For example, each time the word *wind* appears in the catalog it is enmeshed within the framework of the discourse that qualifies it and specifies that a particular meat *calms* (minus sign −) or *excites* (plus sign +) wind. The word needs to be disentangled from that framework.

I have accordingly drawn up a table showing the occurrences of wind, bile, and phlegm together with those of a syndrome characteristic of the *jāṅgala*: namely, "bile-blood" (*raktapitta, pittāsṛj*, or *asṛkpitta*) (table 7). "Bile-blood" refers to discharges of blood caused by bile, in other words, bilious disorders leading to types of hemorrhage. A polarity is established between astringent meats, which halt such discharges, and meats of a hot energy, which provoke them.

Table 7 provides a snapshot of the catalog of meats. Observe the repetition of the same object-terms. It is as if the intention were to imbue certain therapeutic actions with a statistical weight, an importance measurable from the frequency with which they appear. Thus, all meats have "a sweet savor" and all meats "calm wind": that is repeated for each and every meat, almost a total of forty times. By articulating the series of *rasa* or savors (sweet-acid-salty) in conjunction with the series of humors (wind-), I shall later be demonstrating the exact equivalence of the two most frequent formulas:

of a sweet savor = calms wind.

Overall, meats, like milk or winter rice (*śāli*), have a sweet savor (*rasa*), remain sweet even after the savors have been transformed by the process of digestion (sweet *vipāka*), and are of cold energy *(vīrya)*. They thus calm wind and encourage the production of phlegm. Sweet *rasa*, sweet *vipāka*, and cold *vīrya* thus form a homogeneous constellation of dietetic and pharmaceutical properties that together result in the discouragement of wind. More precisely, the "savors" *(rasa)*, the changes they undergo through digestion *(vipāka)*, and the "energy" *(vīrya)* of a medicinal substance represent different levels of apperception, different factors that affect the reactions to a drug, a constellation of attributes permitting each substance to locate within a logical space with a number of dimensions. For the moment, simply note how one property translates statistically at the level of the discourse: the formula "calms (or eliminates) wind," which is repeated almost forty times, together with all the minus signs in the left-hand column in table 7.

The dividing line separating this table into two sections finds justification as soon as all the other technical terms are also taken into consideration: light, astringent, dry, or heavy, unctuous, nourishing, virilifying. The main contrasts emerge immediately, however: *jaṅghāla* and *viṣkira* meats calm all the humors; but as from stanza 79 (devoted to the *bileśaya*, the animals which have a burrow), meats which excite bile and phlegm make their appearance. They excite phlegm because they are unctuous, heavy, and sweet; they excite bile because (in contrast to meats generally) they are of hot energy. Actually this division is made as early as stanza 73, so that the predatory animals (lions, and so on) and the domesticated animals (horses, and so on) belong to the second part of the catalog and share the qualities and defects (the heaviness and unctuosity) of marshy meats.

The text itself must be consulted to determine in which cases inversions of the signs (from + to – or from – to +, in table 7) indicate a

TABLE 7
Occurrences of the Humors

	No.	Wind	Bile	Phlegm	Bile Blood	
jaṅghāla	54	–	–			
antelope	55			–		
	56	–	–	–		*
	58				–	
viṣkira	60	–	–	–		*
	61	–	–	–		
grey partridge	62	+		–	–	**
	63a	–				
	63c	–	–			
peacock	65	–				
cock	66	–				
pratuda	68	+	–	–		
bhedāśin	69	+	+	+		
	70				–	
	71			+	–	
lion, etc.	73	–				
porcupine	79	–	+	+		
hare	80	+/–	–	–		**
varan lizard	81	–	–			
	82	–				
snakes	83	–				
	84	–				
grāmya	86	–	+	+		
goat	87		–	–		**
sheep	88		+	+		
ox	89	–				
kūlacara	95	–	–	+		
elephant	96	–	+	–		
	99	–	–			
	100	–	–			
	101	–	–			
pig	102	–				
rhinoceros	103	–		–		
	104			+	–	
plava	106	–			–	
goose	107	–				
kośastha	110	–	–	+		
	111b	–				
	111d	–	–			
nādeya	114	–			+	
	115	–	+/–			**
	116ac			+	+	
sāmudra	116f			+		
	119	–	+/–	+		
	121	–				
infected	128b	+	+	+		
thin	128d	+				
	135a		+			
	135b	–				

* *Eliminate all the humours* (sarvadosaghṇa).
** Sādhāraṇa *qualities, 'middling' (neither too much nor too little).*
\+ *excite, provoke.* – *calm, eliminate.*

general fact that applies to a whole category, or simply points to exceptions. For example, the fact that the *bhedāśin* (stanza 69) and the sparrow (*kuliṅga*) (stanza 71) are distinguished from the rest of the *pratuda* category is exceptional. But the *pratuda*, birds which peck (pigeons, and so on) do, in point of fact, encourage wind through their dryness and astringency. Among the *jāṅgala* animals, we should therefore distinguish between those whose flesh is absolutely healthy (meats which calm *all* the humors) and those whose flesh presents the defects that are characteristic of an excessively dry life environment. It is the *pratuda* that excite wind. The subdivisions of the catalog are thus distinguished by a sequence of reversals:

—meats that are generally cold, sweet, and also sweet when digested, calm wind and excite phlegm;

—but *jāṅgala* meats, which combine astringency and a sweet savor, also calm phlegm;

—but, first and foremost of the *jāṅgala* meats, the *pratuda* meats, which are also astringent, excite wind.

On a number of occasions the idea of compensatory contraries appears: "not too much" (*nātyartham*), "middling; neither too much nor too little" (*sādhāraṇa*): the grey partridge, the hare, and the goat calm excitation of phlegm as well as "sluggishness of wind" (*mandavāta*).[23]

Now we must follow up a number of ellipses in the translation. A formula such as: "of sweet savor *(rasa)* and digestion *(vipāka)*" contracts, under the constraints of the prosody, to "of sweet *rasa* and *pāka*." A prefix has been dropped: *pāka* remains instead of *vipāka*. Similarly, *saṃgrāhin* is replaced by *grāhin*, just as if in English one were to write "strictive" in place of "constrictive." From such grammatical concision, one moves on, quite naturally, to the effects of logical concision as shown in the example: *dīpana* ("which inflames") for *analadīpana* "which stimulates the (digestive) fire." Another example of capital importance is: *doṣaghna* ("which eliminates the humors") in place of *sarva-* or *tri-doṣaghna*, "which calms *all* the humors, *the three* humors." The interpreter must systematically try out all the elliptical variants in order to determine the meaning in the technical language.

Only rarely do the formulas used in the verse passages have a descriptive value, and even where they do, the description in most cases justifies the dietetic or pharmaceutical properties. *Kūlacara* quadrupeds (the elephant, the buffalo, and so on), for example, are said to be "cold, strong, unctuous" (95c). "Strong" might be an allusion to the vigor of the animals; but a possible metonymy should also be recognized: *balin* ("strong") for *balya* ("fortifying"). It is not a question of the animal itself but of the meat that the animal will provide. The adjectives describing the meat—"cold" and "unctuous"—clearly have no descriptive value; they should be interpreted as strictly conventional, as indicating in technical language particular pharmaceutical processes and effects. The meaning of each term is determined by its position within an overall system of technical terms. Let us therefore consider the co-occurrences and the grouping of the adjectives.

Take, for example, the group "unctuous-hot-sweet-virilifying" (98a). It appears time and again but may be dispersed over a whole stanza, or incomplete, or padded out with other adjectives. "Heavy" sometimes replaces "unctuous" as in "heavy-hot-sweet-virilifying" (61a, b) and "sweet-heavy-virilifying" (77a). A whole series of substitutions, a whole system of combinations, as it were a rotation of the lexical stock, may be noted:

unctuous-hot-calms wind (65c)
unctuous-virilifying-calm wind (106b)
hot-calm wind-virilifying (119c)

What are the rules governing this rotation?

A MULTIFACETED KNOWLEDGE

A classic problem in the natural and social sciences is that the *criteria* used to classify *objects* also require classification. Here, the objects are medicinal substances, and the criteria for ordering them are their savors, qualities, and therapeutic or pathogenic effects.

The most simple method of setting them in order is a linear one that gives rise to hierarchies of technical terms. For example, the series of *dhātu*, or "tissues," that constitute the human body:

chyle-blood-flesh-fat-bone-marrow-semen (130),

enumerated in order of their increasing heaviness, or the six categories of meats provided by the different animals:

aquatic-marshy-domesticated-carnivorous-whole-hoofed-*jāṅgala*, classified in order of their increasing lightness. To arrange all of these terms on the same scale, all we need do is select a variable—in this case, lightness—for an operator which will indicate a linear increase or decrease. Hemistiche 136d is constructed in this way: "they are progressively (*yathottaram*) light"; each successive term is lighter than the one preceding it. The same operator is applied to 136e: "and less prone to produce fluxes"; each successive term is less productive of fluxes than the one preceding it. Here, then, is a series of names (animals, plants, and so on):

$$r < s < t < u < v < \ldots$$

which, in this order, are more and more (*a*) or less and less (*b*), whereby *a, b, c* . . . represent variables such as "light," "cause of fluxes," and so on. It is the simplest method of classification imaginable. The operator *yathottaram*, "in an increasing order, each a degree more than the one before" and its converse, *yathāpūrvam*, "in a decreasing order, each a degree less than the one before" are often used. In addition to this simple classificatory method, Ayurvedic doctors also practice another typological operation, infinitely more complex since it assumes combinations of variables.

This time the variables are not linear (increasing or decreasing) but dichotomous (couples of contraries). Thus *jāṅgala* meats, light-dry-astringent-constrictive, are contrasted with *ānūpa* meats, heavy-unctuous-emollient-diaphoretic. Although these variables appear to be homogeneous constellations of savors, qualities, and actions, how can the method for such a grouping be discovered? We are led to distinguish three different kinds of elements in the technical language:

- the *operators*
- the objects to be classed
  - the *names* of substances
  - the medical *criteria*

1) The *operators*. These are the logical means of a combinative system: "which excites . . . ," "which calms . . . ," "good for . . . ," "not too much . . . ," "more and more . . . ," "generally . . . ," "specially . . . ," and so on.

2) The *names*. The names of plants, animals, and other medicinal substances (milks, fats, minerals) constitute the basic material for typological operations: hierarchies, dichotomies, subsumptions, and so on. The elements "antelope" and "partridge" have the same logical value as

the categories in which they are included: *jaṅghāla, viṣkira.* Whether specific or generic, *names* are the basis for the combinative system of medical properties.

3) The *criteria.* These consist of all the "variables" already mentioned: the excitation or sluggishness of each "humor" *(doṣa)*, the dominance or eclipse of each of the six "savors" *(rasa)*, the ten couples of contrary "qualities" (*guṇa*), and so on.

The *criteria* used to classify *names* are also classified: classification of the criteria of classification. They are distributed over a number of dimensions within the same logical space, forming a single *property space* divided into a number of *facets.* Each substance or category of substances may be defined in terms of its action on the humors, the savors of which it is composed, and so on. It thus presents multiple facets, each of which corresponds to one of the dimensions of an *n*-dimensional space.

A distinction is made between the notion of "property" (*guṇa*) in the wider sense and the stereotyped series of twenty "qualities" (*guṇa*) in the strict sense. Medical dictionaries distinguish between the "names" (*nāma*) and the "characteristics" (*lakṣaṇa*), or "properties" (*guṇa*), of every substance. A *nomenclature* in the strict sense (a system of names) is thus juxtaposed with a *combinative* arrangement of medical properties.

The three humors, the six savors, and the twenty qualities constitute the most important facets or dimensions in this combinative system as shown in table 8.

TABLE 8
THE COMBINATIVE SYSTEM

variables within each facet ↓ / facets →	1	2	3
	wind	sweet	heavy/light
	bile	acid	cold/hot
	phlegm	salty	unctuous/dry
		acrid	sluggish/lively
		bitter	solid/liquid
		astringent	tender/hard
			desiccant/lubricating
			smooth/rough
			subtle/crude
			viscous/fluid

TABLE 9
MORE FACETS

facets →	
4	5
earth	depletive
water	nutritive
fire	drying
air	hydrating
ether	sudorific
	styptic

However, it is always possible to increase the number of dimensions of this ideal space in which each substance is situated by combining the characteristics attributed to it. This produces further facets as shown in table 9.

Depending on which of the five cosmic elements predominates within it, each substance is essentially earthy, watery, fiery, airy, or ethereal. Depending on which of the six modes of therapeutic action it most favors, each drug is depletive, nutritive, drying, hydrating, sudorific, or styptic.

Thus adjectives, whether simple (*laghu*, "light"), derivative (*pittala*, "bilious"; *pārthiva*, "earthy"), or compound (*māruta-nāśana*, "which calms wind"), and nominal forms of verbs such as *laṅghana*, "fast, slimming cure, depletive (action)," and *bṛṃhaṇa*, "feeding-up, nutritive (action)," are multiplied through a kind of verbal inflation, or a mania for enumerations, recitations, seriations, and verbigerations.

Certain homonymies may cause confusion between two facets, as in the case of *vāyu*, meaning both "wind" (the humor) and "air" (the element), or in that of *soma*, meaning both "moon" and, by extension, "water" (the element) and sometimes also "phlegm" (the humor). In the domain of logic, this is a consequence of a religious and metaphysical analogy between the living body (microcosm) and the surrounding world (macrocosm). This combinative system stems from a limited number of familiar images with which the notion of the great vital functions have always been associated: for example, digestion is the work of fire and bile (a fiery fluid). The three humors have a double reality: (1) as a set of images common to all ancient physiologies, an imagery of *fluids* circulating outside us and also inside us, in which saps, winds, and even fire are conceived of as fluids; (2) in medical reasoning, they are also abstract *functions*, the three disorders, the morbific factors the accumulation or disorganization of which may engender diseases.

The point of interest here, on which the entire weight of our analysis is concentrated, is the articulation between the image of a fluid and the concept of a pathological factor, the point at which, leaving the level of images, the Ayurvedic doctor launches into the construction of a conceptual system. That is the moment when wind ceases to mean wind or flatulence but becomes the principle of consumption and rheumatism, the moment when phlegm is no longer simply an image of excessive serosity or unctuosity but becomes the abstract principle of elephantiasis. The leap that this abstraction involves is very different from the kind Westerners, in the Greek and Latin tradition, have tended to make, whereby abstraction means generalization, a reduction of specifications. For the Ayurvedics, in contrast, abstraction means overdetermination, multiplying adjectives, and points of view.

The expressions used here to describe this system, the notions of a "property space" and a "facet design," are borrowed from American sociologists who, in the line of Paul Lazarsfeld, have studied how typologies construct and deconstruct themselves.[24] A prolix series is turned into a concise one by means of selection, fusion, and reduction of the variables; in short, by a process of subsumption. Thus, *unctuous, tender, emollient*, and *nourishing* are subsumed under the genus *sweet*; *cold, dry, light*, and *desiccant* are subsumed under the concept *wind*. "*Substruction*," the name given by Lazarsfeld to define the converse typological operation, should also be described. The problem is to work back from a ready-made typology to the combinative system that produced it. *Wind* and *sweet* result from a simplification; we must reconstruct the complexity from which they emerged and spell out all the variables that they summarize. In the Ayurvedic system, this substruction is of primary importance. It determines the very formulation of the hemistiches or quarter distiches. For example, the following are selected:

unctuous	from among the twenty *guṇa* (qualities)
hot	from among the two *vīrya* (energies)
sweet	from among the six *rasa* (savors)
virilifying	from among the countless *effects* of drugs

so as to compose hemistiche 98a:

"unctuous-hot-sweet-virilifying."

The different facets of the combinative system overlap at one of the variables from which each is composed; each medicinal substance thus acquires a particular constellation of characteristic properties. Better still, the substruction of humors, savors, and so on, is systematically explained:

> Wind is characterised by the qualities of coldness, dryness, lightness, desiccation, constriction; the astringent *rasa* is homogeneous to it, etc. [Then follows a list of the characteristics of each humor and savor.][25]

> A substance that exerts a depletive action is generally light, hot, lively, desiccant, dry, subtle, rough and hard. [Then follows a list of the qualities peculiar to each of the six main therapeutic actions.][26]

In what sense can the words "subtle" *(sūkṣma)* and "rough" *(khara)* be associated with "depletive" *(laṅghana)*? The meaning of the word is neither more nor less obscure in English than in Sanskrit, for in both "versions" (the original and the English) the language involved is not an ordinary but a special one. When the attributes of each humor or savor are enumerated, the process becomes not simply a matter of *deconstructing* the existing categories in order to qualify and refine them but rather the act of pressing on to *reconstruct* the system on other bases, multiplying all the possible points of view. What is involved is not the division of a genus into species (which could be represented by a genealogical tree), or the organization of an overall view by means of inclusion (which might be represented by a trellis design). We are a long way away from the Western logical tradition and would do better to think of China. In contrast to the Chinese treatises, in which the very writing, an *emblematic* writing, conditions the existence of a many-faceted type of thought, the Sanskrit texts are quite devoid of any means of iconographic expression; all the same, the *linear* appearance of the writing should not mask the spatial quality of the thought, for each link in the chain of writing implicitly refers to one or another of its facets. The writing is linear, but the thought is combinative.

The notions of *vipāka* (the alteration of a savor through digestion) and *vīrya* (energy), which introduce extra dimensions, seem to have been forged in order to facilitate reductions within a complex typology. All "digestion" *(vipāka)* is either acrid or sweet; all "energy" *(vīrya)* is either cold or hot. Savors and qualities may thus be reduced to two pairs of contraries: acrid/sweet, cold/hot. However, these new possibilities for reducing the dimensions complicate the system of evaluating and classifying substances by superinducing background factors, resul-

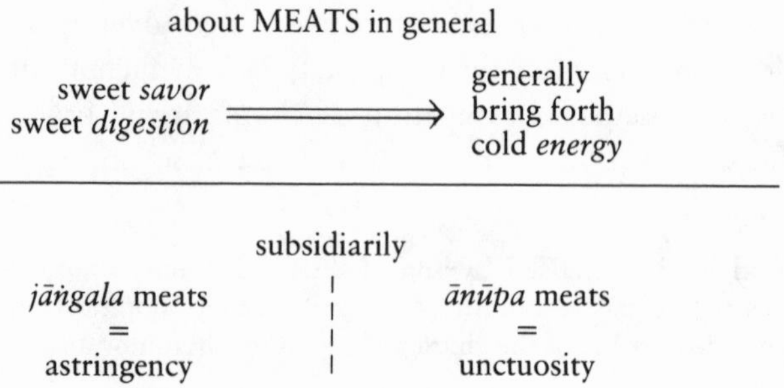

Figure 10. Meats in general are cold

tant vectors. Thus, at first sight, *acrid* and *sweet* are "savors" *(rasa)*; then, by inference and with hindsight, they are the "(alterations in those primary savors due to) digestion" *(vipāka)*. *Cold* and *hot* are first "qualities" *(guṇa)*, and then by inference "energies" *(vīrya)*, resulting from a particular configuration of savors and qualities. The catalog of meats is an excellent example of the multiplication of points of view thus rendered possible.

As illustrated in figure 10, meats, as a whole, are of a sweet *savor*, sweet *digestion*, and cold *energy*: a set of properties linked to the production of phlegm, unctuosity, and fluxes. Within that whole, *jāṅgala* meats, which are sweet but also astringent, are distinguished from *ānūpa* meats, which only possess traces of astringency, in the background, as a "subsidiary savor" *(anurasa)*. But at the same time, another point of view surreptitiously impinges. There are some substances of sweet *savor* and *digestion* that unexpectedly develop a contrary *energy*, a hot *energy*. Among these exceptions we find the *ānūpa* meats.[27] Hence, contrasts between figure 10 and figure 11 become apparent:

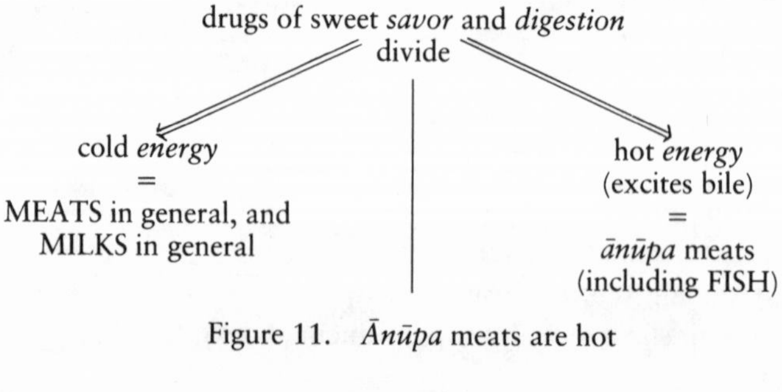

Figure 11. *Ānūpa* meats are hot

This is why, in Suśruta's catalog, meats that excite phlegm—through their *unctuosity*, a quality usually associated with a cold energy—also excite bile—through their *hot energy*, the exceptional consequence of a sweet savor and a sweet digestion. The excitation of bile thus appears on the side of the marshy meats whereas one would have expected it to be on the side of the dry lands.

Furthermore, a possible justification for one dietetic principle of importance emerges: the incompatibility between milk and fish, the incompatibility within a single dietetic regimen between milk, which in general is of sweet savor, sweet digestion, and cold energy,[28] and the "domesticated, marshy and aquatic" meats *(grāmyānūpaudaka)*, which are of hot energy.[29] Substances (foods and remedies) are evaluated and classified by means of dichotomies which lend a scholastic and artificial air to all of this discourse. In all probability, however, this sophisticated combinative system of humors, savors, and qualities, digestions and energies, in most cases simply systematized empirical data, facts of traditional observation or the rules for popular dietetic practices, as is the case here. For among the causes of leprosy the Ayurvedic treatises mention the harmfulness of a diet that associates incompatible foodstuffs such as milk and fish. This is a traditional belief for which ethnographic evidence exists.[30] The second issue (1790) of *Asiatick Researches* included a letter from a Muslim medical practitioner "On the Cure of Elephantiasis." The word denoted a form of leprosy, the "elephantiasis" of the Greeks. This text, from At'har Ali' Kha'n of Delhi, ran as follows:

> A common cause of this distemper is the unwholesome diet of the natives, many of whom are accustomed, after eating a quantity of *fish*, to swallow copious draughts of *milk*, which fail not to cause an accumulation of yellow and black bile, which mingles itself with the blood and corrupts it.[31]

The incompatibility which the Sanskrit texts expressed in logical form is here noted as a curious fact, with an anecdotal tone and in the language of trial-and-error experience. Once again, bile is mentioned but it is no longer the "bile" of the Ayurvedic sages, excited by the hot energy of fish, a specific pathogenic factor in one facet of a rigorously logical system. Under the pen of this eighteenth-century Muslim, it is the "yellow and black bile" of the Hippocratics. In either case, a popular belief is justified by appeal to a scholarly notion. Belief: milk and fish produce a harmful mixture that provokes leprosy. Scholarly explanation: the excitation of bile. It is nevertheless easy to see where the difference lies.

This imported notion of black and yellow bile is also a vulgarized notion which has been dulled, since, no longer coordinated within an overall etiological system, it cannot refer to any background. Indeed, it is quite the opposite of the original (should we say the *classical*?) thought of the Ayurvedics.

Naturally enough, the Ayurvedics started with empirical lists and experiments, but right from the start they elevated taxonomy to the rank of a supreme art. In the following chapters, we shall pursue our study of this system of multifaceted thought.

V: Logic and Cuisine

Just now we plunged, not without a somewhat greedy jubilation, into the superabundance of words. One by one we peeled off the garlands of initially simple adjectives such as sweet or light which, through the very brahminic art of composing collections, series, combinations, and hierarchies, make it possible to construct a multifaceted discourse. That discourse rests on a concrete basis. The delights of words evoke the delights of cooking and do so in a manner barely more intellectual: it is still a matter of choosing, measuring, combining, and perfecting the ingredients. The manipulation of the chemical and organic materials, the extraction of saps and juices, the dilution of sugar and salt, the fermentations, sublimations, decoctions, emulsions, and other fomentations produce, for what we have called the combinative system, its sensory, physical, concrete, craftsmanlike medium. So what do the classic texts prescribe concerning these manipulations and the layout of a meal? An analytical eye cast over the series of different mixtures gently simmering on the hearth, an eye cast over the series of different sauces arranged around rice or wheaten cakes, the gourmet logician's gaze: that is the way we want to look into the medical texts on the subject of cooking in order to draw some conclusions about their logical form.

Recall the layout of an Indian meal! The peripheral position of vegetables and of meat, if meat is consumed. This arrangement is obvious in South Indian cuisine, centered around rice: in the middle on the palm leaf, the boiled rice, and all around it the seasonings are served, to be mixed into the rice with the fingers of the right hand; the seasonings—that is various kinds of *curries*. This word, of Tamil origin, has passed into English and French with a very narrow denotational meaning: a powder made of pimento, curcuma, and spices. In India, however, its significance is infinitely wider, denoting all that would have been known during the eighteenth century as *ragoûts* in France or *relishes* in English. Meats, vegetables, and fruits in cooked combinations form sauces and fricassees to accompany the cereals—rice in the South, wheaten cakes in the North—and to make these more tasty. It is no mere coincidence that the catalog of meats invariably occupies the same place in every medical treatise under the category of foodstuffs and drinks. The meats appear between on the one hand the cereals and leguminous plants and, on the other hand, the fruits and garden vegetables. The catalog of foodstuffs starts with the cereals and to these are added bean or other leguminous broths. Next come the curries, or seasonings *(vyañjana)*: meats, fruits and vegetables. The commentators make a point of noting this logical articulation: "After speaking of the foodstuffs which consist of *bhakta* (boiled rice), the text speaks of meat, the most important of the *vyañjana* (seasonings)";[1] "The catalogue of meats follows on immediately after the soups, because meat is essentially a seasoning";[2] "Having set out the category of cereals for itself, the text analyses the category of meats to serve as additions and seasonings for the cereals."[3] When the Ayurvedics assign a technical role to seasonings in materia medica, they are exploiting an ambiguity: the role of seasonings is both gustatory and pharmaceutical.

A dish can be broken down into the following components: rice at the center, as a staple, and all around it the additions that (from the cook's point of view) heighten the taste and (from the pharmacist's point of view) enhance the bouquet of the savors and the medicinal properties. Following Caraka, for example, in cases of phthisis or consumption, the red variety of *śāli* rice (winter rice) is prescribed "as the basis" of the mixture of foods *(bhojyārtham)*, and a broth of *jāṅgala* meat "as a seasoning" *(vyañjanārtham)*.[4]

This articulation recurs elsewhere in the same chapter, in a catalog that summarizes all the others, the catalog of cooked dishes, in which meat appears in two main forms, as a relish and as a broth. The catalog of cooked dishes repeats the basic catalogs following a similar order. Each category of foods thus appears twice in the materia medica: once

TABLE 10

FROM FOODS TO COOKED DISHES

CATALOG OF FOODS	TYPES OF COOKED DISHES
cereals	"gruels" (*yavāgū*) "in grain form" (*taṇḍula*) "soups" (*sūpa*)
pulses	
meats fruits vegetables	"seasonings"
etc.	etc.

for its natural qualities (in the series of cereals-pulses-meats-) and then again as a culinary ingredient (in the series of gruels-soups-relishes-), in the order indicated in table 10.

The cereals, which in themselves possess particular therapeutic properties, are also *transformed* by various methods of cooking and *combined* with meat, fruits, vegetables, and other additives such as ghee, animal, or vegetable fats to obtain a nourishing and virilifying preparation. Thus *vilepī*, a thick rice gruel, is "combined with vegetables, meats and fruits,"[5] and *odana*, boiled rice, "with unctuous substances, meats, fruits, tubers."[6] A quasi-mechanical enumeration of seasonings:

> Meat, vegetables, fat, oil,
> ghee, marrow, fruits (make) the *odana*
> fortifying, satisfying, cordial,
> heavy and nourishing.[7]

Gruels, fried food, soups, and sauces are meant to produce a synthesis, bringing together the nomenclatures of homologous ingredients. For example, the nomenclature of certain substances of animal origin used as seasonings is homologous to that of the meats:

> The *vasā* (intramuscular fat), the fat, the marrow of *grāmyānūpaudaka* (domesticated, marshy and aquatic) animals are heavy, hot, sweet and calming to wind. Those of *jāṅgala*, *ekaśapha* (whole-hoofed) and *kravyāda* (carnivorous) animals are light, cold, astringent and calming to bile-blood. Those of the *pratuda* and *viṣkira* are calming to phlegm.[8]

This sibylline paragraph, discovered unexpectedly among the catalog of vegetable oils, becomes meaningful indeed as soon as one is prepared to regard it as a kind of a reproduction in miniature of the catalog of meats. The ingredients in question are never used either on their own or in a raw state. They go into compound medicines or dishes, and they all go through transformative cooking.

Cuisine proceeds in the same manner as logic, through combinations (mixtures, sauces) and transformations (the various modes of cooking). Without losing sight of these manipulations and the material images on which they operate, let us examine the reasoning behind this work of synthesis.

COOKING AND MIXING THE JUICES

Two gestures from daily life, mixing and cooking, have been imported into logic. *Cooking*, to be brief, here includes curdling, infusing, and other methods for transforming raw materials. To cite a key formula from the Ayurvedic treatises, pharmacy and cooking set in motion a double process: "the mixing *(saṃyoga)* and the perfecting *(saṃskāra)* of substances."[9] A given material possesses by nature certain properties. The art lies in *combining* those materials whose properties are complementary, meanwhile avoiding incompatibilities, and *perfecting* them through cooking to imbue them with properties other than those that they possess by nature.[10] *Saṃskāra* denotes "the act of perfecting" foods and remedies through the art of cuisine. Whereas the catalog of meats tells of the *natural* properties of each foodstuff, the catalog of *cooked* dishes indicates the "therapeutic qualities and actions which result from the art of mixing *(saṃyoga)* and the art of cooking *(saṃskāra)* meat, the most important of all seasonings."[11] When mixed and cooked with various additives that are unctuous (ghee), acid (pomegranates), or acrid (black pepper), meat develops new nutritive and fortifying powers: a superconcentrate, a synergy of the savors and virtues peculiar to each ingredient. Of all these innate or acquired properties, one can keep a tally by marking each substance, by qualifying each ingredient with one or another particular set of adjectives. This, in effect, is the origin of the phraseology, of the logico-poetic interplay on recurring octosyllabic hemistiches.

In connection with the compensation for opposites, at the beginning of our enquiry, we touched on the notions of *saṃyoga*, "mixture, combination, prescription" and *samayoga*, "equal mixture, congruent junction," a medical prescription to restore the equality of the humors. We mentioned Alcmæon, to whom Greek medicine owed the idea that health results from the *isonomia* of contraries. We suggested that in this context equality means both compensation (for contraries) and moderation (as when one speaks of a person of "equal humor"). In some cases all three humors are exacerbated at once and must all three be repressed. More often, one of them suppresses the other two or two of them suppress the third. There are consequently two aspects to the therapeutic action: it must compensate for contraries and it must moderate extremes. Compensation and moderation is what the doctor may achieve by combining the appropriate savors and qualities—following the ideas of suitability, appropriateness, and opportuneness—in the remedies he cooks up and the regimens he prescribes. At this point a clear convergence can be observed between Indian medicine and Greek medicine. This notion of a harmonious mixture in which antagonistic forces compensate for and moderate one another is quite familiar, for it is none other than the Greek idea of *Krāsis*, the "temperament" of the juices in foods to which the "temperament" of the humors in the body correspond and which makes it possible to achieve the "correct mean," a central theme in the Hippocratic treatise *On ancient medicine*. Different foods contain different juices—bitter, salty, acid, and so on—which are harmful if taken unadulterated and untempered; but mixing and cooking make them lose whatever was untempered and excessive. In gruels given to the sick, one should remove the excessive humoral quality "by mixing and cooking," as the Greek treatise specifically states, and all the disorders which result from the intemperance of the humors cease once these humors are "cooked and mixed."[12] The two words *cooked* and *mixed* form a virtually indissociable pair, and the comparison with the Indian idea of mixture *(saṃyoga)* perfected by cooking *(saṃskāra)* strikes me as particularly revealing.

Such a convergence should not be surprising. In India as in Greece, the doctrine of the humors formulates in medical terms the same cosmic physiology in which two major themes predominate: the circulation of fluids and the great chain of successive cookings by the sun, fire, and digestion. Cooking is a demiurgic activity involving all alimentary substances in a vast interplay of combinations and metamorphoses. The point at which these two traditions diverge, however, is where the Indians, in contrast to the Greeks and Latins, discovered the means to *conceptualize* this vast combinative system. That is what I shall now demonstrate.

In ancient India there existed in all probability a mass of empirical knowledge regarding the flora and fauna. This mass of knowledge remained purely oral and for a number of reasons never gave rise to any literature. All that has come down to us are lists and rules of use. There are clearly two reasons to account for this, one of which is common to both India and the Greek and Latin worlds, while the other affects India alone. The first reason is the anthropocentric character of all the ancient knowledge of nature. The listing and description of living beings do not constitute an end in themselves but are subordinated to a normative aim of some kind, whether it be ritual or political, astrological or medical. In medical treatises as in histories of nature, that perspective is utilitarian; facts and beings are studied from the point of view of how they can be used by man, their value to man. Thus far, then, nothing exceptional. In contrast, what is very new is the appearance in India of treasuries of names and further back in more ancient times the existence of a combinative art of which the dictionaries offer no more than a static residue. Onto an inventory of living creatures, in itself of little importance, there has been grafted a metalanguage which makes it possible to formulate value judgments.

This inclusion of a primary discourse (the nomenclature of living things) within a secondary one (the combinative system of their properties) is perfectly described in a passage of the Collection of Caraka in which the metalanguage necessary for this combinative system can be constructed by separating the category of food into a series of divisions, first into two, then four, then six, then twenty. Ātreya (a mythical figure, one of the originators of Ayurveda) teaches his disciple "the particularities internal to the rules concerning nourishment." Before listing the things that are good or bad to eat, he explains these particularities "from the point of view of the criteria" which make it possible to recognize them:

> Food is seen as a single category from the point of view of its object, the category of what can be eaten; but from the point of view of its sources, it is double since it is composed of both immobile and mobile beings; it is also double from the point of view of its action, if one makes a distinction between beneficent and harmful effects. It is quadruple with regard to its mode of employment since it can be drunk, chewed, crunched or sucked; sextuple with regard to the savors, since there are six savors; vigesimal with regard to the qualities which are, successively, heavy/light, cold/hot, unctuous/dry, sluggish/lively, solid/liquid, tender/hard, desiccant/lubrifying, smooth/rough, subtle/crude, viscous/fluid. They are innumerable in respect of its varieties because there exist a multitude of possible combinations and preparations for all these substances.[13]

A multifaceted system thus exists: twenty qualities, six savors, plus the fourfold series of methods of presenting the foodstuffs—"to drink, to suck, to chew, to crunch."[14] In a parallel passage, Suśruta adduces other facets: food is double in respect of its energy, which may be either hot or cold; quintuple in respect of its elements, which may be earthy, watery, and so on.[15] But the paramount point is that the arrangement of the whole of "immobile and mobile" living creatures within the category of food signifies, as a matter of principle, the exclusion of even the possibility of a botanical or zoological classification: the beings themselves are no longer of any interest, only their dietetic and therapeutic qualities.

At first sight, there appears nothing particularly original about all this. These forms of prescientific thought are already familiar to us in the West. Since this enquiry is limited to the catalog of meats, clearly it should be compared to the famous Hippocratic treatise *On regimen*, which contains a comparable catalog and constitutes, in Greece, the only attempt of any precision at a classification of animals before Aristotle.[16] In both cases exist the same unconscious preconceptions or the same epistemological obstacles, as Gaston Bachelard called them; an example of such obstacles includes the resemblance through the contagion of proximity, an osmosis between the living creature and the environment in which it lives, which suggests that the meat of the duck must be wet because it lives in the marshes, or that the grey mullet and the eel are heavier than other fish because they find their food in muddy water.[17] Furthermore—and this is another point shared by the Ayurvedics and the Hippocratics—as is well known, the author of the treatise *On regimen* founds his dietetic system on the polarity between fire and water, the one being characterized by the hot and the dry, the other by the cold and the wet, and he borrows the paradoxical idea of a wet fire and a dry water from Anaxagoras's cosmology.[18] *Fire is fed by water*: we have already come across this theme, closely reflecting a Sanskrit formula, "the agni-soma-ness of the world," a dialectic between Agni, the sun which captures all the unctuosity of beings, and Soma, the moon whose cold rays nourish the saps and make them increase. Finally, even more important than their preconceptions or the broad themes of their respective cosmologies, the two traditions that we are comparing, the Indian and the Greek, share a common and precise doctrine concerning the ontological link between *essence* and *accident*. At the beginning of the Hippocratic catalog of foods, what in effect accounts for the untidy nature of the inventory, the profusion of rubrics, and the proliferation of adjectives that adhere to a single food is a principle identical to what Suśruta and Caraka formulate as they constantly stress the inherent link that unites savors and qualities with the substances themselves. Hippocrates says: "All sweet matters do not have the same quality, . . . if many sweet matters are laxative, others are constrictive, others drying, others moistening."[19] Translating this into Ayurvedic terms, all substances of sweet *savor* clearly do not have the same qualities. As we have seen, a substance may even possess in the background an *energy* contradictory to the *savors* and *qualities* it bears. The active principles contained in a given substance cannot be reduced to an ideal essence that is always the same in all circumstances; it is necessary to take into account the multitude of accidents and properties that it acquires at one moment only to lose them again at another. To this effect, the Greek treatise *On ancient medicine* (XV) notes that the cold and the hot, the wet and the dry, are never isolated by themselves but always combined. A given substance that is essentially cold possesses in the background a tiny part of the hot, the wet, the dry, and so on. Essences are combined with one another and the whole art lies in the internal hierarchy of the mixing but, even more, essences are combined with a thousand other possible properties such as astringency, and so on. The doctrine of the mixing and cooking of the humors and juices presupposes the existence of a myriad of possible properties and combinations: "For in man there is the salty, the bitter, the sweet, the acid, the astringent, the insipid and *a thousand other things*";[20] "a single thing is at once hot and bitter, or hot and acid, or hot and salty, or *a thousand other* possible combinations."[21] Thus the doctrine comes down, word for word, to a formulation of a principle that is fundamental to Ayurveda.

In India this gave rise to a combinative system of properties, a metalanguage, a system of criteria for recognition and evaluation, the subtlety and coherence of which we are now beginning to glimpse. In contrast, in Greece the principle remained a dead letter. What the treatise *On regimen* proposed was an attempt at a classification of animals which was to remain isolated, without any follow-up. The research undertaken by Aristotle takes a quite separate line and is free from any medical preoccupations. From a comparative point of view, in the domain of physiology the theory of vital breaths and the theory of the humors constitute remarkable points of convergence between Indian medicine and Greek medicine; nevertheless, a deep divergence separates the two when it comes to methods of classification. On the one hand, in the Greek tradition, natural history; on the other hand, in the Ayurvedic tradition, the inclusion of taxonomy in pharmacy and the subordination of pharmacy to a complex interplay of savors and curative properties, which envelops the inventory of the flora and fauna in a welter of synonyms, redundancies, enumerations, divisions, and cross-references. One is tempted to conclude that the passion for arrangement which clearly moved the scholars who produced the Indian *śāstra* or scientific treatises, finding insufficient fuel in the arrangement of things themselves, sought fulfillment in an interminable rearrangement of the criteria of arrangement.

LITERARY FORMS

What mental attitude governed the construction of the kind of verbal kaleidoscope that an Ayurvedic catalog constituted? In Suśruta's catalog of meats we found an alternate use of prose and poetry which drew a clear distinction between the nomenclature and the combinative system. First, the names of the animals are set out, like fragments of colored glass at the bottom of a kaleidoscope. On this first series of words (in paragraphs of prose) other series then converge, assuming the position of a metalanguage (in paragraphs of verse) and lighting up all the various facets of the colored glass: the names of the animals are covered with adjectives. Whenever it is a matter of an inventory, nouns accumulate and are arranged; adjectives proliferate and adhere to them. I will venture to call this style of thought logico-poetic, and it comes as no surprise to find grammar considered the very queen of sciences in classical India. This style of thought has been excellently analyzed by our modern theorists of literature. At this point our discussion shall once again diverge from the level of perception (of the fire in the hearth and culinary manipulations) and move instead to the level of words.

Concrete things, physical facts, and living beings find themselves reduced, abstracted, and devitalized in a discourse that names and qualifies but never argues or recounts. It is as if the Indian scholars spoke only in terms of equivalences, their only method of forming the sequences of the discourse (or sentences) being apposition. One of the two constitutive axes of the language—the combinations, links, and syntactical constructions—is devalued and subordinated to the other—the selection of equivalent terms at a particular point in a chain, synonymies, the choice of variants. This is the process described by Roman Jakobson in a famous article which, incidentally, even refers to the versification of the Sanskrit scientific treatises and also illuminates the essential role of the poetic function in the expression of knowledge. Roman Jakobson points to "two basic modes of arrangement used in verbal behavior, *selection* and *combination*. If 'child' is the topic of the message, the speaker selects one among the extant, more or less similar, nouns like child, kid, youngster, tot, all of them equivalent in a certain respect, and then, to comment on this topic, he may select one of the semantically cognate verbs—sleeps, dozes, nods, naps. Both chosen words combine in the speech chain." The process becomes poetic as soon as one "projects the principle of equivalence from the axis of selection into the axis of combination"; that is to say, as soon as the equivalence is used not only to choose words but also to construct sentences. That is the principle of poetic metaphors. "Equivalence is promoted to the constitutive device of the sequence."[22] This is what happens, in particular, when instead of combining words in an account one juxtaposes equivalent expressions wherever possible, reducing the verb to its nominal forms. The procedure is not confined to metrical versification but can be used in passages of prose equally well.

By way of example, let us take the prose text by Suśruta as cited earlier: *Ānūpa*, the place characterized by an abundance of waters, and so on. Consider a new translation, this time one that respects the structure of the Sanskrit language:

1. Much water, high and low, rivers, rains, forests,
2. gentle-cold the winds,
3. many high mountains-trees,
4. soft-delicate-fat the body (possessed by) the men (that it) contains, etc.

. . . this is *ānūpa*.[23]

What is produced is an indefinite succession of appositions which themselves endlessly exploit the possibilities of forming compound nouns in Sanskrit. Around a concept or noun considered as a pole (*ānūpa* in this case), the various formulas gather, superimposed one on another, their stock increased with each new version (there are parallel texts in Caraka and elsewhere):

x. sluggish the winds . . .
y. dense the ramifications . . .
and so on.

Tradition—the knowledge that history, ever accumulating, passes on—is the sum total of all the different versions, all the variants, each one complementing those that preceded it but never superseding them.

The method should be emphasized here. The theme of this book, which concerns the fauna, geography, and physical realities of ancient India, is not those realities themselves but the system of formulas used to classify them. In the study of traditional taxonomies—sometimes called ethnozoology, ethnobotany or ethnomedicine—a familiarity with Sanskrit provides an advantaged position: we are dealing here with a veritable scientific *literature.* From the system of correspondences and ramifications that a taxonomy represents, we can not only move *downstream* to determine how a particular taxonomy applies to the concrete realities of biology or geography but we can also travel *upstream* to describe the genesis of the literary and poetic forms in which the traditional taxonomies have been molded. We have tried to carry out both operations successively by devoting the earlier chapters to the concrete realities of biogeography and now by addressing the problems of language and an analysis of the logico-poetic interplay of garlands of names and recurring hemistiches.

Let us again review the literary forms—treatises partly (Suśruta, Caraka) or wholly in verse (Vāgbhaṭa)—in which the classical doctrine in expressed. In the most ancient texts (Suśruta, Caraka) expositions in prose are alternated with stanzas, either in isolation or in groups, which have a mnemonic function. They are known as *kārikā*, or in Louis Renou's translation, "memorial verses." The reader should refer to the many analyses which this Sanskrit scholar has devoted to the following literary styles or genres: *sūtra* (aphorisms), *bhāṣya* (commentaries), and *kārikā* (memorial verses), and in particular the combination which characterizes a whole family of scientific texts including the *Arthaśāstra* and the treatises of Suśruta and Caraka, namely the "*sūtra-bhāṣya* style with *kārikā*," either intercalated or grouped at the end of the chapter.[24] Such a perspective makes literature a part of the history of science. Since Hindu medicine gave birth to a science of texts and recitation, a study of style and literary forms will be quite simply a study of how scientific knowledge is formed. The epistemologist must therefore become a student of poetics. According to Renou, the paragraphs in prose have resulted from the ancient *sūtra*, or "aphorisms," being drowned in the mass of the text and mixed with a *bhāṣya*, or "commentary," characterized by an abundance of abstract derivations, long compound words, and the rarefaction of the personal forms of verbs. When placed at the end of a passage, the verses provide a summary: they sum up, conclude, and by virtue of their stereotyped appearance reaffirm the authority of the teaching; the catalog of meats ends in this way (line 138) with one of these summarizing verses. Usually, however, these verses are grouped in sequences where they alternate with prose. At this point, one senses a possibility of logical interplay through a repetition of the same hemistiches arranged in different sequences. For now, however, let us concentrate on the sequences in verse in order to demonstrate this stylistic phenomenon of repetition.

Jean Bottéro has recently drawn attention to the same stylistic feature in the legal codes and treatises on the divination of ancient Mesopotamia. Like medicine, the law and divination are the business of practitioners. The practitioners are presented with concrete cases which must be resolved in accordance with a whole system of casuistry as taught by the treatises. To that end, typical cases are set out in series grouped around a single theme and then "regrouped in paradigms."[25] For a single type of problem, a whole range of circumstances and solutions is presented to cover the entire gamut of possible different aspects; the problem is then arranged in series and recited, just as declensions and conjugations continue to be recited today. In this way, the mind learns to resolve every case by selecting the correct solution from the paradigmatic series of possible solutions already grouped around a single theme. What seems to be characteristic of this literature is an original type of rational thought, a triumph of thinking by using paradigms or series of words fixed by tradition.

EXAMPLES OF PARADIGMS

With this perspective, let us return to Suśruta's catalog. Although the text is brief, there are many repetitions. Many lines as in the following examples contain exact repetitions:

vātapittaharā vṛṣyā
"virilifying, they calm wind and bile" (63c and 95a)

kaṣāyaḥ svādulavaṇas
"astringent, sweet, salty" (64c and 69c)

viṣamajvaranāśanaḥ
"calming irregular fever" (66d and 89b)

Other lines of text provide an interplay of variants with a strictly identical meaning; the formula which we have translated as "of sweet savor and digestion" is thus variously expressed:

madhuro madhuraḥ pāke (56a)
madhurā rasapākābhyām (86c)
madhurā rasapākayoḥ (95b, 106d)
vipāke madhuraś cāpi (70c)
vipāke madhuraṃ cāpi (97c, 100c, 104c)

Around a simple or compound word, other words come and cluster, indicating diverse but analogous properties. The association of *astringent* with *sweet*, for example, leads to a mention of qualities such as *cordial*, *light*, or *dry*, which all tend in a similar direction:

"astringent, sweet, cordial" (55a)
"astringent, sweet, light" (60d)
"astringent, sweet, dry" (68a)

Foods qualified in this way calm disorders of phlegm; the predominant impression is that within the framework determined by the meter, which here requires a two-syllable word at the end of the hemistich, the choice between cordial, light, and dry is a matter of indifference. From a practical point of view, the formulas are equivalent. The names of diseases affected by an operator are also implied in the concordance: "calms bile-blood" (55b, 58a, 62a, 70a, 71c, 104d, 106a), "provokes bile-blood" (114c), "can corrupt blood and bile" (116c). The *jāṅgala* meats "calm bile-blood," while freshwater fish "excites bile-blood": the formula functions as a kind of indicator qualifying a particular article of the pharmacopoeia either in a positive sense (it calms) or in a negative one (it excites).

Let us continue our analysis of the sample chosen, first presenting the purport of the catalog in a synthetic form. The importance of the terms is at least partially conveyed by their frequency of occurrence; through being systematically repeated, a small group of adjectives emerges clearly from the collection of words as a whole. There is one fundamental definition for meats: they are, par excellence, foods or remedies that are *bṛṃhaṇa*, "nutritive." Meat is the most important of the *bṛṃhaṇa* remedies "intended to feed up the patient."[26] In this therapeutic action, meat is more valuable than milk, sugar, ghee, or enemas of an unctuous and sweet type, and so on. Meat is the first named in the series of nourishing agents: "There is nothing like meat to produce plumpness," a well-covered body, the sign of strength and health.[27] *Bṛṃhaṇa* is what "fattens." The word brings in its train other synonyms: "satisfying," "fortifying," and "virilifying," which itself is synonymous with "spermatogenic."[28] A nourishing substance is essentially heavy, cold, tender, unctuous," or, again, "all that is sweet, unctuous, vivifying, nourishing, heavy and excites the mind, is also virilifying."[29] The adjectives are synonymous in that they all convey the same images from different perspectives; their accumulation makes it possible to describe or define the properties of a particular thing through overdetermination. The text would become incoherent each time the terms appeared as such in a series were it not for the fact that they form a homogeneous whole, in this case one dominated by the association of the sweet and the unctuous, which qualifies substances made of earth and water.

This is a first set of criteria and properties to qualify meats in opposition to other types of foods, such as cereals, green vegetables, or fruits. But if meats are in general sweet, unctuous, cold, nourishing, and virilifying, they are not all such to the same extent: there is an internal polarity within the group of meats. Meat is heavy, but some meats are light. In general, meat is sweet, but at one of the poles in the catalog the two savors *astringent* and *sweet* are present together in equal parts, whereas at the other pole the astringent is no more than a subsidiary savor. Suśruta says, for example, that the flesh of the barasingha "is of a savor primarily sweet and secondarily astringent." Such a statement is in all probability based on the principle taught elsewhere that substances in which *earth* and *water* elements predominate are essentially sweet, but with just a touch of astringency.[30]

While *heavy*, *nourishing*, *unctuous*, and *virilifying* are repeated with ever-increasing frequency as one proceeds with the reading of the catalog, other adjectives appear less frequently. Applied mainly in the first two sections to the antelope and the quail, the adjectives *astringent*, *light*, *constrictive*, and *acrid*, which qualify substances made of wind and fire, become increasingly rare and eventually disappear. The stock of stereotyped formulas comprising the catalog of meats is divided into two paradigms, two different classes within a single formulary system. One group applies to light and astringent meats, the other to heavy and unctuous ones.

The first of these paradigms may be constructed by drawing up a homogeneous list of the hemistiches that compose the first three sections of the catalog and mark out the *jaṅghāla*, *viṣkira*, and *pratuda* meats as being essentially *light* and *astringent*. We may simplify the "First paradigm" (table 11) by eliminating the hemistiches that mention the names of the animals involved (names to which literary padding and adjectives composed of the requisite eight syllables are attached). Taking their place in the sequence but set back from the margin are the hemistiches contradictory to the rest of the list: these hemistiches, which belong to the second paradigm (the *heavy* and *unctuous* meats), are here used to mark out the animals (the peacock, the cock, and so on) whose flesh quite exceptionally presents properties contrary to the general properties of their own group. In the series set out on the left of the table, each hemistich could quite well be substituted for each of the others. Within a single paradigm, we find a vast interplay of variants, in the sense that Louis Hjelmslev gave to the word: "correlates with mutual substitution."[31] The meaning is exactly the same whether one say: "constrictive, appetizing, fortifying," or "constrictive, it stimulates (the digestive fire)," or "constrictive, it clears the complexion." The appetite, good digestion, and a clear complexion are all physiological signs of a single type of pharmacodynamic action which calms the excesses of phlegm and stimulates wind and bile. It is perfectly possible to multiply such signs provided it is done in such a way that the discourse divides up into prosodic units of eight syllables each. Once cast, each formula is added to the stock of ready-made units and will recur in other places.

In the end, this stereotyped discourse assumes a stochastic character. The attribution of a particular formula to a particular medical substance is both rational and unpredictable. Rational to the extent that the formulas are grouped into classes within a semiotic system and only one class is applicable for any given article in the catalog. But unpredictable; the antelope may be said to be "cold and to retain urines and stools," the quail to be "constrictive and to stimulate the fire," but it comes down to the same. The one formula could be a permutation of the other, they have the same logical extension. The connotation is different but the denotation is the same.

All concrete information, all empirical data, whether pharmaceutical, physiological, or nosological, are strictly subordinated to this *interplay of language*. But how to make myself understood here? Let me skim again through the text: the black antelope is "astringent, etc."; the fawn one "stimulates the fire, etc."; the quail is "constrictive, etc."; the partridge "stimulates the intellect, etc."

Suśruta does not say that the black antelope stimulates the fire nor

TABLE 11

First Paradigm—*Jāṅgala* Meats

Left column: sequence of hemistiches qualifying light and astringent meats
Right column: formulas contradictory to the sequence in which they are included and which serve to indicate those meats which are exceptional (peacock, cock, and so on)

(55a) *kaṣāyo madhuro hṛdyaḥ*	
(55b) *pittāsṛkkapharogahā*	
(55c) *saṃgrāhī rocano balyas*	
*(56a) *madhuro madhuraḥ pāke*	
(56b) *doṣaghno 'naladīpanaḥ*	
(56c) *śītalo baddhaviṇmūtraḥ*	
*(58a) *śītā 'sṛkpittaśamanī*	
	(58c) *sannipātakṣayaśvāsa-*
	(58d) *-kāsahikkārucipraṇut*
(60a) *laghavaḥ śītamadhurāḥ*	
(60b) *kaṣāyā doṣanāśanāḥ*	
(60c) *saṃgrāhī dīpanaś caiva*	
(60d) *kaṣāyamadhuro laghuḥ*	
	(61a) *īṣadgurūṣṇamadhuro*
*(61b) *vṛṣyo medhāgnivardhanaḥ*	
(61d) *grāhī varṇaprasādanaḥ*	
*(62a) *raktapittaharaḥ śīto*	
(62c) *kaphotthesu ca rogeṣu*	
(62d) *mandavāte ca śasyate*	
	(63a) *hikkāśvāsānilaharo*
	(63c) *vātapittaharā vṛṣyā*
*(63d) *medhāgnibalavardhanāḥ*	
	(64c) *kaṣāyaḥ svādulavaṇas*
	(64d) *tvacyaḥ keśyo 'rucau hitaḥ*
	(65b) *-dṛkśrotendriyadārḍhyakṛt*
	(65c) *snigdhoṣṇo 'nilahā vṛṣyaḥ*
	(65d) *svedasvarabalāvahaḥ*
	(66c) *vātarogakṣayavamī-*
	(66d) *-viṣamajvaranāśanaḥ*
(68a) *kaṣāyamadhurā rūkṣāḥ*	
(68b) *phalāhārā marutkarāḥ*	
(68c) *pittaśleṣmaharāḥ śītā*	
(68d) *baddhamūtrālpavarcasaḥ*	
	(69a) *sarvadoṣakaras teṣām*
	(69c) *kaṣāyasvādulavaṇo*
*(70a) *raktapittapraśamanaḥ*	
(70b) *kaṣāyaviśado 'pi ca*	
*(70c) *vipāke madhuraś cāpi*	
	(71b) *kaphaśukravivardhanaḥ*
*(71c) *raktapittaharo veśma-*	

* Formulas which also belong to the "second paradigm" (see below)

- (55a) astringent, sweet cordial
- (55b) calms bile-blood and disorders of phlegm
- (55c) constrictive, appetizing, fortifying
- (56a) sweet, of sweet digestion
- (56b) calms humors, stimulates the fire
- (56c) cold, retains urines and stools
- (58a) cold, calms bile-blood
  - (58c) suppresses conjunction of humors, consumption, dyspnoea
  - (58d) cough, hiccup, lack of appetite
- (60a) light, cold, sweet
- (60b) astringent, calm the humors
- (60c) constrictive, stimulates (the fire)
- (60d) astringent, sweet, light
  - (61a) rather heavy, hot, sweet
- (61b) virilifying, increases intellect and fire
- (61d) constrictive, clears the complexion
- (62a) cold, calms bile-blood
- (62c) both in disorders stemming from phlegm
- (62d) as in cases of sluggish wind it is appreciated
  - (63a) calms hiccup, dyspnoea, wind
  - (63c) virilifying, calm wind and bile
- (63d) increase intellect, fire, strength
  - (64c) astringent, sweet, salty
  - (64d) good for the skin, hair, and loss of appetite
  - (65b) [strengthens] . . . the senses of sight and hearing
  - (65c) unctuous, hot, calms wind, virilifying
  - (65d) diaphoretic, stengthens the voice
  - (66c) [calms] disorders of wind, consumption, vomiting
  - (66d) and irregular fever
- (68a) astringent, sweet, dry
- (68b) feed on fruit, excite wind
- (68c) cold, calm bile and phlegm
- (68d) retain urine, give few stools
  - (69a) among them, [the *bhedāśin*] excites all the humors
  - (69c) astringent, sweet, salty
- (70a) calms bile-blood
- (70b) astringent, desiccant
- (70c) of sweet digestion
  - (71b) increases phlegm and semen
- (71c) the domesticated [*kuliṅga*] calms bile-blood

that the fawn antelope is constrictive nor that the quail stimulates the intellect nor that the partridge is astringent. Should we conclude that these creatures do not possess those qualities? On the contrary. It is absurd to read the text as a succession of unconnected observations. Instead of dividing up the discourse as follows:

- the black antelope is astringent
- the fawn antelope stimulates the fire
- the quail is constrictive
- the partridge stimulates the intellect

let us consider the overall groups (figure 12):

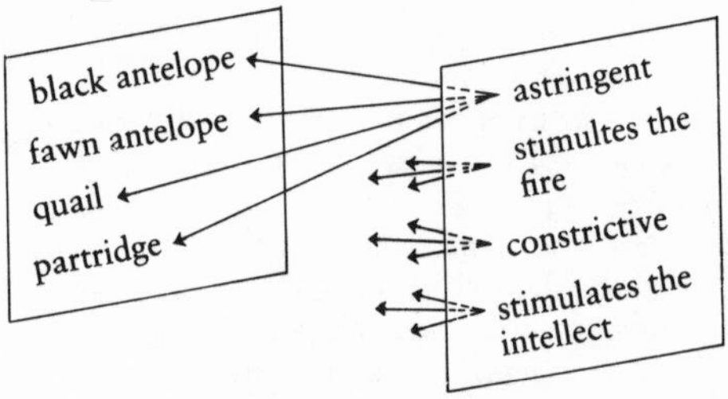

Figure 12. Sets and paradigms

To one and the same group of meats, all the formulas of the same paradigm apply, indiscriminately and overall.

It might be objected that the distribution of formulas is not always strictly consistent and that contradictions may be noted. In many cases, however, contradictions are justified. The black partridge is an equivocal example. While it "stimulates the intellect and the fire" (61b), properties of a light and astringent meat, it is also "rather heavy, hot, sweet" (61a). Is this an incoherence? The difficulty disappears as soon as one notices, in Caraka and Vāgbhaṭa, a detail that Suśruta does not provide: the partridge is *sādhāraṇa*, neither too light nor too heavy, because it frequents both dry and marshy lands.[32]

Nevertheless, we should not disguise the difficulties of interpretation, the existence of counterexamples and of ambiguous combinations of properties. It is difficult to understand, for example, how the *mṛgamātṛkā* (antelope or cervidae family) which is cold and calms bile-blood (58a), can at the same time cure consumption, cough, anorexia, and so on (58c–d). The first of these formulas indicates astringent and drying properties, whereas to cure consumption, cough, and anorexia one should stimulate phlegm by an unctuous and nourishing treatment. It would be easy to point in this way to many individual difficulties that bear on a particular *article* in the catalog; but we should recall what we have noted in an earlier chapter in connection with the identification of plants. While details usually remain doubtful, we are on firmer ground when we argue from the internal logic of a *series* of vegetation. In order to get around the obstacle represented by the individual doubtful or unknown identity of a particular Sanskrit name for a plant or an animal, we adopted the course of concentrating on groups or series. Now it seems that the evaluation of medical substances presents the same difficulties as their identification. The same can be said for the combinative system as for the nomenclature: the idea of an overall coherence becomes more viable once the interpreter determines not to get lost amid the details.

All the same, another more serious objection could be raised concerning the very existence of those paradigms that I believe it possible to identify. These paradigmatic wholes whose members are interchangeable are never explicitly presented as such. It is only as a working hypothesis that the interpreter takes a gamble on the coherence of these collections of adjectives and these repeated hemistiches. There is nothing to prevent any one term of a group, a particular adjective or hemistich, from entering into a combination with different terms from another group and accordingly indicating a different referent. Thus, even if the medical phraseology may be divided into different groups, the content and number of the groups of adjectives and hemistiches thus distinguished are not fixed.

We need only note the manifest predilection of the Indian doctors for collections, repetitions, equivalences, and polarities. The more or less homogeneous sequence of formulas distinguishing the *light* and *astringent* meats is balanced by another sequence composed of contrary formulas which qualify the *heavy* and *unctuous* meats.[33] The idea that these represent two paradigms merely develops the idea of a polarity between two groups of medical substances.

EXAMPLES OF SUBSTRUCTIONS

Time and again in the classical treatises, a desire to formalize the system of medicinal properties manifests itself in the form of curious calculatory exercises to which whole chapters are devoted. Such exercises have included: classifying the savors in terms of the humors, calculating the sixty-three possible combinations between the savors,[34] classifying the savors in terms of the qualities, and so on.

To pass in this way from one facet to another is not to simplify the system but to complicate it. What we try to do is move from the ready-made typology back to the combinative system as it emerges. For example, we have three humors and six savors. Does that mean one humor for two savors? Six for three times two? Are the six savors included within the three humors? They are not. We find neither subdivision nor inclusion but on the contrary three triads of savors for three humors, with rotation of the terms within each triad:

sweet-acid-salty	calm wind
sweet-bitter-astringent	calm bile
acrid-bitter-astringent	calm phlegm

and reciprocally:

acrid-bitter-astringent	excite wind
acrid-acid-salty	excite bile
sweet-acid-salty	excite phlegm[35]

There is no symmetry to the rotation; the savors are not all ascribed the same importance. Let us attempt to sketch out an explanation by setting out a few "substructions," or successive reconstructions, of the system of the *doṣa* (humors), *rasa* (savors), and *guṇa* (qualities).

An analysis of one particular difficulty, bearing on the use of the six principal *guṇa*—heavy, light, cold, hot, unctuous, dry—will allow us to demonstrate the interconnection between the two paradigms, or classes of sterotyped formulas, one of which qualifies the *light* and *astringent* meats, the other the *heavy* and *unctuous* ones. The cold-hot pair, which usually (taking pharmacopoeia as a whole) makes it possible to oppose to all the others (i.e., cold ones) those substances in which acridity predominates (i.e., hot ones), plays only a minor role in the catalog of meats. Certainly, the *jāṅgala* meats are "acrid" *(kaṭuka)*[36] and, as explained at the beginning of this study, in the dry lands bile predominates together with wind. Suśruta, however, stresses the *astringency* of *jāṅgala* meats, despite a few discreet references to their *acridity*. Similarly, *jāṅgala* meats are *cold*. In order to understand the statistical distribution of these adjectives, we must discover how the *rasa* are distributed in relation to the *guṇa* and, more precisely, how *astringent* and *acrid* are

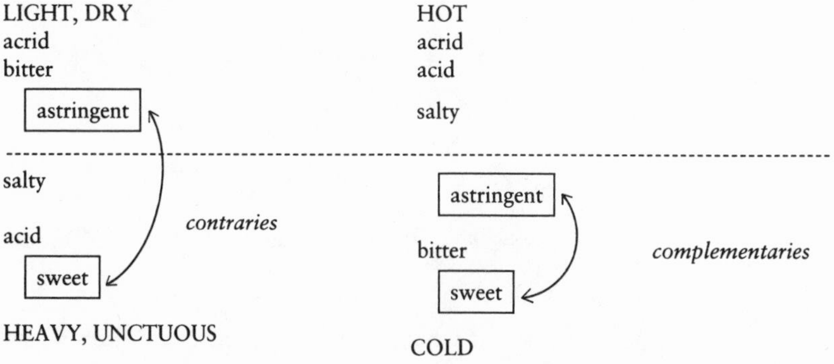

Figure 13. Contraries vs. complementaries

distributed in relation to *cold* and *hot*, *unctuous* and *dry*, *heavy* and *light*. The texts vary on this subject and the classificatory grid that we are borrowing from Suśruta may well be contradicted elsewhere. It is but one means among many others of approaching the problem.

> Some say that by virtue of the relationship of the world to Agni (sun) and Soma (moon), the *rasa* are of two kinds: *saumya* (in which Soma predominates) and *āgneya* (in which Agni predominates). Sweet-bitter-astringent are *saumya*, acrid-acid-salty are *āgneya*. So, sweet-acid-salty are unctuous and heavy, acrid-bitter-astringent are dry and light. *Saumya*, cold; *āgneya*, hot.[37]

The distribution of the *rasa* varies according to which *guṇa* are chosen as criteria. The astringent *swings alternately*, first toward light-dry, then toward cold (figure 13). The meats in general are cold, because they are sweet and astringent; from this point of view, the two *rasa* astringent and sweet are complementary. Yet at the same time the meats are distributed between light-dry, due to their astringency, and heavy-unctuous, due to their sweetness; from this new point of view, the two *rasa* astringent and sweet are contrary to each other.

This distribution, "sweet-acid-salty calm wind," is similar to the one cited above. It is also similar to the distribution that can be made of the five physical elements earth-water-fire-air-ether in relation to the humors:

> earthy-fiery-watery substances calm wind, earthy-watery-airy ones calm bile . . . , etherial-fiery-airy ones calm phlegm.[38]

The fundamental feature of these combinations is their asymmetry. This asymmetry first appears in the primacy of the sweet, in which earth

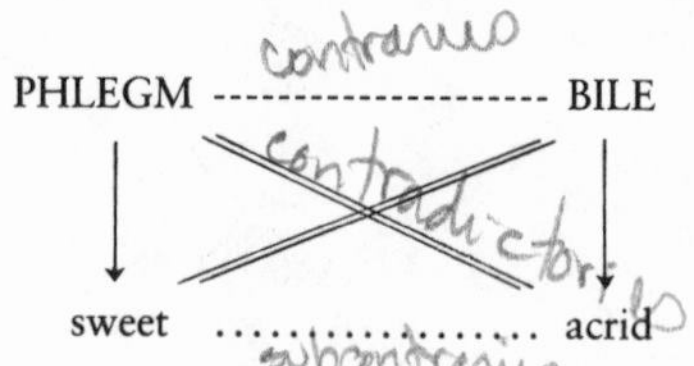

Figure 14. Logical square
Contraries: bile and phlegm
Contradictories: bile and *sweet*; phlegm and *acrid*
Subcontraries: *sweet* and *acrid*

and water predominate and of which all the other *rasa* are simply successive specifications. The sweet is the first *rasa* of all with which the moon, which provides the rains, comes to impregnate the earth. The sweet opposes both bile and wind but for different reasons: bile because of its watery coldness, wind because of its unctuous heaviness.

Wind, the first of the three humors to be cited—in the traditional order—is on a different level from the other two humors. Between bile and phlegm there is a symmetry. Bile and phlegm symbolize the opposition between fire and water, an opposition of contraries: Agni and Soma, *āgneya* and *saumya*, the dryness of fiery substances and the unctuousness of watery ones, lack and plethora, desiccation (in the dry lands) and oedema (in a marshy environment). A helpful illustration may be borrowed from Western classical logic: the schema of the "logical square" (Apuleius's square) and the distinction between several different kinds of oppositions. Bile and phlegm are "*contraries*" (both belong to the same facet); but bile and the sweet are "*contradictories*." The savors oppose the humors; the savors are subordinated to the humors; in relation to the series of the humors, the series of the savors is "*subaltern*." Figure 14 is of an altogether provisional nature. It is meant to show the relations between humors and savors without going right back to the logical foundations of what we have called a multifaceted system of classification. Nevertheless, the few logical concepts illustrated here are illuminating. (One may also refer to Robert Blanché's *Structures intellectuelles* to be discussed later.)

Wind is then introduced into this fight between fire and water, where it remains in an alternating and dominant position. The primacy and ubiquity of wind are mentioned repeatedly in the texts. In contrast to bile and phlegm, which are localized, wind is everywhere and nowhere, the very symbol and basis of movement:

> A fever born from bile and wind needs the cold, born from phlegm and wind the hot. Wind, the vehicle par excellence, can, in conjunction, produce both

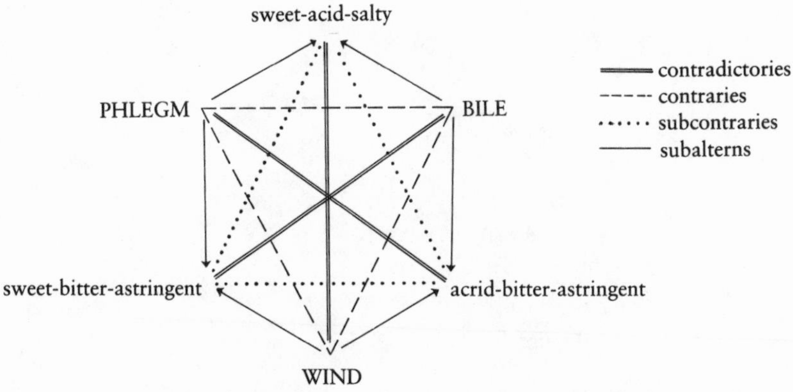

Figure 15. Logical hexagon of humors and savors

> of these effects: joined with bile it imparts an inflammation, associated with phlegm it imparts the cold.[39]

Wind serves as a vehicle: through contact it assimilates the qualities of the environments through which it passes and transports and transmits them. It enters alternately into conjunction with fire and water. We are reminded that *jāṅgala* associates wind and bile and that *ānūpa* associates wind and phlegm. This can be illustrated by complicating the logical square, generalizing it in the form of a logical hexagon, as in figure 15, inspired by an idea developed by the logician Robert Blanché in his *Structures intellectuelles*, a remarkable work which is of the first relevance to the logic of qualities and the study of property spaces.[40]

To **A** (universal affirmative propositions), **E** (universal negative), **I** (particular affirmative), **O** (particular negative), two additional places may be added: **U** (the disjunction of **A** and **E**) and **Y** (the rejection of **A** and **E** and the conjunction of **I** and **O**). Blanché thus obtains a generalized form of Apuleius's square as in figure 16.

To illustrate the rejection of **A** and **E**: wind is neither phlegm nor bile. To illustrate the conjunction of **I** and **O**: wind shares both in the association of sweet-bitter-astringent and also in that of acrid-bitter-astringent, even if on its own it is neither sweet nor acrid. Thus, drugs of an acrid-bitter-astringent savor provoke wind, despite the fact that drugs that provoke wind are not all acrid.

Between the heavy and the light, the unctuous and the dry, the sweet and the acrid, all the qualities and all the savors, thought proceeds by means of either *yes or no* or else by *more or less*, constructing two kinds of conceptual organizations which Blanché has called "the star of oppo-

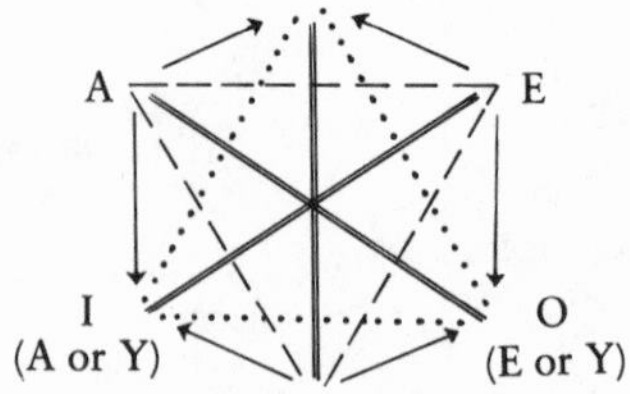

Figure 16. Blanché's logical hexagon

sition . . . and the linear structure of gradation." What is immediately revealed by the logical hexagon is the passage from one to the other made possible in this example by the subordination of the savors to the humors. The combination of sweet-acid-salty, which acts against wind, appears consequently to be a weaker degree of phlegm; and, more generally, each of the three associations mentioned in the texts thus far cited: sweet-acid-salty, sweet-bitter-astringent, and acrid-bitter-astringent seem in part subordinated and in part contrary to the humors surrounding it. This equivocation, this asymmetry is precisely what makes it possible to pass from *couples* of contrary terms to hierarchized *series* of terms. "The structure of opposition is inflected toward that of gradation to the extent that each subaltern term asserts its independence in relation to the one to which it is subaltern and changes to the point where, set opposite the latter, it takes on the appearance of a kind of contrary; a contrary that is no doubt only weakly contrasted but which nevertheless sets itself sufficiently apart for the difference to turn into an incompatibility."[41] Here, the subaltern propositions (subordinated to the humors) are the triads, which combine savors that are alternately opposed or conjoined to each other: sweet (phlegm) with acid-salty (bile), acrid (bile) with bitter-astringent (wind), and so on, so that in a surreptitious fashion the *couples* of contrary terms—sweet and acrid, sweet and astringent—merge into the hierarchical *series* in an order of increasing lightness: sweet-acid-salty-acrid-bitter-astringent. The entire system is constructed on this interplay between couples and series.

Suśruta's catalog of meats provides an example:

Introduction: aquatic, *ānūpa*, domesticated . . . "but they are also classed into two" (polarity).

Conclusion: aquatic, *ānūpa*, domesticated . . . "they are in order of increasing lightness" (scale of values).

First, then, we have a couple: *jāṅgala* and *ānūpa*, the dry lands and the marshy ones, a pair which is eventually transformed into a hierarchy. The "middle" land *(sādhāraṇa)* is defined in abstract by a rejection of extremes: neither too wet nor too dry, neither too cold nor too sunny; this is the place where there is an equality of the contrary humors. A hemistich such as "astringent, sweet, salty," which appears in the middle sections of the catalog (64c, 69c), symbolizes this in-between position where contraries neutralize one another by associating savors which, on the logical hexagon, form the *triangle of subcontraries*: astringent-sweet-salty, respectively subordinated to wind-phlegm-bile, the triangle of contraries. Although wind ought in principle to have remained in an alternating position, associated with phlegm in *ānūpa* and bile in *jāṅgala*, in fact gradation and hierarchy win out. The various categories of animals: aquatic-marshy-domesticated-carnivorous-whole-hoofed-*jāṅgala* succeed one another more or less in the same order as the series: sweet-acid-salty-acrid-astringent ("bitter" is not mentioned). *Sweet* and *astringent* should not be understood as mutually exclusive, but as the lowest and the highest on the same scale. There is one significant displacement: astringency, at first in the foreground ("astringent-sweet"), subsequently falls into the background and the marshy meats are "specifically sweet but of a subsidiary astringent savor." The opposition between wind (*astringent*) and phlegm (*sweet*) overrides the opposition between bile (*acrid*) and phlegm.

The classification and evaluation of medicinal substances thus operates through a perpetual oscillation between polarities (or pairs of contraries in which one is valued highly to the detriment of the other) and hierarchies (or graduated series). In a concrete fashion, names of things and the adjectives that qualify them are thus presented in pairs and series within octosyllabic hemistiches, in the versified parts of the medical treatises and herbals. Hence the usefulness but also the defects of these paradigms of interchangeable hemistiches whose existence I believe we have established. Two contrary paradigms make it possible to develop a polarity. For instance, running parallel to the *light* and *astringent* meats, the "Second Paradigm" (table 12) is a sample of hemistiches that qualify the *heavy* and *unctuous* meats. They constitute a relatively homogeneous sequence that is quite distinct from the "First Paradigm." Thus an opposition is presented between two groups of

TABLE 12

SECOND PARADIGM—NOURISHING, HEAVY, AND UNCTUOUS REMEDIES

(73a)	*madhurā guravaḥ snigdhā*	(73a)	sweet, heavy, unctuous
(73b)	*balyā mārutanāśanāḥ*	(73b)	fortifying, calm wind
	. . .		. . .
(77a)	*madhurā guravo vṛṣyāś*	(77a)	sweet, heavy, virilifying
(77b)	*cakṣuṣyāḥ śoṣiṇe hitāḥ*	(77b)	good for the eyes, good for consumption
(77c)	*sṛṣṭamūtrapurīṣāś ca*	(77c)	evacuate urines and stools
(77d)	*kāsārśaḥśvāsanāśanāḥ*	(77d)	calm cough, piles, dyspnoea
	. . .		. . .
(97b)	*snigdhaṃ madhurakāsajit*	(97b)	unctuous, sweet, dispells cough
(97c)	*vipāke madhuraṃ cāpi*	(97c)	of sweet digestion
(97d)	*vyavāyasya tu vardhanam*	(97d)	aphrodisiac
(98a)	*snigdhoṣṇamadhuro vṛṣyo*	(98a)	unctuous, hot, sweet, virilifying
(98b)	*mahiṣas tarpaṇo guruḥ*	(98b)	the buffalo is satisfying, heavy
(98c)	*nidrāpuṃstvabalastanya-*	(98c)	it increases sleep, virility, strength, milk
(98d)	*-vardhano māṃsadārḍhyakṛt*	(98d)	it makes flesh firm
	. . .		. . .
(102a)	*svedanaṃ bṛṃhaṇaṃ vṛṣyaṃ*	(102a)	diaphoretic, nourishing, virilifying
(102b)	*śītalaṃ tarpaṇaṃ guru*	(102b)	cold, satisfying, heavy
(102c)	*śramānilaharaṃ snigdhaṃ*	(102c)	unctuous, calms fatigue and wind
	. . .		. . .
	(Cooked foods)		(Cooked foods)
(343d)	*bṛṃhaṇī balavardhanī*	(343d)	nourishing, fortifying
(349a)	*guravo bṛṃhaṇā balyā*	(349a)	heavy, nourishing, fortifying
(351b)	*snehanaṃ balavardhanam*	(351b)	unctuous, fortifying
(352b)	*rocanaṃ bṛṃhaṇaṃ guru*	(352b)	appetizing, nourishing, heavy
(354b)	*-māṃsaujaḥśukravardhanam*	(354b)	increases flesh, vital fluid, and semen
	. . .		. . .

(SOURCE: Suśruta, *sūtra* XLVI)

meats with contrary qualities, a polarity between *jāṅgala* and *ānūpa*. The same group of formulas that here serve to qualify the heavy, unctuous *ānūpa* may be used elsewhere to qualify, for example, aphrodisiacs or treatments for consumption. A whole interplay of cross-references is set up: meats are *bṛṃhaṇa* (nourishing) = the *bṛṃhaṇīya* (the nourishing treatments) are based on meats. About feeding up, for instance:

> He who feeds himself on unctuous,
> sweet, heavy and lubrifying drugs
> [relies on *bṛṃhaṇīya*]
> and on marshy and aquatic meats, etc.[42]

All these hemistiches are as many additions to our samples. However, a given sequence is not altogether homogeneous; it contains a considerable proportion of counterexamples and ambiguous formulas, ones which belong to both contrary paradigms simultaneously because they mark out exceptions and because thought is wavering between opposition and gradation, with opposition defined as the parallelism between the hemistiches that belong to two contrary paradigms and gradation defined as the distribution, within a given, relatively homogeneous sequence, of a number of hemistiches which are at odds with the rest, so as to suggest something like "it is this, but not quite," or "it is not that, but all the same, it is a bit."

Another example will confirm our analysis: the catalog of milks is based on a similar division between two classes of hemistiches. In general, milk is of sweet *savor* and *digestion* and of cold *energy*, but distinctions are made depending on its source:

cow, *goat*, *camel* give a relatively dryer milk;

ewe, *buffalo*, and so on give a very heavy and unctuous milk that produces abundant fluxes.

In a first sequence (milk is *relatively dry*), contrary formulas are intermingled, some of which indicate a possible astringency (left-hand column), while others indicate heaviness and unctuosity (right-hand column):

(50a) *alphābhiṣyandi gokṣīram*
                (50b) *snigdhaṃ guru rasāyanam* /
(50c) *raktapittaharaṃ śītaṃ*
(50d) *madhuraṃ rasapākayoḥ* //
                (51a) *jīvanīyam*. . .

(51c) *gavyatulyaguṇaṃ tv ājaṃ*
(52b) *viśeṣāc choṣiṇāṃ hitam* //
(52a) *dīpanaṃ laghu saṃgrāhi*
(52c) *śvāsakāsāsrapittanut* /

(50a) Cow's milk produces few fluxes
(50b) unctuous, heavy, elixir for long life,
*(50c) cold, calms bile-blood,
*(50d) sweet of savor and digestion,
(51a) vivifying. . . .
(51c) with qualities similar to cow's milk, goat's milk
(52b) is especially good against consumption,
(52a) stimulates (the fire), light, constrictive,
(52c) calms dyspnoea, cough, bile-blood. . .[43]

Hemistiches 50c (it calms bile-blood) and 50d (sweet) could equally well appear among those hemistiches that indicate heaviness and unctuosity. They belong to both paradigms at once: such formulas are marked by an asterisk as in the "First Paradigm." Meats and milks, whether heavy or light, unctuous or astringent, are sweet of *savor* and *digestion* and consequently develop a cold *energy*, as has already been noted at the end of chapter 4. They will therefore combat bile-blood and more generally all disorders of bile: the corresponding formulas fall at the intersection of the two paradigms.

The catalog of milks may be schematically illustrated in the same way as the catalog of meats:

about MILKS in general

sweet *savor*
sweet *digestion* ⟹ generally bring forth cold *energy*

---

subsidiarily

cow's milk, and so on	ewe's milk, etc.
=	=
alpābhiṣyandin (50a)	*mahābhisyandin* (55c)
"producing few fluxes"	"producing many fluxes"

Figure 17. Milks

This light/heavy or dry/unctuous opposition emerges against a background of common characteristics (sweet, cold) and is also to be found in the choice of formulas:

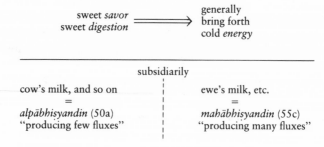

Formulas common to both paradigms:
"cold, it calms bile-blood"
"sweet of savor and digestion"
. . .

Next, opposition:

"stimulates (the fire), light, constrictive"	"unctuous, heavy, elixir of long life"

The catalog of milks only becomes intelligible once one distinguishes between the two series of formulas and perceives the contradiction between hemistiches 50a and 50b, between 51d and 52a. Beneath the apparent linearity of the writing, one can then detect the alliance of two contrary themes, the *intersection* between two groups of contrasted features, the *ambiguity* of a substance that is relatively dry—and yet unctuous, rather light—but with a basis of heaviness. The first sequence which intermingles contraries in this way is balanced by the rest of the catalog (unctuous and heavy milks):

Ewe's milk, sweet, unctuous (54c),
heavy. . . .
Sweet, producing abundant discharges (55c),
the milk of the buffalo. . . .

They represent as many formulas to complete the sample already given as our "Second Paradigm."

WORD AND PERCEPTION

To conclude this chapter, we should stand back a little from the details of our analyses and situate them in a general perspective. We might have uncovered an altogether new form of discourse—that is, both a type of literary composition and a set of patterns for reasoning, in which logic is indissolubly linked with poetics.

What seems to emerge here is a deep interrelationship between medical knowledge and poetry. A distinction is traditionally drawn between science and literature in Sanskrit: on the one hand, the *śāstra*, or treatises concerned with the sciences appended to the Vedic Revelation—medicine, grammar, and law—and on the other hand, the *kāvya*, or compositions in ornate style—lyrics, panegyrics, romances—which bear the mark of aesthetic intentions. But we should reach back beyond that distinction. Once again following Roman Jakobson, we should demonstrate the "poetic function" of language in the medical texts—that is, the phraseology of the language, the combinative interplay of formulas, the way in which the hemistiches recur in the versified sequences.

Admittedly, the Sanskrit treatises constitute an "erudite" literature, a "technical" literature, but that is not the main thing. Above all, they represent transcriptions of an authoritative Word, they are "normative" texts, their aim is to get the knowledge that they transcribe recognized as such: authentic, orthodox. That is why the referential or cognitive function of language (Jakobson's terminology) assumes a secondary importance: the emphasis is placed on the message itself, its *authority*. Poetry is a language endowed with authority and therefore functions as a means to formulate traditional knowledge.

The conclusion will be twofold. A formal analysis should first expose the rhythmic and syntactic parallelism in the cited texts. Then literary facts should be set back within the framework of Hindu tradition. As already suggested, the language of Ayurveda, in its very forms, carries and conveys a topology; the traditional phrases teach the disciples space configurations which elude their own very limited powers of perception; the texts teach one to recognize what it is that one needs amid all that one sees.

Let us remain for now on the level of a purely formal analysis. As is well known, Roman Jakobson and the whole school of linguists, folklorists, and theoreticians of literature who founded the famous Opoïaz or "Society for the study of the poetic language" in Russia in 1916–17 have systematically extended the study of the function of poetic language beyond the limits of poetry in the strict sense. To that kind of approach, as Jakobson has shown, Sanskrit didactic poetry is quite relevant: "Mnemonic lines . . . like "Thirty days hath September," modern advertising jingles, and versified medieval laws . . . , or finally Sanskrit scientific treatises in verse which in Indic tradition are strictly distinguished from true poetry *(kāvya)*—all these metrical texts make use of poetic function without, however, assigning to this function the coercing, determining role it carries in poetry. Thus verse actually exceeds the limits of poetry, but at the same time verse always implies poetic function."[44] All the examples mentioned here emphasize the stereotyped nature of the poetic language, its authority as a piece of teaching. This conclusion was implicit in Louis Renou's description of the *kārikā* style and of *kārikā* as "memorial verses" (quoted above). It is sometimes said that the versification of scientific texts has a utilitarian purpose: it makes it easier to learn them by heart. This explanation, however, is too simplistic. It is not so much a matter of aiding the memory as of the promotion, prescription, and scansion of knowledge.

The fundamental problem of poetry, Jakobson goes on to say, is that of *parallelism*. The word evokes a whole mass of contemporary studies on folklore and oral poetry, but there is no immediate need to multiply our references here or to underline the role of parallelism in the Vedas and the Sanskrit epics.[45] The principle was noted by Gerard Manley Hopkins as early as 1865: "The artificial part of poetry, perhaps we shall be right to say all artifice, reduces itself to the principle of parallelism. The structure of poetry is that of continuous parallelism, ranging from the technical so-called Parallelisms of Hebrew poetry and the antiphons of Church music up to the intricacy of Greek or Italian or English verse. But parallelism is of two kinds necessarily—where the opposition is clearly marked, and where it is transitional rather or chromatic. Only the first kind, that of marked parallelism, is concerned with the structure of verse—in rhythm, the recurrence of a certain sequence of syllables, in meter, the recurrence of a certain sequence of rhythm, in alliteration, in assonance and in rhyme. Now the force of this recurrence is to beget a recurrence or parallelism answering to it in the words or thought and, speaking roughly and rather for the tendency than the invariable result, the more marked parallelism in structure whether of elaboration or of emphasis begets more marked parallelism in the words and sense."[46] The articulation of speech encourages the recurrence of semantic stereotypes. The parallelism within the very space of the text—in other words, the formal similarities displayed by writing on the blank page (or palm-leaf, in the case of the Indian manuscripts)—induces a parallelism of meanings within the logical space, the property space to which the text refers.

Our use of the notion of *space* to describe a text (the space of a text) or a system of signs (property spaces) in their purely formal content may be considered strange, or pointlessly complicated. This image, however, commonly used in linguistics and poetics, can help us to understand the intimate connection in the Sanskrit medical texts between the logical system of characteristics, or *lakṣaṇa*, indicating the nature and effects of medicinal substances and the poetic interplay of recurring hemistiches, a logical system and a poetic interplay which the discourse juxtaposes. The equations, divisions, inversions, and other logical transformations constituting the combinative system of pharmaceutical qualities have been molded in an artificial language in order to manifest the way the thought has been articulated and stereotyped.

The relation between rhythm and semantics in poetry is one of the main tenets of Russian Formalism, a well-known school of literary criticism, according to which the layout of the words in poetry aims to liberate perception from its habitual automatism. Says V. V. Chklovski: "What matters in parallelism is the sensation of non-coincidence in a resemblance"; it aims to displace the objects of the discourse, to provoke an effect of surprise, or to transfer a given object "from the way that it is habitually perceived into the sphere of a new perception."[47] Poetic language creates a medium of ideal meaning, a new semantic atmosphere which cuts across the world of everyday perception. The procedures of recurrence or parallelism aim to make manifest these separations that are internal to thought. We need hardly illustrate this conception of poetry, for today it is part of, so to say, our basic poetical culture.

Recurrence, parallelism: it is the same, as Hopkins already noted! Whether it be the periodic repetition of one formula through a whole gamut of variants, or else a pair of formulas constituting a negative parallelism such as:

> "Few fluxes . . .
> Many fluxes . . ."
>
> "Little water and few trees . . .
> Much water and many trees . . .
> Gives fires, eliminates phlegm . . .
> Gives phlegm, eliminates fire . . .
>
> *raktapittaharaḥ śīto*
> "cold, calming bile-blood"
> *raktapittakarāś coṣṇā*
> "hot, provoking bile-blood"
>
> (A parallelism partly based on a pun: the substitution of *k* for *h*, which transforms °*hara* "calming" into °*kara* "provoking")

and a thousand other examples of the kind. Whether it be a repetition of formulas in oral recitation or a juxtaposition of formulas in a written text, in both cases a given sequence, formulated in *kārikā* style, constitutes—did I make my point?—a multifaceted system.

In the vocabulary of materia medica, a distinction can be made between two components: the names of drugs and their qualities. The names denote the most concrete things, the flora, the fauna, biogeography. The medicinal qualities, in contrast, must be situated on the most abstract level of language. When the texts teach that wind accumulates in summer, bile during the rains, and phlegm during the winter, it can be said that the series of humors *wind-bile-phlegm*—the most abstract of terms and ones that stem from a metalanguage—is applied onto the series *summer-rains-winter*, terms that belong to a more concrete language; then the cycle of the seasons, in its turn, is used as an abstract framework within which foods and bodily techniques are classed in a concrete fashion. We thus pass through different strata of language, from the most abstract to the most concrete; and again, from the conceptual opposition between dry land and marshy land, we may move either downstream to the distributional patterns of the flora and fauna over the terrain, or else upstream to the structures of the language in which the theory is formulated. There we find the poetic interplay of recurring hemistiches, which makes it possible to formulate the *jāṅgala/anūpa* polarity in a thousand different ways. But on any level of the language, the same intellectual structures are found: star-shaped or linear structures (as the logician would call them), recurrences or parallelism (as the student of poetics would say). They appear most clearly at the most abstract level, in the combinative system of the *lakṣaṇa*, but they also govern the geography and the distribution of the flora and fauna as taught in the texts. *Traditional space is structured by the language*; spatial configurations are formulated in the texts before they are ever perceived on the ground.

We should never forget that the doctor, like any other specialist in the brahminic concept of knowledge, would by himself be incapable of discussing the characteristics or effects of such and such substance that he was about to use. There would be no question of experimenting or of reasoning other than on the basis of the traditional teachings. The model of knowledge is perception, and insofar as our perception is blind, imperfect, the word transmitted in the texts comes to our aid. We can make only a brief reference to Madeleine Biardeau's work on the theory of knowledge in brahmanism, but let us at least note one of her major conclusions. Indian logicians "recognize that the summit of all knowledge is perception: having reached that peak, thought can rest, in satisfaction. They never ask for an intellectual comprehension such as knowledge of the interior of a thing or a being. . . . The desire to know is never gratuitous, it always implies that one expects a benefit, not from knowledge itself but from the object to be known. They do not seek to understand, because they do not think they need to in order to possess. *Everything that is useful is given*, either in perception or in Revelation and the Tradition which completes it."[48] The medical texts bear witness to this pragmatism and anthropocentricity, as Suśruta testifies:

> No need to examine them, no need to reflect on them, they will make themselves known, the remedies that the clear-sighted must prescribe in accordance with tradition.
>
> Their characteristics and effects are self-evident and they make themselves known, the medicinal plants; scholars should in no way quibble about them.
>
> Were there a thousand reasons to do so, the *ambaṣṭhā* group will never set itself to purging! The wise must therefore adhere to tradition, without arguing.[49]

No examination, no research, no enquiry or attempt to find a reason for the data: that is what I meant when saying that the model of natural history was alien to India. Its place is filled by the collection, recitation, and combination of the formulas consecrated by Tradition. Whether it is given to us by perception or through the Word, knowledge comes to us from outside and remains on the surface of things. It is the utility of the objects of discourse that constitutes the problem of knowledge: Of all that we see around us, what is best to use? In the making of that choice, Tradition is the law. And to the extent that the distribution of things and beings is anthropocentric, the principles of that distribution, the schemata for organizing space elude perception and belong to the domain of the word.

VI: The Flesh of Eaters of Flesh

This enquiry started with geographical maps. Then came pharmacy and cooking, the most concrete and familiar of operations. Now, unexpectedly, our discourse on the jungle deviates: a logical square is introduced, with poetry, formalism, and the theory of literature. But take heart! The most arid part of this jungle is behind us. We return now to more vital realities—blood and tissues—in this study of a single theme on a number of superimposed levels: first biogeography, next pharmacy, and now physiology. The logico-poetic perspective adopted in chapter 4 provided a general view of the data collected in the course of the first three chapters on spatial configurations and the distribution of fauna. The classification of animals turned out to be subordinate to the system of pharmaceutical properties. Biogeography was incorporated within pharmacy. But pharmacy, in its turn, presupposes a whole cosmic physiology: the world, the great chain of foods. Living beings, eaters soon to be eaten, transmit one to another the nourishing essences drawn from the earth. The last chapters will tackle physiology. Ancient physiology in India, as in Greece, was a part of cosmogony and shared certain primordial images with it: the image of cooking the world, the conflict between water and fire, the scale of beings. The present chapter is chiefly devoted to one link in the great chain of being: the carnivorous animals, the meat of the eaters of meat. Such a theme permits the sketching out of a general description of Ayurvedic physiology.

We have come a long way from the strictly ecological considerations which opened the book; the relations of living beings to a particular soil multiply and become more complex as the sequence stretches farther: moon-space-wind-rain-earth-plant-eater of grass-eater of flesh . . . , the sequence through which the juices and savors characteristic of that soil are diffused. "Nourishing" are the meats?—The meat of eaters of meat is doubly so! The virtues of the meats that they have eaten are added to those of their own flesh, producing a superconcentrate. The first principle of this physiology—bound to remain purely speculative—is not difficult to surmise: the concentration of the materials superactivates the essences that they contain.

Far beyond the standards of present-day Europe—cineasts will be familiar with the leading men's plumpness in Indian films—corpulence is a sign of power. Let us review the eminent property of meats: *bṛṃhaṇa*, they "fatten the body." A *bṛṃhaṇa* food is a "maker of flesh" *(māṃsakara)*, it produces muscle; vegetable oil is *bṛṃhaṇa* because it makes the body firm by fattening the tissues.[1] The "firmness of flesh"[2] is one of those happy consequences of the presence of phlegm. Phlegm disorders lead to plethora, a flaccid and flabby body, while phlegm equilibrium ensures firmness in a well-covered body. Plumpness should not be confused with obesity.

Technical terms are clearly different for "plumpness" *(bṛhattva, puṣṭi)* and "obesity" *(sthaulya)*.[3] Plumpness results from a harmonious growth of the tissues; cachexia, in contrast, is defined as a "wasting" *(kṣaya)*. Overwork, fasting, or a diet not unctuous enough, overexposure to the sun and wind, and too abrupt an elimination of phlegm and excretions provoke desiccation, loss of weight, and wasting of the tissues. In obesity, on the other hand, there is "plethora" *(atimātra)*. Food that is too unctuous and a life that is too sedentary provoke a superabundance of organic liquids which proceed to block all channels and openings. There are two aspects to the polarity between dryness and unctuosity as shown in figure 18:

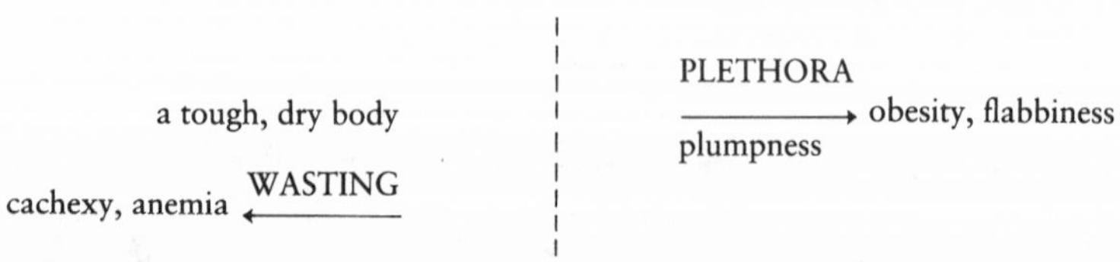

Figure 18. Wasting vs. plethora

From this point of view (but it is a very limited one, as will be explained in a moment), physiology amounts to a double process of "growth" and "decline" of the body's constituents. And it is true that any disease manifests either an excess or an insufficiency; there is evidently a kind of *economy* of the tissues and vital forces. Does that mean that medical diagnosis can be reduced to determining, in each case and for all diseases, whether what is at work is a process of concentration and constriction of the tissues or, on the contrary, one of wasting and relaxation? One is put in mind of the doctrine of the Methodists, the Greco-Latin medical sect which we have already had occasion to mention: they maintained that every disease was either a *constriction* or a *relaxation*, or a mixture of the two states. But we have already seen how alien this reductionist, simplificatory attitude is to the Ayurvedics who, in contrast, attach such an extreme importance to circumstances, ecology, and the patient's habits. Perhaps the only point in common is that, in default of a real physiology, a science as yet nonexistent, both doctrines set up an economy of nutrition, with things now coming in, now going out, a growth and decline of the tissues.

Whenever we come across an instance of polarity—a polarity between dryness and unctuosity, between *laṅghana* (cure by slimming) and *bṛṃhaṇa* (cure by feeding up), between *kārśya* (cachexy) and *sthaulya* (obesity), or finally between Agni and Soma (the sun which captures saps and the moon which makes them increase)—every time a higher value is set upon one of the two terms than on the other. In fact, that is what makes it a polarity: one of the terms serves as a foil, it represents the antivalue of a particular given value. But depending on the circumstances and the point of view adopted, the order of the evaluation may be reversed. Sometimes the emphasis is laid on corpulence, the sign of strength in a well-nourished body in contrast to anemia and cachexy; at other times it is, on the contrary, the spareness of a tough, dry body that is valued more highly, in contrast to flabbiness and obesity. The texts cited in chapter 1 set a high value on the spareness of the *jāṅgala* man whose body was "tough and dry" or "tough and hard"; it was contrasted to the body of an *ānūpa* man, which was "flabby and fat" or "very delicate" *(sukumāra)*, an adjective elsewhere associated with unhealthy and lascivious indolence.[4] Conversely, however, "thin, dry" *(kṛśa)* may in other contexts lead to "emaciation, cachexy" *(kārśya)*, which calls for a *bṛṃhaṇa* treatment to restore a sterling "plumpness" to the body.[5] A polarity of images is thus established. The basic material of ancient physiology consists of familiar images and behavior which discourse then formalizes and complicates. Why did the analysis of discourse assume such importance, to the point of constituting the kernel of this book (chapters 4 and 5)? Because discourse and what we have called prognosis, the science of signs and therapeutic indications, property spaces, and phraseology occupy the place that was later (much later, not before the sixteenth century) to be taken over by anatomopathology in modern medicine. Let us now set out the essentials of the Ayurvedic concept of the human body.

CONCENTRATION OF THE MATERIALS AND SUPERACTIVATION

It comes from images common to all ancient physiologies: the circulation of fluids within organic materials, the internal cooking processes by which the organism extracts the nutritive juices from foods. Onto this common basis other, more particular concepts are then grafted—for example, the doctrine of the seven *dhātu*, or "tissues," whereby chyle, blood, flesh, fat, bone, marrow, and semen are changed into one another through a process of successive cookings. Chyle, cooked by a fire which is specially designed for it in the depths of the organism, produces blood; blood in turn, through cooking, engenders flesh, and so on. Each element is provided with its own particular fire, which then converts a fraction of this element into its successor in the series. The image of the seven successive fires suggests the chain of metabolic processes by which the living tissues are contructed.

Hence the comparison that Ayurvedic revivalists are today tempted to draw between the organic fires and the enzymes. This was one of the themes most dear to the late C. Dwarakanath. A secretary of the famous Chopra committee (1948), a professor at Jamnagar, and from 1959 an advisor to the federal government on indigenous medicine, Dwarakanath worked on updating Ayurveda by comparing it to modern science.[6] One of his pupils, Dr. Bhagwan Dash, who similarly held office in the Ministry of Health in New Delhi, has also produced a work on the physiology of nutrition which is reflective of this integrative trend.[7]

Both men explain that the seven fires "obviously refer to substances which, like enzymes, catalyse the synthesis of seven kinds of nutrient substances required for the use of the seven species of *dhātu*, each *agni* aiding the conversion of nutrient substances in what may permissibly be called 'precursor substances' of the formed *dhātu* already present in the body."[8] Each *dhātu* is present in two successive states: fluid and solid, first as a precursory element, next as a constituted one, depending on whether the chemical syntheses are in the process of taking place or have already done so. In short, each *dhātu* first exists in a nascent state within the hot and nourishing fluids which then solidify and crystallize into stable tissues. It is a distinction that repeats the one formulated in the eleventh century by Cakrapāṇidatta, in a text meticulously studied by Dwarakanath.[9] This text declares that the elements exist in two forms: *poṣaka-dhātu*, "the element which nourishes," and *poṣya-dhātu*, "the element which must be nourished"; in other words, a chemical activity and the product of that activity, a nutrition and the organic tissues deriving from it, a "naturizing" nature and a "naturized" nature. The first example of this ambiguity of a chemical state, the first product of these exchanges between matter and energy, is *rasa*, or "chyle." Circulating through the network of channels in the body, chyle carries to the other *dhātu* the foods necessary for their development, a fraction of which, when "recooked," is converted into blood.

Chyle as a constituted element presupposes a precursor which is separate from it. That is why the Sanskrit authors distinguish carefully between *rasa-dhātu*, "chyle as an organic element," and *anna-rasa*, "the juice (extracted) from the nourishment," the juice formed from foodstuffs assimilated by digestion. Nutrition is a transformation of *anna-rasa* into *rasadhātu*, an assimilation into the body of the *rasa* extracted from nourishment.

The idea of an assimilation—in which what was alien is rendered identical—presupposes an alternation between a stable state and a nascent state, the ready-made and things in the making, cooked matter and transforming heat. This theory of nutrition through transformation and sublimation of the living tissues clearly falls short of making a distinction between tissues and organs. The very idea of an organ makes no sense in Ayurvedic physiology, because that physiology is unacquainted with the fundamental distinction we owe to Aristotle and from which all subsequent Western biology has stemmed, namely, the distinction between the *homoiomeric*, or uniform, parts of the living body and the *anhomoiomeric*, or composite, parts. Says Aristotle, in the beginning of his *Historia Animalium*: "The parts which are found in animals are of two kinds: a) those which are incomposite, *viz*., those which divide up into (homoiomeric or) uniform portions, for example, flesh divides up into flesh; b) those which are composite, *viz*., those which divide up into (anhomoiomeric or) non-uniform portions, for example, the hand does not divide up into hands, nor the face into faces."[10] The former are the tissues such as flesh, bone, blood; the latter are the organs and the members. Book II of the *De Partibus Animalium* tells us that the tissues (the uniform parts) only exist for the sake of the organs (the composite parts) on which all physiological functions and actions depend.

We find nothing of this kind in India, which knew only of a physiology of essences and metamorphoses, not of any physiology of organs and functions. But once situated in the correct perspective, that of a mythical and fantastical knowledge, the theory of the seven *dhātu*, or vital tissues, exemplifies a whole scholastic system stretching from the subtleties of Cakrapāṇidatta to the publications of his modern emulators. Their reasoning, which we shall attempt to retrace, is valid only within the framework of a physiology founded on elements divisible into homoiomeric, or uniform parts, and which is ignorant of the idea of an organ. Although the organs of the human body are named, using words habitually and conventionally translated as the "heart," the "liver," the "intestine," and so on, no explanations of the physiological facts are provided: the parts of the body are mentioned only as reservoirs or receptacles to which fantastical contents are attributed.

Let us start from the formula which expresses their successive creation: "From chyle is born blood, from blood flesh, from flesh fat, etc."[11] Chyle, blood, flesh, fat, bone, marrow, and semen are transformed into one another by cooking. This schema is also found in other domains of the Hindu tradition, particularly in codes of law and ritual.[12] It develops a very general theme and gives it concrete expression in the specific domain of medicine: the theme of the cooking of the world. We shall be returning to this topic. At this point we run into a difficulty of interpretation raised for the first time by Cakrapāṇidatta in the Middle Ages. He raised the question of how, without ending up in absurdities, one could imagine a complete and continual transformation of each tissue into its successor in the sequence of production of the successive seven. In its naive formulation, which implies, for example, that *all* chyle is transformed into blood and *all* blood into flesh, the schema is unacceptable. Imagine a prolonged fast: after a few days all the chyle has changed into blood, all the blood into meat, and by the end of a month, Cakrapāṇidatta concludes, the entire body of the fasting man would, in theory, be composed solely of semen![13]

Other schemata must therefore be devised which somehow respect the principle of identity: the tissues do not melt into one another but instead retain their individual identities. We thus arrive at a second explanation: the growth of each tissue results from the repeated consumption of food "the qualities of which are identical to it"; conversely, its decline or wasting results from food "the qualities of which are contrary to it." In other words, *like nourishes like*. It is by eating meat that one increases one's own meat, by drinking blood that one increases one's own blood; similarly, fat nourishes fat, cartilage nourishes bones, and so on. When, in order to increase a deficient tissue, the medical practitioner is unable to prescribe the exactly identical substance because it is not suitable for eating or is considered disgusting, he must use substitutes in which similar qualities to those of the deficient tissue predominate. In the case of a deficiency of semen, for example, the doctor will prescribe milk and clarified butter, in which unctuosity predominates.[14] It is no longer a matter of the successive creation of tissues but rather of the specificity of each.

Cakrapāṇidatta must be given the credit for having noted this difficulty of interpretation and for having resolved it by drawing a quite remarkable distinction.[15] He maintains that three possible schemata exist for organic growth. The first, as previously noted, is unacceptable. Cakrapāṇidatta calls it the *schema of curdled milk*. Milk curdles en bloc; similarly, the transformation of one tissue into another also takes place en bloc: all the chyle becomes blood, and so on. One of the criticisms levelled at the first schema is of particular interest to us because it justifies in advance a remedy we shall soon be considering: fresh blood to be taken in certain cases of hemorrhage. In such cases, blood taken as a food immediately reconstitutes blood as an element of the body and with a rapidity that would be inconceivable, the commentator points out, were we to look no further than this first schema. It is, in effect, with the argument of the rapidity of the action of reconstituting medicaments that Cakrapāṇidatta counters this first explanatory schema. Instead of appealing to the example of fresh blood, however, he uses a different yet equivalent example. According to the *schema of curdled milk*, Cakrapāṇidatta says, "spermatogenic food will produce semen only after a long time has elapsed, since it must pass through the entire series of transformations from one tissue into another; yet the action of spermatogenic substances such as milk is immediate. According to the *schema of pigeons in a barn*, in contrast, it is clearly explained that, thanks to a special faculty *(prabhāva)*, the spermatogenic food finds itself rapidly associated with semen and so makes it increase."[16] The *prabhāva*, or "special faculty," of a substance is a principle of specificity and selectivity, a faculty of acting *electively* on a particular tissue, which would be impossible if the substances assimilated by the organism had necessarily and completely to pass through the entire series of tissues.

Cakrapāṇidatta then invents two further analogies or schemata, this time ones which respect the specificity of each tissue in the sequence of their successive production: pigeons in a barn, each one pecking grain for itself, and of channels in a rice paddy (and the ramifications thereof). The *schema of channels in a rice paddy* is borrowed from Suśruta who uses the image to describe the ramifications of vessels within the human body.[17] Chyle, as an organic element, thus serves as an *excipient*, or vehicle, for transporting all the nutritive essences throughout the network. When the juice extracted from the nourishment comes into contact with the first of the seven tissues, namely chyle, only some of it is used to make that tissue grow. The rest of this nutritive juice, transported by the chyle, then assumes the odor and color of blood, which in its turn uses a little of it for its own growth. The remainder then passes into the flesh, fat, bone, and so on. Each of these tissues are irrigated in turn by the chyle and draw from it the particular foods which are specially destined for it.[18] The description of this process of distributing the nourishing juices around the seven fundamental tissues or constituents of the body makes use of verbs of movement, the meanings of which remain extremely vague (extract, reach, enter, and so on). Thus the description makes it impossible to determine any anatomical locations with any precision.

Only in contemporary times and no doubt influenced by European medicine have the Ayurvedics been concerned with indicating physiological phenomena cartographically. A significant turning point in the history of the Ayurvedic tradition occurred at the beginning of this century: the appearance of treatises of anatomy written in Sanskrit and even in verse by eminent pundits.[19] Their engravings are veritable artifacts. They copy the anatomical diagrams to be found in English handbooks, replacing the English captions with Sanskrit names. This drawing of scientifically accurate images of the stomach, the intestine, and other parts of the body and providing them with Sanskrit names still does not amount to conceiving of them as organs. Through a kind of retrospective rationalization, the image of channels in a rice paddy is replaced by a modern image, one familiar to any twentieth-century high-school student; namely, the anatomical diagram, which illustrates the ancient text without affecting its mode of thought: digestion remains an irrigation. The juice of the nourishment taken into the small intestine passes from there into the liver and the spleen, which serve as reservoirs for the blood. The rest of the chyle, which has taken on the odor and color of blood, then passes into the heart. From this organ radiate all the vessels that successively irrigate the other tissues: flesh, fat, bone, marrow, and semen.

The figure of the *pigeons pecking in a barn* is merely a variant of this. The irrigation of the tissues is selective from the start. The nourishing juice is divided into seven parts which follow seven different kinds of channels classed in order of increasing length and narrowness.[20] The channels that respectively feed the chyle, the blood, and the other tissues are differentiated and described in hierarchical terms. According to Cakrapāṇidatta, the rice paddy and the barn are two equally valuable analogies; they teach one to conceive of the successive production of the tissues in a fashion that is no longer linear:

juice of the nourishment → chyle → blood → flesh → other tissues

but discontinuous:

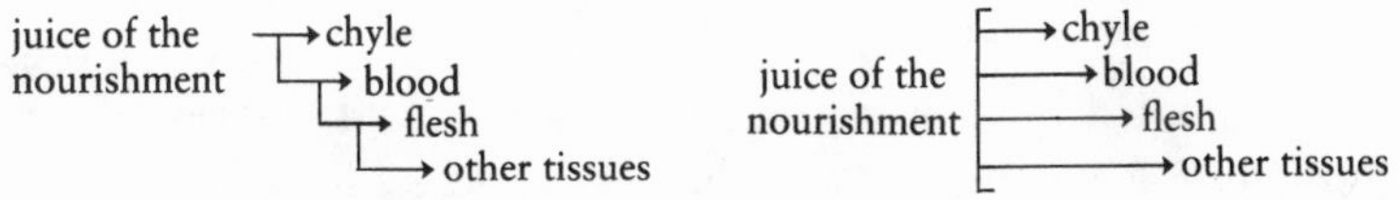

Figure 19. Successive production of the tissues

Each term in the series can increase or diminish independently from the others and under the influence of factors specific to it. Such are the essentials of movement within the body, with the understanding that it would be perfectly possible to multiply the erudite details with respect to all sorts of channels and openings, compartments, kinds of cooking, and excretion, without it being necessary to modify this model.

Whereas what we today call physiology is the science of organic functions, we find in Ayurveda precisely the opposite, namely, a medicine of properties or virtues, a medicine of metamorphoses. Whereas physiology comes into being as a science at the point where it becomes distinguishable from the study of pathogenesis, here the contrary is true: the evolution of the body tissues, or *dhātu*, is strictly determined by the interplay between the three *doṣa*, the "humors, pathogenic entities." This epistemological structure has already been defined: the physical facts are enmeshed in the mass of normative prescriptions. Now, we can describe this hierarchy of levels of knowledge which, in traditional physiology, subordinates the picturesque level of *images* (roughly depicting the physical facts) to the logical grid of *qualities*, which makes it possible for the doctor to take action against the disease.

On the level of images, we have, as already noted, the image of seven successive fires cooking the seven tissues and the image of a network of nutrient-carrying channels that become increasingly elongated and thin as they are required to supply increasingly recooked or sublimated tissues. This level also includes the description, as a whole, of the process of digestion. The bones, for example, allow the semen given off by the marrow to swell up through their pores as in a new clay pot which is still slightly porous; the nutritive juice accumulates in a plethora in the internal channels like massing clouds before a rainstorm bursts.[21] Let us now move on from all of this imagery toward concepts and principles. Even in the texts cited above, one can already read a term-for-term correspondence between the qualities of foods and organic qualities: "It is one by one and each on its own account that the qualities of substances nourish those which correspond to them within the body"; thus the earthy nourishes the earthy, and so on.[22] Another underlying idea is that of the compensation of contraries; for example, when they are in excess and provoke a plethora, "the *mala* (the impurities, excreta, organic waste), treated by contrary qualities, hot by cold and cold by hot, are brought back to normal and this restores the equilibrium between the *dhātu* of the body."[23] The compensation of contraries is simply the other side of a term-for-term correspondence between the qualities of foods and the qualities of the *doṣa* (humors), *dhātu* (elements), and *mala* (impurities of the body): the *heavy*, as a quality carried by a *heavy* food, increases the *heavy* elements of the body and provokes a wasting in tissues of the opposite quality. It is just the same principle according to which: "Always and in all creatures, *sāmānya*, "identity, generic similarity," provokes growth, and *viśeṣa*, "difference, specific variety," is the cause of diminution."[24] Caraka applies this principle in an important text belonging to a quite different level of knowledge from those thus far discussed. Despite its title *Analysis of the Body*,[25] it produces all but an anatomy or physiology. It shows how the pathogenic entities of wind, bile, and phlegm act on the human body to produce diseases. It is a speculative pathogenesis, a reflection on balance and imbalance between the humors from which results either growth or wasting of the tissues. The text opens by defining the human body as *samayogavāhin*, "a vehicle for congruous junctions," the basis for the fundamental articulations. It is the junction of an element of the body with foodstuffs of similar qualities which produces that element's growth; in other words, the doctor totally controls movement within the body by means of an appropriate diet and through the combinative system of qualities. Caraka elaborates:

> Thus, for all tissues and qualities, growth results from junction with what is identical, and diminution results from the contrary.
>
> Consequently, flesh makes flesh increase much more than the other tissues of the body, and blood makes blood increase, fat makes fat, *vasā vasā*, cartilage bone, marrow marrow, semen semen, and the embryo the foetus.
>
> But when foodstuffs possessing that identity, the identity we have just defined, are not to hand or when, even if they are available, it is impossible to prescribe them on account of impropriety, revulsion or any other reason, and yet it is nevertheless necessary to provoke growth in the body tissue the qualities of which are identical with those of the forbidden foods, then one must prescribe foods which, although different in nature, possess those identical qualities in abundance.[26]

Substitutes like ghee, for example, should thus be used to increase semen. Even normally impure and prohibited foods such as raw blood may be prescribed in cases of dire necessity.

Thus to digest is to concentrate within oneself the active powers carried by the nourishing juices. Note the position of central importance occupied by the agricultural metaphor of an irrigation of the tissues. This irrigation can be described on two levels in the hierarchy of the planes of knowledge. The first level of description involves a set of images: the chyle circulates through the network of channels in the body, carrying the juices through a series of cookings that concentrate and sublimate the savors and qualities materialized in them. The second, more abstract level involves pathogenesis: "the vehicle par excellence" is wind, which assimilates within itself the properties of the other humors, tissues, and substances coming into contact with it and then carries them on and transmits them. Wind becomes a medium in an interplay. As we have seen, the humors—and especially wind—have an ambiguous reality. As images, they are fluids; as concepts, they are pathogenic factors. Finally, in the analysis of the human body, two points of view are superimposed, one on the other. From the point of view of the materials in movement, the humors are fluids irrigating the tissues. From the point of view of health and disease, they represent various facets in the combinative system of humors, savors, and qualities.

In the series of seven tissues, there are two which undergo particularly violent processes of concentration, superactivation, and sublimation, namely, blood and meat. The theme of violence, with all its moral implications, is present at the heart of physiology.

VIOLENT THERAPEUTICS: RAW BLOOD, THE MEAT OF CARNIVORES

The images depicting the internal movements of the body prefigure and bring out certain forms of remedies. The first and foremost remedy is broth, which concentrates and superactivates the ingredients during the boiling process. We have repeatedly noted the polysemy of the technical vocabulary. The use of *rasa* to mean "broth" serves as a new example of such multiplicity of meaning. Savor (any one of the six "savors"), sap or juice (*annarasa*, the juice from foods), chyle (*rasadhātu*), or even unctuosity in general, as when we stated in chapter 1 that the sun captures all the *rasa* of beings: these are just a few of the meanings of this master-key word. We now discover another technical meaning. The model for all broths is *māṃsa-rasa*, "meat-broth." Like the classical French word *bouillon*, *rasa* on its own implies meaty ingredients, even if vegetables are sometimes included. *Rasa* standing for *māṃsarasa* is an example of ellipsis and is noted to be such in the list of rhetorical figures given in an appendix to the treatises of Suśruta and Caraka. Thus *jāṅgala-rasa* means "broth of meats from the dry lands."[27] Compare this with the classic definitions to be found in French, as in Diderot's *Encyclopédie*, article *Bouillon*: "Decoction of the flesh of animals produced over a moderate heat in order to extract the juice. . . . When *bouillons* are used as remedies, certain plants whose virtues are appropriate to the person using them are usually added to them and they are then known as medicinal broths." The original meaning is certainly a meat broth.

These broths should not be confused with soups. Caraka makes a distinction between "thin broth" and "thick broth," depending on the quantity of meat it contains.[28] Finally, even if it would appear to go without saying that all these "elaborated" or "cooked" *(saṃskṛta)* foods or medicaments were prescribed to be taken orally (and it is easy to see how misleading those adjectives can be), they might equally be administered anally, in the form of enemas. The *Carakasaṃhitā* in particular mentions in its last pages hundreds of different recipes for enemas, most of which are no longer used today—perhaps, indeed, they never were. The basis of such enemas is a meat broth; there are, as we shall see, even some with a basis of *raw blood*.

Furthermore, a distinction should be drawn between the raw and the cooked. Meats are always consumed *after* having been cooked. One proof of the importance of cooking from a physiological point of view, quite apart from the purification to which it submits the foodstuffs, is the occasional use of *chain*, or *serial*, cooking. Meats are cooked and *recooked*, in order to concentrate their virtues. Thus we find "echoing" lists of meats, each of which is cooked in the broth produced from another:

> *Other virilifying broths*
> Sparrows in a partridge broth,
> partridges in a cock broth,
> cocks in a peacock broth,
> or even a peacock in a goose broth
> melted (or reduced) in fresh ghee,
> (are so many) broths to be prescribed, made acid with fruits
> or sweetened, depending upon what is appropriate (for the patient),
> very aromatic and fortifying.[29]

This schema for the superactivation of drugs by means of successive processes of cooking or digestion is the justification for one of the two violent therapies now under consideration: eating the flesh of eaters of flesh. First, however, a few words concerning the other violent therapy —drinking raw blood—are in order, since the principle is the exact converse. In both cases the *violence* of the remedy is as it were a sign of its efficacy. In the case of the drinking of raw blood, the extreme rapidity of action involved is a significant factor: raw blood reconstitutes the reserves of a blood-deficient body immediately. In contrast, when one eats the flesh of eaters of flesh (cooked, of course), this duplication concentrates the substances and superactivates the medicinal broths.

Although fleeting and little known, the theme of raw blood—a surprising one in the context of Hinduism (in which cooking is a purification)—is nevertheless attested to on several occasions in the Great Triad. As we shall see, it will serve as a countertest for the analyses that we shall be making later on and is one of the points that clearly manifests the equivocal nature of the Ayurvedic doctrine, caught as it is between violence and vegetarianism. It would prescribe the drinking of the raw blood of an antelope, goat, or various other animal species, essentially in the case of a sudden wasting of blood considered as *dhātu*. Appropriate cases for such a prescription might include hemorrhage, crises caused by bloodletting, fainting fits, and amenorrhoea. We will leave aside the matter of the blood of cocks, crows, and peacocks, antidotes used in *external* applications on snakebites and instead concentrate on prescriptions to be taken *internally* in either of two possible ways: as drinks or as enemas (indicated for the same type of disorders as well as for colic pains). This type of remedy is also indicated for cases of violent evacuation, such as dysentery or vomiting. From the many references scattered through the texts,[30] let us cite two in which the principle of the treatment is explained either in the text itself or in a commentary. Bloodletting as a remedy has fallen into disuse in modern times but was highly regarded in the (ill-determined) times described in the classical texts and was one of the five *śodhana*, or "purifying" treatments, practiced during the intermediary seasons (spring, the beginning of the rains, autumn) which required the hospitalization of the patient. According to Suśruta, the diet that in principle accompanies a bloodletting includes the drinking of the blood of *eṇa* (black antelope), *hariṇa* (antelope in general), sheep, hare, buffalo, or pig. Ḍalhaṇa then explains that the patient must drink this blood "to increase [his own] blood" and that it must be consumed in its natural state, "not corrupted and not cooked."[31] Caraka provides the second example. Too violent a purge sometimes produces a rectal hemorrhage of red blood called "living blood" *(jīva-rakta)* which may be accompanied by prolapse of the rectum.[32] The emergency treatment involves the patient drinking the fresh blood taken from a living *mṛga* (antelope or deer), bovine, buffalo, or goat, because living blood immediately combines with living blood; this same blood must be administered in an enema with ground sacrificial herbs added. Cakrapāṇidatta provides a vivid explanation: "By reason of the *prabhāva* (the special faculty) of the blood, the fresh blood (the remedy) immediately changes into blood (the element in the body)."[33] We can here recognize the physiological schema of the specific ways of nutrition of each tissue, and the notion of *prabhāva*, the "special faculty." *Prabhāva* denotes both a general identity in the properties of blood both as a remedy and as a tissue and also a particular affinity between one and the other. Hence the verbal duplication "living blood combining with living blood" *(jīvābhisandhānaṃ jīvam)*.

There is a similar duplication in "the flesh of eaters of flesh" *(māṃsaṃ māṃsāśinām)*.[34] The image is of a concentration of the meat:

> There is in effect nothing like meat
> to produce plumpness;
> and especially, because it has been nourished
> with meat, the meat of eaters of meat.[35]

One must feed to
persons emaciated, debilitated and cachexic
as a result of long illness,
lightly acidulated broths of the (meat of) *prasaha*
eaters of meat,
light nourishment. Because they are sharp, hot, evacuant,
they rapidly stimulate the digestive fire.
And because the meat is fattened by meat,
their nourishing effect is extremely rapid.[36]

Recall in Caraka's treatise that the *prasaha*, animals "which pull at their food," are of two kinds: the croppers of grass and the carnivores. As has been shown through a comparison with Suśruta, this composite category of Caraka's includes both beasts of prey (which give lighter meats) and domesticated animals (with heavier flesh).[37] Thus in the prescription given above the lighter meats of the *prasaha* are selected: perhaps that is why Caraka twice explicitly repeats that broths of *prasaha* eaters of meat are light.[38] Another reason could be that the culinary "perfecting," the *saṃskāra* of these broths, transforms the natural heaviness of *prasaha* meats into lightness.[39]

In Suśruta's more precise classification the meats used are not only the *prasaha* in the strict sense of the word—that is, birds of prey such as the crow—but also the *guhāśaya* wild beasts of prey "which have a lair": such as the lion and the tiger. Given the rarity of this type of ingredient—the product of hunting which is a royal privilege—it is an extraordinary prescription. It is important, however, to note that doctors were often reserved for the service of royal families; but what is most striking about this prescription is that it runs directly counter to a dietary rule formulated repeatedly in codes, epics; namely, the prohibition against the consumption of the meat of all except five of the *pañcanakha* animals, "those which have five nails (or claws)." This is known as the rule of "the five with five nails" *(pañca pañcanakhāḥ)*.

The beasts of prey are named in a number of different ways. We have already come across the *kravyāda* "the eaters of raw flesh" and the *vyāla* "ferocious beasts." *Pañcanakha*, "those which have five nails," however, is the term used in most of the normative texts when it is a matter of prohibiting the beasts' consumption, although it rarely appears in the treatises of the Ayurvedic Great Triad.[40] Frequently the rule is presented in a positive form. An exception exists to the prohibition that affects this category of *pañcanakha* in general: it *is* permitted to consume the meat of five of them, *the five with five nails*, a stereotyped series comprised of the *śvāvidh* (porcupine), *śalyaka* (porcupine, hedgehog, or pangolin), *godhā* (varan, monitor, lizard), *śaśa* (hare), and *kūrma* (tortoise). Several texts add a sixth term, the rhinoceros; others substitute the rhinoceros for one of the names of the porcupine so that the number five is respected. As Heinrich Lüders wrote in 1907 in a short but decisive article on this issue: "This limitation to five animals was clearly a pan-Indian opinion."[41] A discussion of the rhinoceros—the significance of its purifying qualities when consumed during a sacrifice to the ancestors[42]—shall be temporarily put aside.

For now let us briefly consider the interpretation of the doublet *śvāvidh* and *śalyaka*, terms usually described as synonymous in the Sanskrit commentaries and lexicons.[43] To translate the first term as "porcupine" and the second as "hedgehog," as most translators do, is in my view mistaken. What justification is there for implying that when one of two synonyms in the same list seems redundant, the two words must necessarily denote two different genera? Why should they not refer simply to two species of the same genus or two varieties of the same species, or even to the very same animal on different *levels of language*? From our point of view, however, the identity of the referent is really of scant importance. So let us move on directly to make the two essential observations that we, who are familiar with the Ayurvedic catalog, are in a position to note in connection with this classic list of five animals with five nails. In Suśruta, the first four animals appear at the head of the list of *bileśaya*, "those which have a burrow." As if by chance, they all happen to be those among the *pañcanakha* which do not attack man and are not predators. Or, expressed conversely, which animals are the *pañcanakha*? The tortoise, the elephant, the rhinoceros, and the monkeys must certainly be mentioned, as they appear in the Sanskrit commentaries and lexicons.[44] The essential core of the category of *pañcanakha* is nevertheless made up of those which Suśruta calls *guhāśaya*, "those which have a lair." These animals include the lion, tiger, wolf, hyena, bear, panther, wildcat and jackal, among others, all of which are five-toed creatures.[45] The Ayurvedic distinction between *bileśaya* and *guhāśaya* indirectly illuminates this famous dietary rule of the *pañca pañcanakhāḥ*. At the same time, however, by prescribing broths of the meat of the lion or the tiger, for example, as a remedy for consumption, chronic diarrhoea, or hemorrhoids, the Ayurvedic doctrine runs counter to brahminic prohibitions.

The exceptionally nourishing character of the meat of eaters of meat was mentioned earlier in Suśruta's catalog.[46] He returns to the point elsewhere, adding a number of psychological considerations:

> Man may, in accordance with the rule, eat
> the flesh of eaters of flesh;
> when his *manas* is perfectly pure
> his flesh is fattened by the flesh (that he eats).[47]

The *manas* is the "common sense" over and above all the organs of the empirical senses, the internal organ ensuring the link between the *ātman* (the eternal principle) and the life of experience; let us call it the "mind." Ḍalhaṇa comments: "A pure mind means a mind free from pain, anger, etc. Jejjaṭa explains that tiger meat, etc. is given in disguise (to the patient); in that way (he retains) a pure mind."[48] Before focusing on this concept of purity, free from anger and pain, let us pause to consider the principle of fraud or disguise, which is also mentioned by Caraka and Vāgbhaṭa.[49]

It is essentially in cases of consumption that the doctor resorts to this violent and cunning form of feeding meat to the patient struggling against one of the gravest diseases of all, *rājayakṣman*, "royal consumption." Here is the regimen to be prescribed, according to the *Caraka-saṃhitā*:

> To those who are wasting away and losing their meat,
> the one who knows the rules will give
> in prepared dishes the meat of eaters of meat
> which is especially nourishing.
> To the consumptive he will give peacock
> and under the name of peacock others too,
> vultures, owls and jays
> well prepared according to the rule.
> Crows under the name of partridge,
> and under the name of *varmi* [a fish] snakes;
> fried, under the name of fish intestines
> he will also give earthworms.
> Foxes, large mongooses,
> cats, in prepared dishes,
> and young jackals, the doctor
> will give them under the name of hare.
> Lions, bears, hyenas,
> tigers and others of this type,
> eaters of meat, under the name of antelope,
> he will give them to make the meat grow.
> The meat of elephants, rhinoceros and horses,

prepared with spices, the doctor
will give them under the name of buffalo,
meat to make the meat grow.
Especially of the beasts and birds
whose bodies are fattened by meat,
the meat is the best meat-maker,
and valuable through its sharpness, heat, lightness.
For meats which, through lack of habit,
are unpleasing although it is necessary to prescribe them,
he will use false names; easy to eat
will they then become.
If the patient knows the truth, disgusted, he will not eat
or will vomit what he has eaten;
it is thus disguised and under a false name
that these meats must be given.[50]

Fantastical prescriptions, I admit, if only because they presuppose a whole economic infrastructure capable of producing on demand lions, bears, hyenas, tigers, and other game—in short, a royal existence! Furthermore, the luxuriance of this accumulation of names of ferocious beasts and the throbbing duplication of the phrases "meat the meat-maker, meat of eaters of meat" combine to produce a discourse of extraordinary violence. I should nevertheless point out immediately that it is a violence expressed within the framework of the brahminic tradition; it does not destroy the rationality of that tradition. Although the discourse is admittedly fantastical, there is no magic or sorcery in it; all of these manipulations take place within the framework of normal medical practice, "according to the rule" (*vidhi-vat*), says Suśruta in the text cited above. Caraka also says: "well prepared, according to the rule."[51] At the beginning of this passage, the doctor is called *vidhāna-vid*, "the one who knows the rules"; the rules pertaining to dietetics and therapeutics, and more generally all the rules that make Ayurveda a *śāstra*, an orthodox science. There could be no better testimony to the rationality of the doctrine even in the case of the prescriptions that run most contrary to religious rules of purity and nonviolence. It is within the very system of rules that an emergency renders recourse to such violent therapeutic action necessary. Moreover, the action is accompanied by a string of justifications, as the account that I have given shows in detail.

I can imagine the amused or perhaps irritated dismay that may be felt by the general reader and many doctors trained in the Western scientific tradition when they take an interest in Hindu medicine with the laudable hope of expanding the framework of their own culture and instead discover the archaic and savage prescriptions as here brought to light. Yet they should not conclude that these texts are absurd or full of magic. Medicine, in the sense of a science as we understand it today, is not really relevant to Hindu medicine. Nevertheless, everything in these texts is orthodox, rational, and justified provided they are replaced within the universe of meaning that is proper to them—that of the brahminic tradition, within which they express the irruption of vital needs, distress, and emergency.

Caraka reproduces in detail the whole mythological history of royal consumption. Its first victim was the god Soma, the Moon, who was guilty of an excessive erotic passion for Rohiṇi; he was punished for it by the wasting of all of his *sneha*, all the unctuosity of his body. "Consumption" is therefore something much more than a simple disease; the image of a burnt-out body, with its unctuosity consumed, has the force of a quasi-religious sanction. Following a whole cycle of physical and moral decline, a king who has neglected his duties and has abandoned himself to lust finds himself laid low with royal consumption. Such is the theme of a famous poem by Kālidāsa:[52] "The wasting, exhaustion of the unctuosity" *(snehakṣaya)* of the body, and Cakrapāṇidatta glosses "exhaustion of the essential *(sāra)* constituents, of semen *(śukra)*, of the vital fluid *(ojas)*."[53] There is a significant play on words in the very name *rāja-yakṣman*. It means "the disease *(yakṣman)* of the king *(rāja)*," to wit, King Moon, King Soma, the first to be attacked by this evil for which the cause is a sin. Because Soma signifies the moon that makes the rains, and also the waters, the very idea of unctuosity is connotated, so that in medical texts *soma* is sometimes used as a technical term denoting simply phlegm. In a famous article on "The concept of kingship in ancient India," Louis Dumont has drawn attention to the fundamental association between rain and law: "Rain and order go together as do disorder and drought (*Śatapatha Brāhmaṇa*, XI, 1, 6, 24). Later, in the legend of Triśaṅku as in that of Devāpi, the reign of an illegitimate sovereign is manifested by drought. In the *Jātaka*, the king is a rain-maker."[54] A land deprived of rains and the royal person of the king himself afflicted by consumption thus constitute two forms of a single image of drought sanctioning disorder. A second translation is also possible: *rāja-yakṣman* is also the "king-disease," the king of diseases.[55] The wasting of all the elements of the body in a sense sums up the whole of pathology, but more important still, as early as the Vedic period (in its Vedic form *yakṣma*), the word denotes disease itself, seen as constitutive of human nature.[56] As can well be imagined, such an evil calls for extreme treatments. If they fail, the only way that remains open for the Ayurvedic practitioner is recourse to the sacrifices prescribed in the Vedas, the very theme which ends the chapter that Caraka devotes to royal consumption.[57]

Let us return to the psychological aspects of the treatment. Here is a case in which the doctor resorts to deception for a good cause. Yet of the ethical rules that Caraka prescribes for men who desire a healthy and long life, the very first is precisely *not* to lie. Cakrapāṇidatta cannot ignore a typically scholastic objection: Has not the Master been led to contradict himself by prescribing here (chapter on ethics) truth and there (violent treatments) deceit? The commentator himself proceeds to provide the answer:

> The text says: "*one must not lie*"; although, by declaring that one should give "*crows under the name of partridge*" etc., this very treatise, in the chapter on *Rājayakṣman*, prescribes speaking falsely, it cannot be said that there is any contradiction for false speech is only affected by the vice of lying when its effect is to harm others, but in this case it is in order to save another's life that one does not speak the truth.[58]

The patient who increases his flesh with the flesh of eaters of flesh is thus able, notwithstanding, to retain a perfectly serene mind: such is the effect of this life-saving lie. Better still, it is by regaining the unctuosity of his body, through the increase in the *ojas*, "the vital fluid," that the patient, his mind set at rest, regains a "pure spirit" *(śuddhaṃ sattvam)*.[59] This alliance between contraries is absolutely fundamental: consumption of the most disgusting of meats and purity, conceived as serenity, an absence of distress and anger. Louis Dumont has noted the association between rain and order; similarly, this association between the *purity of the mind* and the *plumpness of the body* cannot be emphasized too strongly. In the Ayurvedic texts, it is precisely in connection with this theme that we find the very word *ahiṃsā*, meaning both nonviolence and the purity of whoever abstains from all violence. The paradox is that the principle of nonviolence can coexist with violence as a therapeutic means. We shall have to justify this alliance of contraries by stepping back from the literal meaning of the Ayurvedic doctrine in order to perceive its social purpose. This we shall be doing in the next chapter, but first we must finish collecting our evidence.

Of all the possible causes of consumption and cachexy, says Caraka, the most serious is distress. Fear, anger, passion, and other psychological causes play a role of primary importance in the wasting of the body's constitutive elements. Yet "abstinence, detachment" *(nivṛtti)*—might we call it ataraxia?—is the best means for "increasing plumpness."[60] Here lies the paradox. Into this idea of tranquillity and knowledge, which nourish the mind *(manas)* and, consequently, are even more nourishing than meat for the body, our instinct is to read a distinction that is traditional in Western thought: between the soul and the body, between material nurture and spiritual nurture. But such a distinction proves irrelevant here. Abstinence and purity nourish the body, possess medical properties, and prolong the life of the patient, preserving his vital fluid through proper maintenance of the internal channels to avoid blockage by plethora or dryness by consumption. In short, purity is a practical principle, a means of obtaining a well-tempered unctuosity in the human body. Caraka's expression should be understood from this perspective: "*Ahiṃsā* (nonviolence) is the most perfect of all the means of increasing the longevity of living beings, virility is the most perfect of fortifiers, knowledge is the most perfect of nourishing treatments."[61] A *therapeutic system of force* and virility is inserted into a much wider medical and religious tradition which superimposes on it a *therapeutic system of purity* and nonviolence. At its own particular level, each of the two contrary principles is completely orthodox. So it is that a single doctrine can promote nonviolence, abstinence, and vegetarianism and at the same time in certain circumstances prescribe deceit, raw blood, and the flesh of carnivores.

VII: Vegetarianism and Nonviolence

Let us continue to trace back along the sequence of foods, since this book is constructed on the idea that within a given soil the saps which the plants draw from the earth are transmitted to the animals, then to man, then finally to the gods through the aroma given off in the flames of sacrifice. The most striking link in the great chain of being is the carnivorous animal, the eater-eaten, the flesh of the eaters of flesh. The next link, however, is assuredly the most important; namely, man, the hunter and eater of meat. A decisive turning point in our analysis has now been reached, since the ambiguity of this worldview appears in full force. Into the framework of a society ideally governed by the brahminic norms of purity, the friendship for all beings, and the vegetarianism which such a friendship entails, medicine introduces pragmatism, emergency, vital necessity, and violence. It is an ambiguity or, more precisely, a *tension* internal to all brahminic hierarchies. Recall our first discovery that revealed the jungle as both the wild and the chosen land of Hindu kingdoms. Similarly, hunting is not only a violent and impure occupation but also a royal privilege. This chapter will attempt to explain the sociological implications of such a fundamental ambiguity. No jungle without royal hunting. No Hindu medicine without a king.

THE PLACE OF THE KING: HUNTER, EATER OF MEAT

The art of healing imposes the use of violence on the medical practitioner: violence toward animals if meats must be eaten, violence toward the patient if bloodletting, surgery, or obstetrics must be carried out. These sectors of Ayurveda have been abandoned in modern times for precisely this reason. The use of violence degrades the position of medicine in the hierarchy of pure and impure activities but in no way destroys its orthodoxy. Ayurveda, like all *śāstra* or traditional sciences, maintains its allegiance to the law of *dharma* (the sociocosmic order). Simply, the Ayurvedic practice is situated in the lower register of *artha*—"the useful," "what is good" for health, wealth, and prosperity—in the middle-range zone of the rules for daily life, where purity is never unadulterated. To act with success, one has to dirty one's hands a little.

In all its prescriptions for a healthy life, Ayurveda reconciles two models, or normative types. The first model is strictly brahminic, espousing nonviolence, compassion for all beings, and vegetarianism. The second model refers to the exercise of power and the *kṣatriya*, the princes, seen in their social function, which involves the art of warfare. This explains one of the most curious aspects of the medical treatises: the king is the most important of all patients, *the king is the patient par excellence*, because his state of health expresses the *artha* (well-being) of all his subjects. The misfortune of a king who falls sick in times of war signals the downfall of his subjects, and that is why Suśruta devotes to the medical protection of this high personage a special chapter rather curiously entitled "On the army on campaign."[1] Many of the prescriptions confidently formulated in the treatises of the Great Triad relate to princely medicine. The complexity and cost of the therapeutic procedures and the rarity of some of the remedies presuppose luxury, adequate leisure, patronage almost, a king capable of honoring the merits of his personal doctor. It is not without reason that Suśruta's catalog of foods closes with a passage describing and organizing the royal kitchens, the ritual of His Majesty's meal: such is the task of the brahmin doctor to ensure that it be innocuous, pure, and therapeutic.[2] Were we to disregard the luxury and purely fantastical elements present in the Ayurvedic catalog of foods and limit ourselves solely to a consideration of the most plausible and easily applied prescriptions, the fact would remain that the catalog presupposes, at the least, hunting and the consumption of game.

At this point we find ourselves back with a theme that we touched on in chapter 2 in relation to the antelope, the Jungle animal par excellence. Over the as yet uncultivated land, the great flat, dry expanses of the jungle available for Aryan colonization, hunting represents the expression of a right; it is a royal institution. Let us draw upon the conclusions of Louis Dumont, for they are pertinent to our enquiry. We should bear several factors in mind: first, the complementarity of the brahminic and the royal functions in ancient India; and second, the division separating the *religious norms*—of which the brahmin was held responsible to maintain and teach—and the *political power* belonging to the *kṣatriya*—the category of warriors and princes—for these constitute a major factor in comparative sociology. To some extent, the dietary regime is a touchstone in this respect. Regarded as a superior form of feeding, vegetarianism progressively imposed itself on all the strata of Hindu society. Interestingly, however, the vegetarianism preached on the level of the brahminic norms did not exclude the widespread consumption of meat in daily life. Contemporary social anthropology has brought to light a fundamental fact of ethnographic experience in India: the *kṣatriya*, the prince and warrior, in contrast to the brahmin, traditionally remained an eater of meat.[3] The meat diet was a feature of royalty and served not only as an observable fact of life but also as a representative model of life.

On the subject of food in the form of meat in India, a distinction should be made between two different yet complementary points of view: that of the priest and that of the hunter or, in other words, that of the brahmin and that of the *kṣatriya*. This first viewpoint leads to vegetarianism to the extent that the *Dharmaśāstra*, the normative texts of brahminism, allow Hindus of caste to eat certain meats as listed in the texts, but with two stipulations attached: first, they should do so only in the course of a religious ceremony, and second, the meat must be that of an animal ritually sacrificed by a brahmin priest. Seen in this perspective, sacrifice appears to be the only authorized source of food in the form of meat except (as we shall see) in cases of emergency—when one is dying of hunger or consumption. Consequently the doctor, because he prescribes meat, participates in the impurity that affects the hunter. The *Laws of Manu* teach that a brahmin should not accept food from the hand of "a doctor, a hunter, a man who spills blood."[4] It should be kept in mind, however, that this is a specifically normative attitude and that these are prescriptive texts. As well as the science of *dharma* (the good, the law, the norms forming the basis of the social and cosmic order), there is a science of *artha* (material interest) formulated in the rules of conduct and treatises of government for the use of princes, such as the *Arthaśāstra* (cited at length in chapter 2). The *Arthaśāstra* devotes a chapter to the rules governing the sale of meats and the protection of game, according to which it is the king's duty to decree "safety" (*abhaya*), freedom from danger and fear, for certain species of animals in reserved sectors of the forest. Capturing, killing, and mistreating birds "whose safety is declared (by law)"[5] are punishable offenses. At the same time, where hunting is allowed, a levy is taken on the products of the hunt. The royal "hunting grounds" *(mṛgavana)* constitute a special category of the forests and provide meat and skins in abundance.[6] Thus, after sacrifice, hunting constitutes a second authorized and regulated source of food in the form of meat. Stock raising after all implies hunting, since the protection of the domesticated animals which have wandered in the forest to graze is dependent on the successful mission of "trappers and hunters" to "put an end to the violence and fear that reigns on account of bandits, beasts of prey and enemies of the kingdom."[7] In the space symbolically structured in this way, the pasturelands are situated outside the cultivated lands, in the *aṭavī*, the forest where barbarian tribes live.

Furthermore, the opposition often formulated between *paśu*—"livestock" which provide sacrificial victims—and *mṛga*—"game" (wild animals)—does not exclude the possibility, under certain circumstances, of sacrificing wild animals. In his catalog of meats, Suśruta provides one example where he notes the purifying and macrobiotic qualities of rhinoceros meat when eaten on the occasion of a sacrifice to ancestors. The sacrifice of the rhinoceros—or of other wild animals—on the occasion of a *śrāddha* (worship addressed to the spirits of the dead) is often mentioned in the texts of the Law.[8] It presupposes catching the victim in the forest. It is not hard to see the possible concrete links between hunting and sacrifice, although the two social activities or functions in principle remain separate.

There are thus three kinds of reasons for authorizing the eating of meat: 1) in the context of sacrifice, 2) in cases of vital emergency, such as famine or disease, and 3) in providing the model of royal life. In a certain category of texts, especially in the *Dharmaśāstra*, only the first two of these justifications are mentioned. One is the norm: the consecration of meats within the framework of sacrifice to the spirits of the dead or to the gods; the other is the exception, permissible when life is in danger. We shall be considering briefly these first two reasons in detail. Let us focus now on the third point of view, the royal ideal of life, a theme particularly adopted in epic literature. The gigantic epic of the *Mahābhārata* constitutes (predominantly in its didactic parts) an encyclopedia of Hinduism that provides an excellent complement to the Dharma codes, but from a heroic perspective in which the position of the *kṣatriya* is given greater prominence. Consider as one of many examples the chapter in the Book of Teaching (otherwise known as Canto XIII of the *Mahābhārata*) devoted to praising and promoting nonviolence and vegetarianism; despite its main subject, it also praises hunting and the fortifying virtues of meats. It is worth summarizing the sequence of ideas:

> No food [according to lines 6 to 8] is better than meat with respect to the *rasa* (the nourishing juice) and particularly in cases of cachexy or overwork; but [line 9] the merits of abstinence are great; there is no one more vile than he who desires—and note the expression—*to increase his flesh with the flesh of another*. There follows a passage in praise of compassion for all beings. But a new sequence then takes over, introducing the point of view of hunters and warriors: a special rule applies to the *kṣatriya* for they commit no sin by consuming meat procured through their own valiance [line 14]; in dedicating to the gods and the spirits of the dead all the beasts of the forest (as possible victims for sacrifice), Agastya consecrated the merits of hunting [line 15]; hunting is not a sin provided *the life of the hunter is as much at risk as that of his prey* [line 16]. But then the text takes yet another turn: nothing is of greater merit than pity, nonviolence, and vegetarianism.[9]

Hunting, like dueling to the death on the battlefield, can be assimilated to a sacrifice (as a result of which the victim is consecrated) in which the hunter (and the warrior) is both the *sacrificer* (he kills) and the possible *victim* (he is killed). This risk is an inherent part of the royal function itself. The *dharma* of the *kṣatriya* is either to conquer or to die a heroic death. Warfare and hunting provide so many opportunities for the *kṣatriya* to accomplish his function as *sacrificer*. The role of the prince in a sacrifice is that of the *sacrificer*: he is in the background, the one on whose account the sacrifice is offered. According to Madeleine Biardeau, if the prince himself is killed in battle, "this is sacrifice in the pure state, in which the sacrificer offers himself as victim instead of finding substitutes for himself"; but if it is true that combat must therefore be interpreted as a form of sacrifice, then "the *kṣatriya* turns out to be justified in the most violent of his actions, so it is not surprising that kings may practice hunting and that the murder of animals is considered parallel to that of enemies."[10]

To this justification of violence of a moral and religious order—that is, after all, the *dharma* of kings—medicine adds a pragmatic note: meat cures cachexy, and so on. Following consecration of an at least rudimentary kind, game may be consumed. The *dharma* and the ideal of nonviolence are reconciled with the idea of the *artha*, which includes warfare, hunting, and the necessities of medicine.

Eating meat is in accordance with a traditional idea purveyed principally by Ayurvedic medicine. However disgusting meat may appear as seen against brahminic norms, a diet based on meat is nevertheless prized from the point of view of a therapy to encourage strength and virility as concentrated within the person of the king by means of treatments. Such treatments involve aphrodisiacs and cures to promote youthfulness, in which meats play a major role. This matter thus involves many different perspectives which coexist even as they oppose one another. Historians of vegetarianism in India have virtually ignored the doctor's point of view. Yet the Ayurvedic sources are eloquent and add an entire, if little known, corpus of documentary evidence to the information hitherto available.

REVERENCE FOR THE BOVINE

In his *Contributions to the history of vegetarianism and reverence for the bovine animals in India*, Ludwig Alsdorf makes a point of mentioning the catalog of Suśruta. He describes Suśruta as "a relatively late witness" for dietary practices in which the meat of the ox not only is not found shocking but is even prized.[11] He draws attention in particular to the word *pavitra*, "purifying," which is used by Suśruta to qualify the meat of the ox.[12] Alsdorf also draws attention to the presence of the meat of the ox among the cravings of pregnant women as described by Suśruta. Each craving is a prognostic sign of the temperament of the as yet unborn child, and a desire to eat the meat of the ox foretells of a child notable for vigor and endurance.[13] But Alsdorf's conclusion is no more than a chronological one: he sees a proof of the continuing practice of eating meat in the early centuries A.D. in the fact that the last revision of the *Suśrutasaṃhitā* in the sixth or perhaps even the tenth century retains these laudatory references to the properties of the meat of the ox in an intact form. Let us take a closer look at the texts. The fact that the meat of the ox is *pavitra* is but one aspect of the matter and must be seen as part of what appears to be a contradictory whole.

On the one hand, the word *pavitra* is frequently used in Suśruta's treatise to denote, if not sacred things, at least those that are endowed with magic powers of some kind. The offering of a rhinoceros to the spirits of dead ancestors is *pavitra*; but the word is also used of precious stones or of the wearing of a turban, which has a ritual significance in India.[14] The word *pavitra* thus gives the meat of the ox a religious or magic connotation in addition to and distinct from its purely medical properties.

On the other hand, in Caraka's treatise we find a surprising statement: "The most unhealthy of the meats of quadrupeds is the meat of the ox."[15] This statement appears together with the lists that record the *hitāhita*, the things that are "best and worst" for each of the major categories of pharmacopoeia, the things "(par excellence) indicated and contraindicated"; in short, the most outstanding elements, both in a positive and a negative sense. For example, we find that

the best meats are:	*the most unhealthy meats are*:
among the quadrupeds, the antelope,	among the quadrupeds, the ox,
and among the birds, the quail.	and among the birds, the *kāṇakapota*.

This totally negative evaluation of the ox is in contradiction with what even Caraka himself says in the catalog of meats which, quite to the contrary, describes the many virtues of the ox in curing disorders of wind, catarrh, irregular fever, and so on.[16] What should be made of this apparent contradiction?

It is tempting to conclude that Suśruta's formula: the ox is purifying, and Caraka's: it is the most unhealthy of meats, come down to the same thing. Both are tacked onto the strictly medical qualities; their effect is to set the ox apart by marking it out from the rest of the animals. It matters little whether the demarcation is positive (purifying) or negative (unhealthy): its *raison d'être* is extramedical. It refers one to the Hindu tradition as a whole. The medieval commentators have nothing to say about such formulas which indirectly, and on the pretext of including the ox in the pharmacopoeia, remind us that 1) the ox is sacred, and 2) its meat is forbidden. Such at least is my interpretation of these two formulas. "Purifying": it is sacred. "The most unhealthy" (*or* par excellence, contraindicated): the meat of the ox must be forbidden. So this constitutes an irruption of vegetarianism into a medical text.

EMERGENCY AND DISTRESS

If the pertinent texts as a whole are regrouped, we notice that the importance of a meat diet in Ayurvedic medicine by no means excludes a promotion of vegetarianism; the two themes coexist. Suśruta, Caraka, and Vāgbhaṭa each provide two series of texts: one series praises the virtues of meat; the other prescribes abstinence and, above all, "nonviolence" (*ahiṃsā*), which is fundamentally linked with vegetarianism. This superposition of two different normative registers is occasioned by the need for a compromise between the brahminic ideal and the exigencies of therapeutics. By way of explanation, let us quote the following formula taken from a *Purāṇa*: "Whoever eats meat commits no sin either when it has been consecrated or *when it serves as a remedy*."[17] Quoting Manu, in his work cited above, Alsdorf once and for all drew attention to the quest for a compromise in the perpetual debate on the subject of eating meat. What yet remains to be shown is the crucial role of the doctors in this debate.

The text most often cited in this connection belongs to the literature of Dharma and accordingly adopts a juridical and religious point of view. The thirty verses of the *Laws of Manu* (V, 27–56) devoted to the rules governing the eating of meat deserve our full attention. On the one hand existed the obligation to *consecrate* meats, and on the other hand the possibility of raising the prohibitions affecting the eating of meat in circumstances of distress. Verse 27 states that "once consecrated, meat may be eaten, when Brahmins desire it, when one is ritually committed to do so in accordance with the rule or *when life is in danger*." The consumption of meats is linked with sacrifice; that is the immutable rule of *dharma* (the sociocosmic order). Meats are always consecrated; if not by sacrifice, at least by a few rudimentary ritualistic gestures, such as the sprinkling of water or the recitation of Vedic formulas. That, at any rate, is what Manu prescribes and what appropriately influences the discussion at hand: the prescribed norms, not the observed facts. At the same time, however, emergencies are allowed for, and life when threatened is taken to be a value in itself worth preserving.

Onto these prescribed norms is then grafted a strictly religious dialectic between *life in the world*—social life; the struggles and perils of daily life; family, political, and ritual responsibilities—and *renunciation of the world*, which presupposes abstinence and vegetarianism. Life in the world authorizes the eating of meat in two precisely specified situations: 1) within the framework of sacrificial activities, and 2) in cases of distress. In itself, the eating of meat is ineluctably tainted by violence. *Hiṃsā*, or "violence," is a desiderative form of the verb HAN, "to kill." This is expressly stated in verse 48 of the *Laws of Manu*: "No meat can be obtained without *hiṃsā* upon living beings." But sacrifice—or by extension an at least rudimentary consecration of the animals used—suppresses that violence. Hence the famous verse (39): ". . . to kill in sacrifice is not to kill." Verse 44 elaborates: "This *hiṃsā* prescribed by the Veda [namely, blood sacrifice] . . . should in reality be understood as *ahiṃsā*." (*Ahiṃsā* denotes a "nondesire to kill," an absence of the desire to kill; in short, nonviolence.) A serious interpretational problem now arises: that of the religious and social status of blood sacrifice (the Vedic form of sacrifice) in the Dharma texts. Setting the problem aside for now, let us simply note the compromise that is reached: a meat diet is authorized but against a background of praise for vegetarianism, as explained in verse 46: "There is no sin in eating meat." With the stipulations that the animal belongs to one of the permitted species and that some at least rudimentary form of consecration takes place, as concluded in the same verses: "That is the natural way (*pravṛtti*) of creatures; great, however, are the fruits of abstinence (*nivṛtti*)."

Since we are here studying how medical knowledge is articulated within the Hindu tradition, what is essential about these thirty verses of the *Laws of Manu* is the method by which they take natural processes into consideration. In the scale of beings, man's place is among the carnivorous animals. Verse 29, although previously cited, is particularly relevant to this issue and merits review: "Immobile beings are the food of those which move, those without teeth are the food of those with teeth, those without hands are the food of those with hands", as well as another formula, typical in its physiological violence and aimed at *fattening one's own flesh with the flesh of another*. Verse 52 reads: "There is no worse sinner than he who desires to fatten his own flesh (by eating) the flesh of another, without honoring the ancestors or the gods" (in other words, outside the context of sacrificial activity, nonconsecrated meat). It is within this realistic, naturalistic perspective that we should interpret the other theme—*emergency* and *distress*—that appears in the texts of the Law and is relevant to our own medical preoccupations. Situations of famine or disease are anticipated, in which the earlier stipulation (the consecration of animal victims) and the prohibition affecting a large number of animals are no longer valid. The brahminic rules of nonviolence and purity thus find themselves complemented, their idealism counterbalanced by a whole system of precautions to be taken in cases of emergency; this is the *āpad-dharma* or "*dharma* for times of distress." In this connection, Manu recalls a number of legendary examples of the most virtuous of Brahmins who ate ox-meat or dog-meat to prevent a death from starvation. Therapeutic intervention should thus be set within this very context: the catalog of meats certainly describes not delicacies but remedies.

It is not surprising to find the same compromise between Nature and the Law in the medical treatises as in Manu's code, and the subordination one to another of two registers of rules for human behavior. Just as within a Dharma treatise that which is other than *dharma*—namely, whatever is accidental, biological, or is a natural violence toward creatures—is situated in its subordinate and complementary position, similarly or reciprocally, within a medical treatise where the subject is precisely the accidental and suffering, the rules of *dharma* are specifically formulated, and in the very same terms: praise of nonviolence and compassion for all creatures.

Let us cite first an important testimony to the links connecting Ayurveda with the religious tradition. It is the myth of the origin of diarrhoea, as told by Caraka.

> In primitive times, sacrificial animals had to be consecrated but were not, on that account, put to death. During the following period, after the sacrifice of Dakṣa, in the sacrifices offered up by the sons of Manu, Nariṣyat, Nābhāga, Ikṣvāku, Nṛga, Śaryāti, etc., the victims submitted to death of their own volition. This period was then followed by another when Pṛṣadhra, who was offering up a *dīrghasattra* (a prolonged session of sacrifices), found that there was a shortage of victims and had the idea of sacrificing cows. At the sight of this, all the animals were seized with terror. It was the consumption of these cows killed in sacrifice, the heaviness, heat and inappropriateness and the consumption of a non-prescribed food which, adversely affecting the fire and the intellect, produced diarrhoea for the first time, on the occasion of the sacrifice of Pṛṣadhra.[18]

The *Purāṇa* give a number of versions of the legend of Pṛṣadhra, one of Manu's numerous sons; the theme always centers on the murder of a cow. Whether the crime is committed inadvertently or is aggravated by the consumption of flesh, it occasions the degradation of Pṛṣadhra who is reduced to the rank of the *śūdra*, the fourth and lowest category in the hierarchy of castes. The purpose of this and other legends concerning the sons of Manu is to account for the origin of the various castes, all springing from a common ancestor.[19] Medical touches are inserted in an overall normative perspective: disease is a sanction for crime, the horror of murder is compounded by the indigestible heaviness of meat, and moral sentiments become indissociable from physiological effects.

The professed vegetarianism of Caraka, in his account of the origin of diarrhoea, does not preclude his prescribing (further on in the same chapter) a broth of *jāṅgala* meats or even the blood of an antelope or goat.[20] The same phenomenon of a juxtaposition of two contrary points of view occurs elsewhere too, as in the chapter on therapy for mental disorders. While one of the curative treatments consists in satisfying the appetite of the patient with ghee and meat in order to calm his spirits, the chapter nevertheless closes with a homily in which vegetarianism is praised for its prophylactic effects:

> He who abstains from meat and alcohol and who eats only what is indicated—the pure and pious man, in whom the *sattva* (spirit, the principle of knowledge and purity) predominates, escapes from mental disorders both innate and acquired.[21]

Particularly in Caraka's treatise, which draws more heavily than the others on texts of the Law, formulas of such a religious nature generally constitute the framework for chapters whose content is secular, thus providing them with an introduction and a conclusion.

The concepts appealed to are similar in every domain of the tradition; in Caraka, for example, we once again find the extremely ancient opposition between "activity" (*pravṛtti*) directed toward temporal enterprises and commitment to action, and "non-action," "abstinence" (*nivṛtti*), which is deliverance or detachment: "The root of the world and of all afflictions in *pravṛtti*; *nivṛtti* is its cessation. *Pravṛtti* is unhappiness, *nivṛtti* is happiness."[22] It is within the religious context of an opposition between life in the world and renunciation that the principle of abstinence and vegetarianism should be interpreted; but at the same time it is necessary to stress the importance of *pravṛtti*, the activity which is natural to creatures and which leads them to eat one another. As I shall show in the next chapter, the animals serving as victims in blood sacrifice are thereby simply assuming the function for which they were created in the scale of rebirths. The legend teaches that before Pṛṣadhra's crime, sacrificed animals submitted to their deaths "of their own volition."[23] That is one way of recognizing the ineluctability of *pravṛtti*. A few centuries later, Cakrapāṇidatta was to put the point again quite bluntly: "For living beings, eating meat is only accompanied by violence as a result of the passion (*rāga*) which animates them."[24]

Rāga is the passionate attachment of living beings to things of this world. Such an attachment finds expression both in *hiṃsā*, "the desire to kill," and in sacrifices which in the last analysis are unable to procure deliverance since, far from delivering men, they chain them to the cycle of rebirths.

Explaining these classical texts, which serve to reconcile vegetarianism and eating meat, is always a delicate matter for Indianists, for we must take into account both the part played by the *structures* of collective thought and also that of *history*, the details of which now escape us. On the one hand, we need to explain to the Western reader how it was possible for these opposed rules of life to be practiced *simultaneously* at every period: the opposition (between vegetarians and meat eaters) being integrated within a hierarchy (of brahmins and *kṣatriya*). On the other hand, we must also consider from a historical angle the degree of compromise involved in a realistic interpretation of these texts, for they are evidence of a period prior to the triumph of vegetarianism. A few centuries later we find a similar embarrassment in the face of the consumption of meats in both the medical texts and the Dharma literature: although justified in the texts, in practice it was progressively discredited.

In his *Homo hierarchicus*, Louis Dumont reminds the reader of a characteristic expression used by the medical commentators on the codes of Manu and Yājñavalkya: they remark that blood sacrifice had become "odious to people." In the Ayurvedic tradition too, at the same period,[25] when Ḍalhaṇa and Cakrapāṇidatta are obliged to comment on the fundamental theme of friendship for all creatures, they run up against the contradiction constituted by the fact that elsewhere raw blood and fresh meat are prescribed. Suśruta declares that the medical practitioner must show friendship toward all creatures. Ḍalhaṇa then asks, "How can one speak of friendship for creatures when one prescribes fresh blood taken from animals which are still living?" The answer comes as no surprise; it is a transfer from Manu's text (cited above): "Because it is, in effect, the application of a rule"; in prescribing fresh blood, "the medical practitioner no more commits a crime than he who kills animals in the accomplishment of a sacrifice."[26] This is an orthodox tradition promulgated by a collection of *śāstra*, or normative treatises: the classical texts quite literally authorize the Ayurvedic prescriptions. The medical practitioner can never be at fault if he applies the formulas consecrated by Suśruta and Caraka. The commentator's attitude here is typical of a pundit. The idea that the doctor is acting in a situation of distress and only employing violence out of necessity is always implicitly understood, and thus it proves possible to circumvent the difficulty of the internal contradiction or tension between the ideal (nonviolence) and the necessity (violence).

A parallel text in Cakrapāṇidatta, in contrast, draws full attention to this fundamental duality of perspectives, the dialectics between compassion and distress, a compassion which makes one regret taking the life of any creature even while, in order to relieve distress, one must resort to violent remedies. One of the ethical principles taught by the *Caraka-saṃhitā* is "friendship" *(maitrī)* and "compassion" *(kāruṇya)* toward all creatures. This evokes the following commentary, exceptional for its impressive precision:

> Friendship is a mode of behavior *(pravṛtti)* free from animosity with respect to all creatures as to oneself. But is it not contradictory [to what is said elsewhere] to insist "*that one should practice friendship assiduously?*" When (in *sūtra* XXVII, 311) the author of this same treatise prohibits the meat of an animal shot by poisoned darts or dead from natural causes and prescribes the fresh meat of antelope or of other game killed in the prime of life, is he not thereby teaching a violence *(hiṃsā)* that is manifestly in contradiction to friendship *(maitrī)?* No, that is not the case. If one reflects that for living creatures eating meat is only accompanied by violence if passion is involved, the master of Ayurveda, for his part, is teaching which meat is indicated, which contraindicated, in such or such diseases, but he is not prescribing the eating of meat nor [the committing] of violence. In effect, even while he teaches that alcohol is good for the regimen of a healthy or a sick man, he also prohibits the use of alcohol. Similarly, when prescribing a meat diet in a disease such as royal consumption, and similarly, in the chapter "Regimen to be followed in accordance with the season," in the passage (*sūtra* VI, 43) which for autumn recommends "quail meat, etc.," the purpose is to teach of the good effects that can be produced by quail meat, etc.; it is not to prescribe violence. But those who are sick and those who are well all share the fruit of violence.
>
> Another example: the Vedic rule according to which "*as a rite of black magic, one may practice the sacrifice of the śyena (falcon).*" Given that black magic [too] is a consequence of passion, the Vedic rule does no more than present the *śyena* as a means of black magic, but that does not stop the practice of black magic from being a negation of *dharma*. However, here there is a difference: if a man's life can only be saved by meat acquired by violence and if he exercises that violence, such violence is not a source of sin since a Vedic formula lays down the rule that "in all circumstances one must safeguard one's life"; but when there are other means of saving one's life and the purpose of the violence is merely to obtain plumpness, it is assuredly a source of sin. Besides, say Ayurveda did prescribe violence, even then, if one speaks of violence, it is to [indicate] the sin. For Ayurvedic rules *(vidhi)* do

not teach the way to realize *dharma*, rather the way to realize health, as it is phrased (in *sūtra* I, 53): "the objective of this science is to maintain the equilibrium of the *dhātu*."[27]

The commentator goes right back to the philosophical roots of the debate concerning the *adharmic* nature of magic (non-*dharma*, a negation of *dharma*), in *Mīmāṃsā*, the science which aims to interpret the Vedic texts. The concept of a "rule" *(vidhi)* is of central importance. Conceived on the model of the Vedic injunctions—and the word indeed denotes a type of Vedic formula—it means command, *exhortation*. Without going into details, I would refer the reader to the analysis given by P. V. Kane in his *History of Dharmaśāstra*, as he specifically comments on the Vedic formula cited by Cakrapāṇidatta: "Whoever is practicing black magic may sacrifice the *śyena* (falcon)."[28] The rule has no more than a hypothetical value: if one desires the death of an enemy, a possible and effective means to achieve it is through the rite of the *śyena*; but this is certainly no categorical rule, no rule of *dharma*. Magic may be effective but it runs contrary to *dharma*: It is not part of the sociocosmic order and in fact denies it. Magic instead is *adharma*, that is, injustice and sinful violence. By referring in such a manner to this Vedic example, Cakrapāṇidatta is able to make a distinction between the hypothetical rules, which do no more than proclaim the *efficacy* of some practical procedure (a ritual or a treatment), and the categorical rules laid down as norms or *commandments*. Working on this basis, when confronted in Ayurvedic medicine with the prescription of a meat diet, Cakrapāṇidatta proceeds to give two interpretations, each on a different level. A meat diet is, first, an efficacious procedure, and Ayurveda is concerned solely with that aspect of things: health, the equilibrium of the elements of the body, efficacy—in a word, *artha*; the problems of violence and sin and the realization or negation of *dharma* do not fall within its province. At the limit, the rules of Ayurveda, like those of magic, are purely hypothetical: if you wish to grow fatter, eat meat; whether it is sinful to do so is not the point. At another level, though, Cakrapāṇidatta does find a possible agreement between medicine and the realization of *dharma*: in circumstances of emergency and distress. When life is in danger, the rules of Ayurveda do become categorical, commandments of *dharma* for times of distress. But even then, as the text points out, the patient still "shares in the fruit of violence": there can be no meat without violence. However, quite exceptionally, because his life is in danger, the violence he employs is not a source of sin. Through its logical articulations and its use of the traditional concept of *vidhi*, "rule, injunction," this text seems to provide a perfect summation of the problem of therapeutic violence and a meat regimen, and of the two competing perspectives between which the classical doctrine had to construct a compromise.

VIII: Animals in the Sequence of Foods

Let us complete this enquiry by developing the full implications of the very first of our conclusions. At every level the biological data are enmeshed in a mass of normative prescriptions. First, the jungle: defined less by its physical characteristics than as a magnetic pole within the framework of a spiritual or religious ecology. It is the territory of the antelope, the land of sacrifice. Next, animals: understood literally as meat, they represent zoology caught within pharmacy. Then, physiology is caught within pathogenesis. In short, perception informed by the Word, the image subordinated to the stereotype. In every domain there reigns the same ambiguity that we first noted in the *Arthaśāstra*: today, no one can tell for certain whether it is a real kingdom or a construction of an imaginary utopia. It is in the catalog of animal forms that the omnipotence of sterotypes is most clearly apparent. That is by no means an original discovery, and I will do no more than repeat, in the context of the taxonomy of animals, what historians and psychologists of art have long since demonstrated in connection with representations of animals down to very recent times. I am thinking of a number of famous pages in *Art and Illusion*, where Ernst Gombrich shows how the stereotype of the dragon, with its armor plating, determined all representations of the rhinoceros from Dürer's master drawing (1515) right down to the late eighteenth century, even when the artists themselves claimed to have drawn the animal *from life*. The idea (of the dragon) precedes, informs, and idealizes the perception (of the rhinoceros), but in traditional art, in India as in Europe, the entire bestiary is stereotyped in this manner and the consequences are twofold: a lack of differentiation between the real and the fabulous and a subordination of the biological to the spiritual. Animal forms are confused with demonological ones; animals are avatars or vehicles for the gods, empirical observations are indissociably mingled with magic prescriptions. But I fear that there is no masking the fact that India proceeded no farther than the bestiary, whereas others managed to escape from the enchantments of the *dharma*, that ritualistic vision of the universe, and invent the natural sciences.

The immediate aim of this chapter is to determine the respective positions of animal and man in the scale of creatures; once that is done, it should be possible to develop some more general reflections on taxonomy. Man is placed among the carnivorous creatures, and the relationship between man and animals is a utilitarian one: animals serve either as Man's food or Man's enemies. This fully developed theme can be noted when one compares the Ayurvedic catalog of meats to other brahminic taxonomies and to the overall classification of creatures subjected to the *cycle of rebirths*: plants, animals, men, demons, and gods. In this immense sequence of rebirths, schemata of strictly *biological* classification play no more than a minor role; the position of each category of beings is fixed by its function in the system of *ritual* activities. This subordination of physical facts to ritual activities is nowhere more clearly manifested than in the brahminic concept of food, as I shall demonstrate by analyzing a doctrine that is complementary to the doctrine of the soils, namely, the distribution of living beings according to the mode of their generation into four categories: 1) those grown from the ground, 2) those born from wet heat, 3) the oviparous, and 4) the viviparous. These four categories are arranged one by one on a much wider scale which reaches right up to the gods, the scale of the "conditions" in which creatures may be reborn in the course of transmigration.

THE HINDU EQUIVALENT OF THE CHAIN OF BEING

The clear-cut theme of the great chain of being will allow us to attempt a comparison between two styles of thought, two very different traditions: the Greco-Latin tradition, where the theme of the chain of being is unfolded in huge tableaus of natural history; and the Hindu tradition, where such a theme is certainly no less important than in the West, since it determines the scale of reincarnations and the caste system, but which, for all that, takes no account at all of history or the natural sciences.

In his admirable book on botanical and zoological methods of classification down to Antoine-Laurent de Jussieu, Henri Daudin credits Aristotle with two ideas which the Natural History of the Renaissance inherited: the idea of hierarchy and that of continuity.

The idea of a hierarchy of beings takes shape in the *De Anima* and in the division of the soul into various principles: the nutritive soul, the only one present in plants, then desire, sensation, locomotion, and—at the summit—reason, peculiar to man alone. In neo-Platonic philosophy and subsequently in Christian theology, the hierarchy of the faculties of the soul was easily devised to provide the theme necessary for a speculative and religious interpretation of the world; but it also affects the history of the natural sciences to the extent that it was associated with another idea, one which observers since Aristotle have been eager to "verify" by invoking the existence of intermediary forms linking the different classes of living beings, and which, right down to the mid-seventeenth century, determined in particular a belief in the existence of intermediary "zoophytes" in between the plants and the animals (sponges, for instance). This other idea is the law of the *continuity* of Nature which, beginning with inanimate beings and proceeding first with plants and next with animals, rises little by little in a continuous and almost imperceptible transition.[1]

Onto these two principles of hierarchy and continuity there was then grafted a vast body of research concerning the flora and fauna, both real and legendary. The Greeks called it *Historia*, enquiry, the noting and collecting of evidence, things seen and curiosities. I know that *Natural History*, in the strict sense, the science of the classification of living beings in tableaus, series, or networks, only made its appearance in the second half of the seventeenth century, and that it is of course necessary to distinguish a number of variants in the long tradition of *Historia*, depending on whether one is considering the Renaissance or the classical period, the Greece of the third century or the Alexandrian period. It would perhaps be wiser to abstain from making any comparisons relating to such vast themes; nevertheless, here is what I would be inclined to suggest.

By associating the hierarchy of functions with the continuity of

Nature, Aristotle and his successors opened up the path which led European thought from theology to the natural sciences. In India, in contrast, the scale of beings was never any more than a juridical principle: here, beings were classed according to their merits and according to their aptitude or inaptitude at practicing the rituals. The idea of a "science" of Nature is altogether alien to India or, to be more precise, in India it is formulated in a radically different fashion. We have already observed that, in Ayurvedic speculation, the idea of Nature is absorbed by the idea of Food, as zoology is by pharmacy. Here we find further evidence of that fact: the chain of being is presented in the form of a sequence of foodstuffs.

In the first pages of the *Suśrutasaṃhitā*, where living beings are classified according to their four modes of generation, Suśruta says that the human body constitutes both the place of disease or health and the point of application for therapeutic action; the *puruṣa* (human being) is man as an incarnation of the soul, a combination of the *ātman* (the eternal principle) with the five crude elements (earth, water, and so on). Why is man the privileged object of medicine? Because he is the first in the scale of living beings, and all the rest are at his service. Then follows a multifaceted classification of living beings considered from a number of different points of view: they are twofold, immobile (plants) and mobile (animals); and twofold also, *āgneyaḥ saumyaś ca*, depending on whether Agni or Soma predominates within them; quintuple (since there are five crude elements); and, last, quadruple through their modes of generation. To the most important of them all, the *puruṣa*, the human being, a receptacle for diseases, can be applied four means of curing the latter or mastering them. The principle means is food. Food is the root of life; it depends on six *rasa* which are, in themselves, inherent in material substances. "But the substances are *oṣadhi* (plants, remedies)" *(dravyāṇi punar oṣadhayaḥ)*. "And these [the *oṣadhi*] are of two kinds: the immobile and the mobile." The immobile are quadruple:

vanaspati, trees which do not appear to flower
vṛkṣa, trees which give flowers and fruits
vīrudh, bushes and lianas
oṣadhi, annual plants

The mobile are also quadruple:

jarāyuja, viviparous
aṇḍaja, oviparous

svedaja, born from wet heat
udbhijja, which grow from the ground

Finally the text enumerates the parts of plants and animals used in pharmacopoeia.[2]

Man is a consumer of others: that was a conclusion to be expected within the framework of a science for human longevity. In the texts which teach not (as this one does) the realization of *artha* (health, prosperity) but that of *dharma*, the living are first and foremost food for the gods, the material of sacrifice. However, once that nuance has been noted—and except for the mention of a "place" where the conflict between disease and health is played out, the "point of application" *(adhiṣṭhāna)* for therapeutic "action" (technical words)—the text as a whole is in no way peculiar to the medical domain; it might equally well belong to other genres of Sanskrit literature, which make widespread use of the classificatory series of *jarāyuja* (vivipara), *aṇḍaja* (ovipara), *svedaja* (born from humid heat), and *udbhijja* (which grow from the ground).[3] Note the minor role this traditional division plays in Ayurveda: Suśruta never mentions it again, Caraka mentions it only once in passing,[4] and Vāgbhaṭa never refers to it at all. Despite the importance of such a division in the religious domain, it is virtually absent, or at least unexploited, in the medical domain. This stereotyped series of four terms, repeated everywhere but only in an allusive form, can in no way be considered as proof of an effort at empirical knowledge. Never is it used as the framework for the nomenclature of plants or animals, either in Ayurvedic treatises or in the dictionaries—treasuries of names *(kośa)*—or pharmacopoeia *(nighaṇṭu)*. This series of four terms has a quite different significance. Suśruta's presentation of it lacks the indispensible complement that alone confers on this division its true ontological and religious dimensions: the principle of the *ātman*'s transmigration through reincarnations. Thanks to the many different classificatory points of view—divisions into two, then five, four, six (the six *rasa*), eight (four for plants, four for animals)—thanks to all these successive *substructions*, the classification of living beings undergoes a metamorphosis and becomes a classification of foods and remedies. The metamorphosis is aided by a whole set of logical distortions. The series of four modes of generation, for example, is used twice: first, applied to all beings (in this case, those which grow from the ground are the plants); next, applied solely to mobile beings (at which point it must be assumed that animals which grow from the ground do exist). Another example is the overlapping of the three notions—"food" *(āhāra)*, "sub-

TABLE 13
FOUR PLANT FORMS GRAFTED ONTO FOUR MODES OF GENERATION

"mobile" *(jaṅgama)*	*jarāyuja*	viviparous
	aṇḍaja	oviparous
	svedaja	from wet heat
"immobile" *(sthāvara)* or which grow from the ground *(udbhijja)*	*oṣadhi*	annual plants
	vanaspati	trees without flowers
	vṛkṣa	trees with flowers and fruits
	vīrudh	bushes and lianas

stances" or "drugs" *(dravya)*, and plants *(oṣadhi)*—which finally become merged into materia medica, whereby the term *oṣadhi*, which in the strict sense refers to "annual plants" (cereals, etc.), expands to include all substances used as remedies.

We must look closely at these shifts of meaning, these logical distortions, that turn the medical texts into *reductive* discourse: the scale of beings is literally flattened out, its cosmic and religious importance is made incidental; it is reduced to a pharmacopoeia.

When the series of the four plant forms is grafted onto the series of the four modes of generation, we obtain a scale normally presented as in table 13. This is how the scale of rebirths appears in the first pages of the *Laws of Manu*, for example. From the top to the bottom, from Brahmā down to the plants plunged in obscurity and ignorance, the position of each creature results from retribution for actions performed in earlier lives.[5] As shown in table 14, the extension of the first three terms is comparable in Manu (I, 43–45) and Suśruta (*sūtra* I, 30). And to the extent that the series of the four modes of generation applies to all living creatures, which is everywhere the case in Sanskrit literature, the *udbhijja*, born by growing from the ground, are the plants. Indeed, Manu is quite explicit: plants, whether they propagate themselves or grow from cuttings.[6] This point is worth stressing, since certain interpreters have mistakenly read "animals" where the texts say "creatures, living beings" and thereby have made a serious mistake of interpreting the expression as a declaration of the existence of zoophytes.[7]

When it first appears in Suśruta (*sūtra* I, 22), this classificatory series applies to "living creatures as a whole" *(bhūtagrāma)*, but when it is repeated a few lines later (*sūtra* I, 30), it applies only to the animals.

TABLE 14
THREE CATEGORIES OF ANIMALS

	Manu	Suśruta
Jarāyuja	livestock *(paśu)* antelopes *(mṛga)* beasts of prey *(vyāla)* demons men	livestock *(paśu)* men *(manuṣya)* beasts of prey *(vyāla)*
Aṇḍaja	birds snakes crocodiles fish . . .	birds snakes reptiles
Svedaja	insects mosquitoes fleas . . .	*kṛmi* } including { worms, larvae, insects, ants *kīṭa* } *pipīlika*

And at this point, Suśruta mentions *udbhijja* animals, "animals which grow from the ground: trombidions, frogs, etc."[8] However, in classical Ayurveda at least, this meaning of *udbhijja* is exceptional; as far as I know, it occurs only here. I would be inclined to explain it as resulting from a purely formal need to establish a symmetry between two groups of four: four plant forms and four animal forms, a parallelism which entails mentioning animals grown from the ground.

In contrast to the animal series, the series of four plant forms (*oṣadhi*, and so on) does play an important role in Ayurveda and in traditional Sanskrit dictionaries but does not interest us directly. Here again the use of the word *oṣadhi* undergoes a curious extension. In its place in the scale of living forms, its strict definition, "the annual plants," is maintained, yet we have observed that at the same time *oṣadhi* can be given the specialized meaning of "medicinal plants." Suśruta actually says:

> Food in its turn is the root of living beings, and of strength, complexion and the vital fluid; it depends upon six *rasa*; the *rasa* in their turn depend upon *dravya* (substances); the *dravya* in their turn are *oṣadhi*, but the latter are of two kinds, immobile and mobile.[9]

How should the word *oṣadhi* be understood here? "As a consequence of contiguity" *(sānnidhyāt)*, as Ḍalhaṇa puts it in his commentary (or, as we might say, through synecdoche), the word refers both to animals and to plants. It is an altogether aberrant use. We may assume that at this point it was necessary to qualify the word *dravya*, "substance," to indicate that it was specifically a matter of "medicinal substances," the drugs that compose materia medica; but, even so, one would expect the word *auṣadha*, "medicament," to be used. We are told elsewhere that *oṣadhi* as "medicinal plant" is only used where there is some form of birth or germination, while its derivative *auṣadha* does not convey the idea of a birth but instead refers to all remedies, whether they be of animal, vegetable, or mineral origin.[10] Ḍalhaṇa suggests a possible reason for the surprising choice of *oṣadhi*: it is here, precisely, that the minerals are excluded. *Auṣadha* ("remedy") is an extension of *oṣadhi* ("medicinal plant") from which it is derived. Note how by means of a remarkable synecdoche the extension is used but is arrested halfway. Thus, more than plants but less than remedies, since the minerals are excluded, *oṣadhi* here become (exceptionally, as we have translated) living beings to the extent that they compose materia medica.

Now we come to the main point: food is the root of living beings. The text enumerates four means of mastering diseases: *saṃśodhana*, "purification," *saṃśamana*, "calming," *āhāra*, "nourishment," and *ācāra* "rules of conduct." This is another of those classificatory series which, with their sibylline arithmetic, sum up an entire universe. Let us attempt at the risk of being inexact a schematic explanation: the *saṃśamana*, calming medicine, includes prescriptions to be taken orally and external applications to be carried out at home; the *saṃśodhana*, purifying medicine, calls for hospitalization and manipulation of the patient's body by nurses; the *ācāra*, rules of conduct, apply in three domains—the body (exercises and postures), speech (the times for and techniques of recitation), and thought (reflection, attention, volition); thus, all that we would call techniques of the body, pedagogy, and psychology is brought into association with *āhāra*, nourishment, to make up what can certainly be regarded as a therapy but is above all "the regimen of life for healthy people."

Each of these four types of medical action in its turn is then subdivided, using new classificatory series. We should thus specify, as Ḍalhaṇa does in his commentary, that there are four modes of nourishment: "to drink, to suck, to chew and to crunch."[11] The mode of presentation constitutes one of the first criteria for the classification of food remedies; the point of view of the pharmacist, later to predominate in the descriptions of materia medica, is already apparent. If effect is regarded as a criterion, nourishment is triple: "calming humors, calming diseases, allowing healthy people to live."[12] Through its "calming" *(praśamana)* effects, nourishment is immediately included in the panoply of the *saṃśamana*. The justification for subsequently treating it under a separate rubric is the fact that it also plays a preventive role. The four types of medical action are divided into two groups: "In short, the therapy is of two kinds, *śodhana* and *śamana*."[13] In parallel fashion, food and the rules of conduct are associated together as *āhārācārau*, a compound in the dual, to define the conditions of a healthy system of life. The idea of remedy and that of nourishment are thus both parallel and complementary; pharmacy and cuisine are two aspects of medical activities regarded as a single set.

Suśruta molds, reduces, and subordinates creatures as a whole to strictly human needs: "Man is the first, the rest are at his service" (*tatra puruṣaḥ pradhānaṃ, tasyopakaraṇam anyat*). He takes bark, leaves, flowers, and fruit from the plants and skin, nails, fur, and blood from the animals. Taxonomy stops short and finishes up expressed as pharmacy. But let us restore all its religious dimensions to the scale of beings, of which we have presented but a poor reflection. When we do so, we discover a whole cosmology, a whole ontology of food: "and food in its turn is the root of living beings . . .": a formula inscribed in the mainstream of the Hindu tradition, and which can be traced directly back to the *Upaniṣad*.

No enumeration of the immense cosmic chain of foods has a more vibrant ring than that of the *Taittirīya Upaniṣad*. The Brahman is the supreme *ātman*:

> From this *ātman* came forth the ether, from the ether the wind, from the wind the fire, from the fire the waters, from the waters the earth, from the earth the plants, from the plants food. From food creatures are born. Those which are to be found on earth live by food alone and at the end they return to it. For food is the first of creatures. That is why it is called *sarvauṣadha*, "the sum of all the plants."[14]

Some time ago, I had the privilege to hear a free rendering of the longer passage by A. K. Ramanujan, marvelous poet and translator, who teaches at the University of Chicago:

FOOD CHAIN, Sanskrit style

From food, from food,
creatures, all creatures
come to be.

Gorging, disgorging,
beings come
to be.

By food they live,
on food they move,
into food they pass:

food, the chief
of things, of all things
that come to be,

elixir,
herb of herbs
for mortals.

Food, food, Brahman is food:

Only they eat
who know
they eat their god.

For food is the chief
of things, of all things
that come to be:

elixir,
herb of herbs
for mortals.

From food all beings
come to be,
by food

they grow,
into food
they pass.

And what eats is eaten,
and what's eaten, eats
in turn.

A. K. RAMANUJAN
(By courtesy of the author.)

What a despairing but illuminating encounter! See how the gist of what has been for us such a laborious enquiry is captured by the poet in the flash of his word! *Sarvauṣadha*:

"Elixir,
herb of herbs
for mortals."

The earth is a herbarium from which animals draw the nourishing saps. If we follow the sequence up into the animal kingdom we reach the feeding activities of the beasts of prey and the eating of meat by man.

Food is the basis for all human activities, not only those leading to prosperity (the realization of *artha*) but also those leading to heaven (observation of the rites prescribed in the Vedas), and finally those through which one may achieve deliverance (a vegetarian diet, for example). Caraka teaches that every action, "whether a worldly action to ensure one's subsistance, a Vedic rite to reach the *svarga* (the dwelling place of the gods) or the action aimed at deliverance—every action is based upon food."[15] So it is that man slips into his place in the sequence: below him, those he eats; beyond him, those receiving his oblations.

This can be understood first in the biological sense: food gives man the physical means of taking action. In the medical texts that is a commonplace: food, health, and continuing life are "the root, the basis" which make it possible for man to realize his four goals: desire, *artha, dharma*, and deliverance.[16]

But we must also consider the other side of the coin: food is "the basis" of actions or "the root" for living beings in the sense that living beings *constitute the material of sacrifice*. When, in conclusion to the catalog of foods, Caraka predicts happiness in this world and in future lives for the healthy man who day after day follows an "appropriate" *(sātmya)* regimen and assiduously practices medication in the name of Brahmā, charity, and other virtuous actions, he is addressing not just any individual but brahmins in the second stage of their existence, when they are the fathers of families and heads of households. The master of the house takes care to keep the sacrificial fires of the domestic hearth perpetually alight; for that reason he is called *āhitāgni*, "the maintainer of the sacred fires." Making use of an analogy between the sacred fire and *antaragni*, "the internal fire, the digestive fire," Caraka compares the meal to a sacrifice: He will escape all disease, "he who, maintainer of the fire *(āhitāgni)*, provides as offerings to his internal fire *(antaragnau juhoti)* foods that are always wholesome."[17] An additional proof, if proof were needed, of the constant desire to justify material activities and physical processes by considerations borrowed from the all-enveloping tradition, considerations that in the last analysis stem from the religious domain.

The implications of this theme are developed in the *Dharmaśāstra*.

The creator arranged for all living beings, plants and animals alike, to be born to serve as food for the vital principle: plants for animals, game for beasts of prey, those without hands for those with hands, and the cowardly for the brave. Food, sacrifice, and the cycle of rebirths: all belong to the same constellation of ideas. The *oṣadhi*, the trees, the *paśu*, and all the other animals that die and are consumed on the occasion of sacrifices will by way of recompense receive promotion in the scale of reincarnations.[18] We have already seen how the Vedic texts were unwinding the reel, or *sequence*, of moon-space-wind-rain-earth-food. I am endebted to Armand Minard for this expression and its references.[19] The Dharma texts go on to incorporate the biological (the chain of living beings) within the normative (the scale of rebirths). The sequence is a succession of states through which to pass, degrees to rise above in order to progress upward in the hierarchy of creatures. Creatures are types of food, substances are remedies: what it comes down to is that there really are no substances, only relations, transitions, sacrifices, stages which must be passed through. All this looms in the background to the medical treatises even if they, whose sole object is the "continuing life" *(āyus)*, do not need to concern themselves with the remainder of the sequence.

SCIENCE AND MYTH

If we leave aside what I have called the "bestiaries" (the lists of animals as avatars and vehicles of the gods), the only catalog for the fauna, apart from the *Amarakośa* to which we shall be returning, is the catalog of meats. First, it refers back to the jungle, plunging us into the traditional ecology; next it refers us to the flesh of eaters of flesh and the whole physiology of concentrated and superactivated juices. All these different segments of knowledge form a whole; they represent, as it were, a single central problem in different guises. It is a matter of cutting a kind of section through the Ayurvedic doctrine, passing through the jungle to the cooking of meats, in order to lay bare the different levels of approach to one and the same problem—that of the place of *animality* in medicine, the animality of man who feeds on animals. As we have seen, Ayurvedic medicine, which is a science and not just a technique, opens up a new theoretical perspective on Hinduism. It is a reductive perspective since at the center of his preoccupations, the doctor places *artha*, health or prosperity in a continuing life. Nevertheless, all the themes of the enveloping Hindu tradition are present: *dharma*, sacrifice, nonviolence. Simply, in contrast to the more usual idea formed of Hinduism, Ayurveda places the emphasis on force, dire need, animality; and these aspects of Hinduism deserve to be situated in their right place.

Passing from the sequence of rebirths described in the *Laws of Manu* to Suśruta's pharmacy involves a reduction. Eschatology brought down to earth is a whole theory reduced to a catalog of recipes. It is exactly the same kind of reduction as that described by Charles Malamoud in his "Cuire le monde," a dazzling interpretation of Vedic sacrifice which shows how the original theme—cooking to perfect the world—was degraded, coarsened, confined to the ritualization of cooking: in banquets it is a brahmin who does the cooking . . . that is a pale reflection of his original function in the solemn sacrifices founded on the Veda.[20] The medical tradition's degradation of the original theme leads to Caraka's formula cited above: to eat is to offer up foods to the digestive fire; the ideal of sacrifice is reduced to a metaphor, to a metaphoric ritualization of the process of digestion.

Malamoud's purely linguistic comment on an expression such as "the cooking of the world" *(loka-pakti)* is equally valid for "the *āhitāgni* who offers up foods to his digestive fire"; and also for another formula already cited several times, "those without hands are the food of those with hands, and the cowardly are the food of the brave." In each instance one should retain the most meaningful interpretation and not dull the metaphor. But, faced with such formulas, Western interpreters and translators seem, on the contrary, to have been seized by a strange timidity. Thus *loka-pakti* was given a spiritual sense: "good reputation in the world, the perfecting of the world" until Malamoud restored the material image which underlies it, cooking, the culinary art, a whole ontology of cooked foods. Similarly, translators of Caraka, apparently forgetting that they themselves are brahmins (I am thinking of the Jamnagar team of pundits who produced a very remarkable translation into English), refuse to take into account the deliberately religious significance of the vocabulary: *āhitāgni*, the one who maintains the sacred fires, *juhoti*, he offers a libation. And finally, when Norman Brown glosses Manu's statement: the plants are born to feed the animals, game for the beasts of prey, those without hands for man, the cowardly for the brave,[21] adding: cowardly "like the deer," brave "like the tiger," the gloss is totally incomprehensible. Who are these men here in the positions of game and beasts of prey to one another? They are the warriors, the *kṣatriya* involved in the trial of combat and seen from that aspect of themselves which allots them their place in the sequence of foods: their *animality*, whether it be a cowardliness which debases them to the level of little fish eaten by large ones or courage, in an almost Hegelian sense, the virtue of the master, the virtue of the beasts of prey. Here is a summary of the commentary provided for this theme by a passage in the *Mahābhārata*. The hero swoops down upon his enemies, thereby adopting the path of salvation: if he is victor, it is the *dharma* of the warrior to dominate, just as do beasts of prey; if he is vanquished, he wins a glorious death and the heaven of Indra. But the coward who flees from the field of battle and abandons his comrades is demoted to the rank of game and becomes the prey of the victors, like little snakes which are devoured by the great *āśīviṣa*, an extremely venomous species.[22] In a direct sense, warriors devour one another; combat is a sacrifice in which the flesh of enemies constitutes the libation. Once again, we should not blunt the brutal impact of the images and so mask this extraordinary constellation of ideas which associates together feeding, sacrifice, and the animality of man.

The impression given by Ayurvedic therapy is that of a vast makeshift job: it consists of a mass of recipes in which the most bizarre ingredients crop up. Who, after all, really knows the art of collecting the semen of the crocodile (an aphrodisiac), the bile of the jackal (an eyewash), or the urine of the lion (against epilepsy)? These magic substances are associated with the presence of fabulous beasts, either as a result of fantastical idealizations of fauna considered from the Indian point of view to be exotic—such as the *śarabha* of Kashmir—or because the names used to denote real creatures—such as the *śiśumāra*, "crocodile," or the *timi* "shark"—are also in Hindu tradition as a whole applied to mythological monsters, such as the *śiśumāra*, "dragon," and the *timi*, "sea monster." The medical discourse thus appears to be intermingled with the imaginary; in truth, however, it is the Western interpreter who has introduced from the outside these distinctions between the natural and the magic, the ordinary and the fabulous. In reality, all of these associations are presented on the same footing within a single, homogeneous discourse. Ayurveda must be taken en bloc: it stands as a whole and single "myth," a whole and single "science." In traditional culture, myth is a science, as has been abundantly proved by anthropologists. But then the reverse is equally true: an orthodox "science," a science derived from the Vedic revelation, a *śāstra*, is one of the possible versions, one of the possible modes of expression for the prevailing mythology. It is not simply one or another ingredient in the pharmacopoeia that is imaginary but the entire pharmacopoeia itself, *even in its very style*: what it really formulates in the style of a codex, the falsely practical style of a catalog of remedies, is a theory of the relations between man and animality, a general taxonomy of living beings. We are thus set fairly and squarely in the world of the *śarabha* and the *śiśumāra*.

It is important to preserve the mythical dimension of traditional science, a dimension which modern Ayurvedic scholars, in their efforts at modernization, are—alas—eliminating by pruning the classical texts. For example, a "scientific synopsis" of the *Carakasaṃhitā* has recently been published in India. Among other things, it compiles an index of the medicinal substances of animal origin mentioned in the treatise. By virtue of what criteria does this index omit the semen of the *śiśumāra* and the meat of the *śarabha* while including other substances which are just as extraordinary, magical, indeed imaginary, such as crocodile semen and lion urine?[23] Is it because the *śiśumāra* and the *śarabha* are fabulous animals? If so, why not be consistent? For nothing here is scientific in the modern sense, it is all fabulous. To be sure, the aim of the modern Ayurvedists is quite different from ours. As practitioners, they seek to extract as much as they can from the *techniques* prescribed in the texts. As purists and conservationists, we, in contrast, are seeking to reconstruct the principles of a *science*, in all its homogeneity and orthodoxy.

The case of the *śarabha* is a model one. In epic literature and mythology this is a monster defined by its power to overcome the lion. In particular, it is in the form of a *śarabha* that the god Śiva uses his claws to kill Narasiṃha, an incarnation of Viṣṇu in the form of a lion-man.[24] The *śarabha* is an eight-legged monster which lives in the forest. More than this we should have no way of knowing, were it not for the garland of synonyms in the *kośa* (treasuries of names for the use of poets), the *nighaṇṭu* (dictionaries of pharmacopoeia), and the stereotyped definition provided by the commentaries which localize its habitat to the mountains of Kashmir. Now, coming several centuries after the classical treatises, the dictionaries and commentaries introduce a certain equivocation into the names and characteristics that define the *śarabha*. One collection of names and indicative features make it out to be one of the *Antilopinae*-or-*Cervidae* group: a "species of *hariṇa*," "a large *mṛga*" with big horns; another collection defines it as a beast of prey: "a species of tiger," "a large lion," *pañcanakha*, and so on.[25] Such equivocation is an expression of the irruption into Ayurveda of a being which in reality belongs to a different order. Presenting it as one of the *Antilopinae* or *Cervidae* is a way of making the *śarabha* less extraordinary, of bringing it down to the level of ordinary meats; and it is made out to be a light and astringent meat from the dry lands. To define it as a beast of prey, on the contrary, is to convey in classificatory terms the monstrous nature of the *śarabha*: a earthly monster—always assuming it is not really a demon—could not be anything other than carnivorous. In the classical texts, in the strict sense of the expression, that is to say in the treatises of Suśruta and Caraka, the *śarabha* always appears in a form made commonplace: it is systematically introduced into a particular series, the series of meats that are by nature light:

quail-partridge-antelope-hare-*śarabha*-sambar-. . . ,

which is repeated several times with variants:

quail-partridge-antelope-sheep-*śarabha*-hare-. . .
quail-partridge-antelope-chital-*śarabha*-hare-. . .[26]

Thus the terrible or monstrous aspect of the *śarabha* does not appear in either Suśruta or Caraka. *The fabulous being is surrounded by ordinary ones.* What could be more commonplace, among the light meats, than the quail or the hare? It might of course be objected that the *śarabha* is in truth a real animal. In some Indo-Aryan languages, the derivatives from *śarabha* refer to the markhor and the ibex (as is indicated in Table 5). Might not the *śarabha* be one of those wild goats of the Himalayan forests? Whatever the case, it makes no difference. These are species on the margins of the Hindu world, so rare and distant that the name of *śarabha* included in a ready-made list, sandwiched in between the hare and the sheep, still stands out from the rest. When positioned on the same level as the very ordinary creatures surrounding it, this fabulous being suddenly looms up to constitute a point of anchorage for mythology within the medical discourse. Indeed, so positively is it felt to be a fabulous being that modern Ayurvedic scholars—determined to bestow a natural identity on beings whose fabulous character they refuse to recognize—identify *śarabha*—with the wapiti, a deer native to Canada and Siberia which has never even existed in India![27] Chase away the fabulous, and it comes galloping right back!

THE PUNDIT'S TAXONOMIES

One angle of research only briefly mentioned in the preceding chapters, the stylistic study of knowledge, might be a future follow-up in other contexts. Such an investigation would involve comparing how a particular corpus of understanding is expressed and taught in each of the different provinces of the Tradition. Thus, the classification of living beings which takes on the appearance of a pharmacopoeia in the Ayurvedic treatises is also to be found formulated in other styles: in the *Purāṇa*, it is a cosmogonic myth; in the *Laws of Manu* (XII), a hierarchy; in the *Amarakośa*, a catalog. A myth (a story), a scale of values, a dictionary of synonyms: so many forms of taxonomy, each with a different role and purpose. In one case what is sought are the means for writing a poem (this is the purpose of treasuries of names), in another the means for identifying a medicinal plant (the role of the *nighaṇṭu*), in yet another means for regulating rituals (this is the aim of the doctrine of the three *guṇa*, the three components of Nature, in Manu and in the cosmogonic myth). Let us sketch out a comparison, starting with an illustration of the doctrine of the three components of living beings.

Without needlessly straying into the complexities of Hindu cosmogony, we must aim to compare what is essential in Hindu ideas generally concerning the place of animals in the scale of beings with what is taught by Ayurveda within the limits of its own specialized field. The comparison concerns not so much the *content* of taxonomy as the *style* of discourse. The dominant form used to classify plants, animals, men, and gods is the triad of the *guṇa*, the three aspects of empirical existence: *sattva*, the pure and luminous component, *rajas*, passion, and *tamas*, the darkness of ignorance. This schema is primarily used in the myth of the re-creation of the world.[28] At each re-creation in between two cosmic reabsorptions, Brahmā is seized by a desire to create beings of every kind. We can skip the first creation, that of Ignorance. Next to appear in the order of the story are:

1) A first category of creatures full of "darkness" *(tamas)*, which are the immobile beings, the plants;

2) then the beings "with transversal movement," the quadrupeds, still too full of *tamas* and ignorance and inclined to follow the wrong path;

3) Brahmā's creative efforts are then brought to bear on the opposite pole of the scale of beings and thus produce beings "with upward movement," too full of joy for action, the gods in whom *sattva*, the luminous component predominates;

4) finally, dissatisfied with his creations so far, which have produced beings either with no aptitude for the rites or who have nothing left to desire, Brahmā makes a last effort by creating beings "with a downward movement," which are defined by their aptitude in accomplishing the

rites; and these are men in whom "passion" *(rajas)* predominates, impelling them to activate themselves (literally, the "dust," which obscures *sattva*).

Ignoring the details accumulated in the *Purāṇa*, the great archaic compilations of Hindu tradition, let us sketch the basic cosmogonic story which unfolds the triad of the *guṇa*. All three components of nature—*sattva, rajas,* and *tamas*—are present in every being, but in each category one in particular predominates. In man, all three are in excess and this explains why Man always suffers more and is more active. The scale of beings is thus founded on the moral principles of "error" in the plants, "incapacity" in the animals, "contentment" in the gods, and "accomplishment" and "realization" in men. The curve of creation rises from the plants and animals up to the gods and then descends again to man, the emphasis being placed on action, ritual, and retribution in future lives for actions in the present life.

In one sense it could be said that the doctor escapes from this strictly juridical and ritualistic classification in which all beings are arranged in a hierarchy according to their merits. In a tradition dominated by the pundits, Ayurveda introduces a breath of fresh air: the great open spaces, the forest, the seasons, and the animal ecology all have a place within this pharmaceutical vision of all living beings and represents *the seeds of secular thought*. True, this secularism is almost immediately repressed, normalized, impregnated with a religious vocabulary: as we have repeatedly stressed, Ayurveda is a religious science. All the same, a difference of style separates the ritualism of the *Purāṇa* from the utilitarianism of Ayurveda, a significant difference in literary genres which should not be overlooked since it also corresponds to a social division.

We should remember that in classical India the brahmin doctor (and *a fortiori* the doctor who was not a brahmin) did not in principle study the Vedas or any of the related sciences of the Revelation except for the one that he practiced, Ayurveda. An excellent Sanskritist, the brahmin doctor would memorize the *Amarakośa* (see below) as well as perhaps one of the great medical *saṃhitā* and would make assiduous use of the huge related body of literature. He might also be a poet, an astrologer, but as a rule he would not be familiar with the *Upaniṣad*, the *Mīmāṃsā* (the hermeneutic interpretation of the Veda), or the disciplines which develop the dominant themes of Hinduism, sacrifice, the triad of the *guṇa*. The doctor was a specialist and the caste system confined him to his specialty. This point is further illustrated with an anthropological observation drawn from Thurston's *Castes and Tribes*. Its bearing is limited both spatially and temporally since it relates exclusively to the brahmin doctors of the Nambudiri caste in Kerala and reflects caste rules that applied in the early years of the twentieth century. Nevertheless, it gives a good enough indication of the doctor's position in relation to brahminic knowledge in general. The brahmin doctor led an isolated intellectual life sealed off from the Tradition as a whole, which was transmitted to him only through the specialized point of view of the Ayurveda. In Kerala, there were eight lineages of Nambudiri brahmins known by the name of Aṣṭavaidya, an enigmatic title which defines them as "doctors *(vaidya)* [disciples] of the *Aṣṭ[āṅga]*," the science "with eight limbs," which is one of the names of Ayurveda. Compared with other Nambudiri (the highest caste in the hierarchy), the Aṣṭavaidya were considered slightly inferior. That inferiority was expressed in two ways: first, the need to shed blood (in surgery, bloodletting) was said to entail a slight impurity, which affected their ritual status; and second (the same argument expressed differently), they were deemed not to have the time to devote to Vedic recitation, being constantly occupied with their functions as medical practitioners. The inferiority of brahmin doctors is equivalent to that of brahmins who embraced a military profession. *The study of the Vedas was forbidden to them.* They enjoyed access only to the first degree of that study, that is, only once could they read the Vedas or hear them recited.[29]

Let us draw out the consequences of this social inferiority of the doctor with regard to the ethnoepistemological status of the Ayurvedic doctrine. The brahmin is a priest, the doctor a practitioner. Thus the ritualism of the principal disciplines which make up the Vedic Revelation is matched, at a slightly lower level, by the utilitarianism of Ayurveda. Not that a medical treatise is any less elaborate than a *Mīmāṃsā* treatise or a cosmogony, for what it loses in technicality on the philosophical level it makes up for at the taxonomical level: nowhere else do we find the multifaceted system of classification that we have briefly analyzed. But a medical *saṃhitā* lays down the theory for a practice; although it may transmit the overall Hindu tradition, it does so by particularizing it for the use of practitioners. The result is a devaluation of *pure* forms of knowledge—zoology and botany, but also the triad of the *guṇa*—which are systematically presented as *applied* forms of knowledge such as pharmacy, normative ecology, and bodily techniques. Consider, for example, what becomes of the three *guṇa* in the medical texts: they are used, quite simply, to provide the basis for a characterology of the most banal kind. *Sāttvika*, in which the pure and

TABLE 15
DOMESTICATED VS. WILD ANIMALS

"Domesticated" animals *(grāmya)*	"Wild" animals *(āraṇya)*
ox	beasts of prey
goat	beasts with cloven hooves
man	elephant
sheep	monkey
horse	birds
mule	aquatic animals
donkey	creeping animals

luminous component predominates, means a sweet and docile temperament, *rājasa* means one who is vain and violent; and *tāmasa* denotes a person who is flabby and lethargic. The same characterology is used in "medicine for horses and elephants" (a technical discipline at the borderline of Ayurveda and the *Arthaśāstra*) whereby animals are classified into three types: docile, mettlesome, and lethargic. The principle is the same: *sattva, rajas*, and *tamas* are still being used to classify the various beings. But what a comedown! At first we were on the heights of cosmogony; now we have sunk to applied psychology!

Let us return to the catalog of animals. It was never our intention to go through all the traditional lists and indeed we have made only one allusion to the lists of the seven *grāmya* and the seven *āraṇya*, which appear in the *Purāṇa*. From the point of view of sacrifice, which is the basis of this distinction in the animal kingdom, man is one of the *grāmya* (as illustrated in table 15).

The *grāmya* are the sacrificial animals, and even if in some versions the presence of man is masked by the substitution of the pig at this point in the series,[30] traditionally he belongs to the group of sacrificial animals; in the lists of sacrificial animals given by the Vedic texts, which run man-horse-ox-sheep-goat,[31] he is even the foremost of them. First of the *grāmya* is man, and first of the *āraṇya* is the lion: such is the teaching of a passage in the *Mahābhārata* which also adopts the series of the seven *grāmya* but reduces the seven *āraṇya* to the quadrupeds—lion, tiger, boar, buffalo, elephant, bear, and monkey.[32] It would be easy to find further variants. See how all these series of terms intersect, repeat one another, *overdetermine* one another, with one particular term—man in

TABLE 16
AMARASIṂHA'S TAXONOMY

1. The Earth (in general)
    - 2. Town
    - 3. Mountain
        - 4. Plants of the forest
        - 5. Wild animals

6. Man (in general)
    - 7. brahmin
    - 8. *kṣatriya* → elephant, horse
    - 9. *vaiśya* → bovine species
    - 10. *śūdra* → dog, pig

this case—turning out to be situated in different positions depending on the points of view successively adopted: man differs from the animals by reason of his aptitude for ritual actions, but as sacrificial material he also belongs within their group. We have elsewhere cited the list of twenty-eight kinds of animals enumerated in the *Bhāgavata Purāṇa*: six whole-footed, nine cloven-hooved, and thirteen *pañcanakha*, symbolizing the twenty-eight types of infirmities of the intelligence and sense organs.[33] No additional examples are needed to conclude that in every case the principle of classification is simultaneously moral, juridical, and religious.

The best-known taxonomy in classical India—at least to those who have access to Sanskrit culture—is without doubt Book II of the *Amarakośa*, the treasury of names composed by Amarasiṃha (fourth century?). Studying it and reciting it by heart represented the necessary prerequisite for a good traditional education.[34] The words contained in the *Amarakośa* are grouped according to themes, and its table of contents more or less reproduces the order of the *trailokya*, the collection of "Three Worlds" ruled by the law of *dharma*. Book I deals with the heavenly and infernal worlds, the gods and the demons, the snakes, the waters (connected with the underworld), and the catalog of lotuses and fishes. But the internal hierarchies of Book II, which is devoted to the Earth, most particularly concern us here. The linguistic material relating to the Earth (and its inhabitants) is subdivided into ten sections as categorized here in table 16.

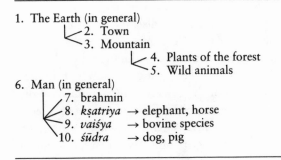

In the form of a number of locutions grouped around a single theme, the *earth* refers to the jungle, the polarity of the Indus and the Ganges, and the polarity between the Aryan heartland and its barbarian margins.[35] From this follows the fundamental division between inhabited space (the Town) and wild space (the Mountain). And in the mountains are found wild plants and wild animals.

Man refers to terms of kinship, names of diseases, and so on. Next comes the hierarchy of the four *varṇa*, or categories, of brahminic society. Here we find linguistic material relating to the cultivated or domesticated flora and fauna. The resulting classification is purely utilitarian and anthropocentric. The names of the domesticated animals are distributed between the social categories to which they are most directly useful: for the brahmins, the "sacrificial victim" in the section of the *kṣatriya*, the raising and training of elephants and horses, considered royal animals by virtue of their military importance; for the *vaiśya*, stock raising and agriculture, with the nomenclature of cereals, vegetables, and the bovine species; and finally, in the section devoted to the *śūdra* (the servant castes), the Caṇḍāla (untouchables) are surreptitiously slipped in together with the mountain tribes (barbarians) and trappers, usually associated with dogs and pigs.

The inventory of the wild flora, the "plants of the forest" *(vanauṣadhi)*, is so rich that even today it constitutes the major botanical manual used in the colleges of Ayurvedic medicine.[36] If the same cannot be said of the catalog of animals, which is also extremely detailed in the *Amarakośa*, that is only because materia medica of animal origin are no longer used. Amarasiṃha, the legendary author of the first of the treasuries *(kośa)*, is noted for his concern to be exhaustive, his interest in concrete details, and the systematic variety of his vocabulary—each term being surrounded by a converging series of "cognitive synonyms," as Anglo-Saxon logicians call them. He seems to have introduced a movement toward the secularization of Indian thought, but such a movement is immediately checked, disciplined, and molded into a religious taxonomy, where every being is set in its place in accordance with the *dharma* that governs the three worlds.

In a sense, the Ayurvedic nomenclatures could be classified as part of that same movement of thought toward the concrete and biogeographical realities, a movement immediately normalized and reabsorbed by the Tradition. But one radical innovation is added, the combinative system of the *lakṣaṇa*. I mean, all the architectonic procedures already described: the interplay of many facets, the substructions, the recurring hemistiches, the transformation of star-shaped structures (oppositions) into linear ones (gradations), etc. It is these procedures which make it possible to produce a layered taxonomy on a number of overlapping registers and which have led us, in our pursuit of a single theme, from the Jungle to the digestive fire, and from the distribution of animals in the savanna and the marshes to the unctuosity of meats sublimated through digestion.

All the other lists of animals and the scale of beings that one finds formulated elsewhere in Sanskrit literature, in the *Purāṇa*, dictionaries, and so on, remain rudimentary because they are all stereotyped (symbolic numbers: three *guṇa*, seven *grāmya*, etc.) and isolated (never combined together). The Ayurvedic catalog, in contrast, involves a line of reasoning (a combinative system, a metalanguage), the direct function of which is to exploit these lists, to make them more complex by opening up further underlying perspectives and to turn each name into the nucleus of a whole semantic constellation of attributes. To borrow Jean Bottéro's expression, this represents a "treatisizing" *(mise en traités)* of taxonomy.[37] It is not simply a collection of lists and divisions, an inventory, but a *śāstra*, a treatise, a pedagogical work. It is concerned not simply to catalog remedies but also to teach the judicious use of them. It is not merely a catalog of medicinal substances but a system of jurisprudence or medical deontology. The art of classification is absorbed by the art of healing.

Conclusion: Unctuosity Sublimed

Within a confining religious tradition, where all beings are hierarchically classed according to their aptitude for ritual, I have sought to concentrate on the most immediate physical realities, those most firmly anchored in the nature of the soil or the physiology of the human body: the savanna and the distribution of waters, the acacias, the territories of animals; then the saps, the juices that swell our organic liquids and the digestion that stimulates the ripening of plants. In Ayurvedic medicine, all of these themes appear to have constituted a start for secular thought but were then retrieved without delay, normalized, and subordinated to the overriding values of brahminism. The jungle, like the human body, provides a favored context for a conceptualization of the relations between the outside and the inside, between wildness and culture, and, at an even deeper level, for a dialectic between the pure and the impure. I have endeavored to show in this study that a reality—in itself physical and biogeographical—also has a social significance and ultimately becomes a theme for religious prescriptions. What attracted me to the concept of *jāṅgala*, the jungle, in the original meaning of the term, was that it set the highest value on the dry lands and in its connotations included the idea of their fertility and the rewards to be had from irrigation. It is wasteland but also fertile soil.

This specifically Hindu theme is not at all obvious in any of the texts; today it eludes us still, primarily for two reasons. The first one has to do with the history of modern sensibility. In our collective imagination, the luxuriance of the tropical forests has usurped the place of the arable lands, and we have invested our image of the jungle with all the charms of exoticism, of primitivism, of an alleged return to wild and virgin nature. In order to perceive that in ancient thought the jungle was something quite different, which held out promise for agriculture, it was necessary to reverse our perspective. That was the first stage in the enquiry.

But there is another reason why the originality of this ecological doctrine centered on the jungle was in danger of escaping us. It is masked by the all-pervading imagery which Ayurveda shares with so many other traditional sciences. Ancient medicine, whether in India, Greece, or China, stems from a limited number of images, everywhere essentially the same: water and fire (the polarity of contraries), the microcosm (the human body as an image of the world in miniature), the humors (pathogenic principles given concrete form in the mucus or serums of the body)—so many images not limited to any particular cultural area or to any particular province of knowledge. At this level of generality, differences become blurred, comparison (between, for example, Hindu medicine and Greek medicine) and the quest for origins (the Vedic or even the Iranian sources of Hindu medicine) may produce no more than commonplace remarks. What, instead, needed to be done was to mark out the differences by focusing the analysis on the points of anchorage of the Tradition (the texts) in geographical reality (the maps of distribution), in other words to produce a cartography, to locate the doctrine of the three soils within the actual land of the Indo-Gangetic plain. True, to impenitent Hippocratics like ourselves, Hindu medicine often purveys a *déjà-vu* impression; but at least the jungle is a specifically Hindu reality.

"A total social fact" is what we have called it. Implicit in the very land but at the same time endowed with an imaginary aura, it is one of those *polarities* which used to delight the eighteenth-century *philosophes* of Europe. The mystical opposition set up between the North and the South in the Europe of the Age of Enlightenment (Montesquieu, Abbé Dubos, etc.) is well known: it was expressed as a triumph for Holland (with its trade and its painting) over Italy, victory for the men of the North struggling against the cold, the marshes, and the mists; the people of Holland modified the climate by dint of their strenuous efforts of tree clearing, drainage, and dike building. Dutch trade flooded northern Europe with spices, sugar, coffee, tobacco, and chocolate. Thus, in his *Réflexions critiques sur la poésie et la peinture* (1719), Abbé Dubos reversed the polarity between the cold and the hot, the spirituous and the ethereal:

> In Holland, England, Poland, Germany and the North, the spirituous salts and juices of all this produce imbue the blood of the northern nations with a soul or, to use the language of the physicians, an ethereal oil which is not to be found in the foods of their own countries. These juices fill the blood of a man of the North with animal spirits formed in Spain and in the most burning of climates.[1]

The North steals the sun and the juices of the South, and eventually usurps its supremacy in the context of a normative ecology. The famous theory of climates in the philosophy of the Enlightenment is but an avatar of the very ancient polarity between Fire and Water, which polarity derives its topicality for different periods from the contemporary *geopolitical* context in which it is invoked: in modern Europe, the emergence of the Dutch bourgeoisie; in iron-age India, the eastward expansion of agriculture in the marshy Ganges valley. Etched into the fabric of discourse, immense facts of social history can thus be read. On the surface, however, these facts often appear cluttered with hackneyed, redundant, and apparently insignificant images, such as resisting the cold, ripening in the sun, drainage, irrigation, nourishing juices.

Let us return one last time to that fundamental polarity the Indians call the "Agni-Soma-ness" of the world, *agnī-ṣomīya-tva*, a compound of Vedic origin twice used by Suśruta in his treatise on medicine.[2] This relation of the world to Agni and Soma—the sun and the moon, the fire and the rain—leads to a division of beings into two groups. All things are necessarily of either *dry* or *unctuous* quality, either *hot* or *cold* energy, and this duality of creatures in turn leads to the division of treatments into two groups, the one *nutritive*, the other *depletive*.

Jean Filliozat has shown in his thesis that the semantic link between *rasa* (organic juice) and *soma* (principle or symbol of unctuosity) first appeared in the hymns of the *Ṛgveda*.[3] Similarly, the pulsation of the world, the alternation of the two half-yearly periods—that is, the emission of the *rasa* by the moon and their capture by the sun, which burns up all the unctuosity of beings—can clearly be viewed simply as a translation into ecological terms of what the *Brāhmaṇa* teaches on the level of myth: on every night of the new moon, "the sun sucks the moon dry."[4] Parallels to this primordial image of Agni-Soma, fire and water, are to be found in all systems of traditional medicine. But how was the transition made from that *theme* to a *system* of thoughts? How did reason exploit this imagistic material? That is what no comparative research can discover so long as it limits itself to comparisons between ready-made doctrines. We must concentrate upon the movement of thought at work, pluralizing images, multiplying points of view, and transforming a single basic theme into a whole series of avatars which then slip into place on various registers in the architecture of this knowledge. We must complicate the basic material in order to evolve the combinatorics, the system of markings, the *lakṣaṇa* system which we have attempted to analyze.

Needless to say, the dialectic of dry and marshy lands, the alliance between the Jungle and the water's edge, is an expression of the Agni-Soma-ness of the world. What is less commonplace is the architecture of Ayurvedic doctrine, with its layering of different levels of knowledge. Halfway up the levels of the doctrine, we have attempted to interpret not trite stereotypes after all but concrete, specialized concepts, which, upstream, form the basis for an abstract combinative system, while lower down they are rooted in the ground itself. One last time let us follow the links in this strange sequence which has led us from the jungle to sacrificial cooking.

In the beginning were the sun and water allied. Men built towns "in dry lands, where there was perennial water." The implication is that Soma is *in* the *jāṅgala*. The sun, which ripens the wheat in the granary plains—the *jāṅgala* at its most prized—, the sun starts off a long chain of cookings through which Soma is assimilated, and which are continued in the kitchen and the digestion. The lightness of *jāṅgala* meats is a distant consequence of this assimilation of Soma by Agni: their astringency tempers, sublimates, and refines the unctuosity they carry.

Of this unctuosity sublimed, there is no more telling illustration than the elaboration of milk in the organism. Its thick fluidity and unctuous whiteness liken milk to phlegm, semen, and *ojas*, the "vital fluid." Although it shares their properties: heavy, sweet, cold, unctuous, yet the milk of the cow, goat, and camel produces few fluxes. It is therefore fortifying, aphrodisiac, and an elixir of youth. But of all its eminent qualities, its purity must be stressed.

I do not mean to imply that milk (cow's milk) exercises strictly purifying functions in brahminic ritual, although these too are mentioned in the Ayurvedic treatises (*pāpmāpaha*, "it wards off sin.")[5] Indeed its other functions are reflected in its nature, in its physical purity. Charles Malamoud has noted the Vedic paradox of the cooked (milk) in the raw (cows). It is cooked by nature. "Whereas the cow is raw, the milk in her is cooked," says the *Śatapatha Brāhmaṇa*, "for it is the semen of Agni."[6] Expressed in medical terms, milk is the "pure essence of *rasa*" *(rasa-prasāda)*, the result of a sublimation of *rasa*. Suśruta teaches that the herbivores' milk consumed by man "is the pure essence of the *rasa* of all plants"; it is as if the organism of the cow, goat, or camel performed an initial cooking, sublimating the nourishing juices that they derive from the great herbarium of the world.[7] Milk, a kind of additional *dhātu* for the organism, is a consequence of the control exercised by the organism over the unctuosity by which it is nourished.

The channels and orifices of the body, and the cloudy or clear liquids which form the serums, mucus, humors, excretions, and secretions provide the most favored basis for a dialectic between the pure and the impure. Each of the organic cookings isolates a "pure part" *(prasāda)* from a coarse residue; each of the *dhātu*, or "tissues," has its counterpart, or its waste, in the series of impurities *(mala)*: sweat, urine, stools, spit, nail-cuttings, and cut hair. Other, more essential residues exist as well, for when wind, bile, or phlegm are disordered they flood the body, block the channels in their superabundance, and then become impurities *(mala)*. In a valuable ethnopsychiatric study, Morris Carstairs has shown how the drawing of a distinction between cold foods and hot foods reflected a desire to nourish the body without exciting the humors. In the opinion of the high-caste Hindus whom he questioned, some foods of *cold energy* (wheat flour, rice, milk, etc.) had the exceptional virtue of producing "a pure and intact semen."[8] Carstairs also drew attention to the extreme anxiety occasioned in India by spermatorrhoea. Any purulent oozing or spitting is assimilated to "wasted semen."[9] The pure and the impure thus take concrete form in the preservation or wastage of the organic fluids. Semen is a symbol. Spermatorrhoea, sometimes real, sometimes imagined, which gives rise to an almost ontological anxiety, is reminiscent of the Ayurvedic syndrome of royal consumption *(rājayakṣman)*, the wastage of all the vital unctuosity.

The division of treatments into two groups is prompted by a desire to produce a well-tempered unctuosity:

1) *bṛṃhaṇa* (nutritive): these treatments increase unctuosity; they can only be of the *saṃśamana*, "calming" type (taken orally, the patient does not have to take to his bed);

2) *laṅghana* (depletive): these treatments temper the unctuosity or

eliminate it; if they temper it, they are *saṃśamana* (calming); if they eliminate it (hospitalization), they are *saṃśodhana* ("purifying").

To describe this double nutritive and depletive action, Caraka naturally enough uses agricultural metaphors of irrigating and draining the body.[10] Grave disorders of the humors, a profuse dyscrasia, are cured by elimination. How can a flooded rice paddy be drained unless the ridge of earth surrounding it is breached? Same for the body! Draining is required. A moderate dyscrasia is cured by both fasting and calming remedies, "as one dries out a draining well by tossing in sand and ashes to complete the action of the sun and wind." A very slight excess in a humor is eliminated spontaneously by fasting "just as a little puddle of water evaporates in the sun and wind."

Appendix: Nomenclature of Animals

The translations suggested are intended only to afford an overall view of the contents of each category. They should be regarded as the results of an exploratory investigation rather than an exercise of categorical identification.

Unless otherwise indicated, the names given between inverted commas are taken from Ḍalhaṇa's commentary.

Abbreviations

D.	K. N. Dave, *Birds in Sanskrit Literature*, Delhi, 1985.
h.	hindi
Hora	Sunder Lal Hora, "Fish in the Rāmāyaṇa," *Journal of the Asiatic Society of Bengal, Letters*, XVIII (2), 1952, pp. 63–69; "Fish in the Sūtra and Smṛti Literature," ibid., XIX (2), 1953, pp. 63–77.
Mh.	M. Mayrhofer, *Kurzgefaßtes etymologisches Wörterbuch des Altindischen*, Heidelberg, 1956–1976.
onom.	onomatopoeia
RvD.	Raghu Vira and K. N. Dave, *Indian Scientific Nomenclature of Birds of India, Burma and Ceylon*, Nagpur, 1949 ("Sarasvati Vihara Series" 20).
Tn.	R. L. Turner, *A Comparative Dictionary of the Indo-Aryan Languages*, Oxford, 1966.

Raghu Vira and Dave have, in a sense, approached this problem from the wrong end, attempting to substitute a Sanskrit nomenclature for the Latin nomenclature in use in modern zoology. Their aim, inspired to a certain extent by a spirit of cultural nationalism, may be judged somewhat naive. They did however submit the ancient names to a meticulous review, and their use of them has on several occasions set me on the track of an interpretation which might otherwise have escaped me. New clues are provided by K. N. Dave in his more recent book.

Source: The catalog of meats (Suśruta, *sūtra* XLVI) translated above in chapter 4.

(1) JĀṄGALA

(1.1) **jaṅghāla** (which have legs)

1	eṇa	black antelope
2	hariṇa	antelope
3	ṛkṣa	nilgai
4	kuraṅga	four-horned antelope
5	karāla	musk-deer
6	kṛtamāla	?
7	śarabha	?
8	śvadaṃṣṭrā	muntjak?
9	pṛṣata	spotted deer
10	cāruṣkara	gazelle?
11	mṛgamātṛkā	?

(1.2) **viṣkira** (which scatter), cf. table in D., p. 269

1	lāva	quail, partridge, h. *lawā (Perdiculata asiatica)*
2	tittiri	partridge, francolin, h. *tītar (Francolinus* sp.)
3	kapiñjala	grey partridge, "gauratittiri" *(F. pondicerianus)*
4	vartīra	quail, h. *baṭer* (*Coturnix* sp.)
5	vartika	quail
6	vartaka	quail
7	naptṛkā	?
8	vārtīka	quail
9	cakora	h. *cakor (Alectoris graeca)*
10	kalaviṅka	sparrow
11	mayūra	peacock
12	krakara	swamp partridge, "kayar" *(Francolinus gularis)*, Mh. *kṛkara*
13	upacakra	?
14	kukkuṭa	cock (*Galloperdix* sp.)
15	sāraṅga	black and white cuckoo, "cātaka" *(Clamator jacobinus)*
16	śatapatra	woodpecker, "dārvāghāṭa" (Mh.)
17	kutittiri	partridge
18	kuruvāhaka	? "kurukuruka" (onom., cf. *kṛkavāku*, cock)
19	yavālaka	?

(1.3) **pratuda** (which peck)

1	kapota	pigeon
2	pārāvata	pigeon, h. *parewā*

3 bhṛṅgarāja	racket-tailed drongo (*Dicrurus* sp.)
4 parabhṛta	koel, Indian cuckoo, "kokila"
5 koyaṣṭika	lapwing (*Vanellus* sp.) Mh. and D., p. 358
6 kuliṅga	sparrow
7 gṛhakuliṅga	domesticated sparrow
8 gokṣveḍaka	heron?, "gonarda" (lows like an ox)
9 ḍiṇḍimāṇavaka	barbet (*Xantholaema* sp.); Mh. *ḍiḍimānaka*; "which makes a loud drumming noise"; RvD., p. 256, D., p. 124: resembles a drummer
10 śatapatraka	= 1.2.16
11 mātṛnindaka	? "putrarañjaka" (cf. Mh. *mātṛvāhakā*, bat)
12 bhedāśin	? "bhekāśin" (eats frogs)
13 śuka	parrot
14 sārikā	h. *mainā* (*Acridotheres* sp.); Tn. *madana*, bat
15 valgulī	bat (Tn. *vālguḍa*)
16 giriśā	hill partridge, "girivartikā"
17 laṭvā	? (Mh. pali *laṭukikā*); "pheñjātaka," and Cakra. on Caraka (*sūtra* XXVII, 51) "pheñcāka", cf. Mh. *pheñcaka* and *phiṅgaka*, Tn. *phiṅgaka*, racket-tailed drongo
18 laṭṭūṣaka	?
19 sugṛhā	weaver bird (*Ploceus* sp.), "with a yellow head," "vayā," h. *bayā* (Tn.); RvD., p. 176, D., p. 88: elaborate nests
20 khañjarīṭa	wagtail (*Matacilla* sp.)
21 hārīta	green pigeon, h. *hariyā*; "haritāla," h. *hāriyal*
22 dātyūha	hawk-cuckoo, "rāhak," Cakra. on Suśruta "dāhak" (h.), on Caraka "ḍāhuka"; RvD., p. 374, D., pp. 293–297

(1.4) **guhāśaya** (which have a lair)

1 siṃha	lion
2 vyāghra	tiger
3 vṛka	wolf
4 tarakṣu	hyena
5 ṛkṣa	bear (#1.1.3)
6 dvīpin	panther
7 mārjāra	cat
8 śṛgāla	jackal
9 mṛgervāruka	?

(1.5) **prasaha** (carnivorous)

1 kāka	crow = (75b) vāyasa
2 kaṅka	heron?; cf. Tn. gujarātī *kā̃kṛũ* "bird of prey"; in epics, it haunts the battlefields
3 kurara	osprey (= 2.2.5)
4 cāṣa	jay

5	bhāsa	lammergeier
6	śaśaghātin	falcon; Tn. *śaśāda, śaśādana*
7	ulūka	owl
8	cilli	merlin
9	śyena	eagle, falcon, "garuḍa"
10	gṛdhra	vulture

(1.6) **parṇamṛga** (tree dwellers)

1	madgu	? (= 2.2.15)
2	mūṣika	tree rat *(Vandeleuria oleracea)* (#1.7.12)
3	vṛkṣaśāyikā	squirrel
4	avakuśa	monkey, "golāṅgula" *(Macaca silenus)*
5	pūtighāsa	civet cat, "sugandhivṛṣaṇa" (perfume glands)
6	vānara	monkey

(1.7) **bileśaya** (which have a burrow)

1	śvāvidh	porcupine
2	śalyaka	porcupine
3	godhā	varan lizard
4	śaśa	hare
5	vṛṣadaṃśa	cat, "mārjāra"
6	lopāka	fox, jackal
7	lomaśakarṇa	?
8	kadalī	?
9	mṛgapriyaka	snake, "gonasa" (Tn.)
10	ajagara	snake
11	sarpa	snake
12	mūṣika	rat, mouse (#1.6.2)
13	nakula	mongoose
14	mahābabhru	mongoose

(1.8) **grāmya** (domesticated)

1	aśva	horse
2	aśvatara	mule
3	go	ox
4	khara	donkey
5	uṣṭra	camel
6	basta	goat = chagala (verse 87)
7	urabhra	sheep
8	medaḥpucchaka	sheep, "dumba" *(fat-tailed)*

(2) ĀNŪPA

(2.1) **kūlacara** (which live on the banks)

1	gaja	elephant
2	gavaya	gaur
3	mahiṣa	buffalo
4	ruru	barasingha

5	camara	yak
6	sṛmara	?
7	rohita	? (#2.5.1)
8	varāha	boar
9	khaḍgin	rhinoceros
10	gokarṇa	?
11	kālapucchaka	?
12	udra	otter
13	nyaṅku	?
14	araṇyagavaya	= gaur

(2.2) **plava** (which float)

1	haṃsa	goose (*Anser* sp., Anseriforms: swan. . .)
2	sārasa	crane, *sāras* (h.) crane *(Grus antigone)*
3	krauñca	crane, demoiselle crane *(Anthropoides virgo)*
4	cakravāka	sheldrake, brahminy duck *(Tadorna ferruginea)*
5	kurara	(= 1.5.3)
6	kādamba	*Anser indicus* or *Anser anser* ("black")
7	kāraṇḍava	goose
8	jīvañjīvaka	?
9	baka	egret *(Egretta alba)* or white ibis, D., p. 386
10	balākā	heron, egret, "bagulī," h. *bagulā* (Tn. *baka*)
11	puṇḍarīka	? (Caraka: puṇḍarīkākṣa, cf. mallikākṣa)
12	plava	pelican, "prasevakagala" (sack beneath beak)
13	śarārīmukha	heron; Tn. *śarāḍi*
14	nandīmukha	comb-duck *(Sarkidiornis melanotos)*?; cf. RvD., p. 437, D., p. 448 (protuberance on beak); "āṭī" (Mh. Tn. *āti*); Suśruta, *sūtra* VIII, 3 (āṭīmukha)
15	madgu	cormorant, "jalakāka"
16	utkrośa	sea eagle (*Haliaetus* sp.)
17	kācākṣa	?
18	mallikākṣa	pochard (*Nyroca rufa*); RvD., p. 447, D., p. 458 (white iris)
19	śuklākṣa	pochard
20	puṣkaraśāyikā	?
21	konālaka	? (Tn. *kuṇāla*)
22	ambukukkuṭikā	rail (Rallidae); RvD., p. 370, D., p. 292
23	megharāva	?
24	śvetavārala	Indian courser; D., p. 333

(2.3) **kośastha** (which have a shell)

1	śaṅkha	conch (*Turbinella* sp.)
2	śaṅkhanaka	?
3	śukti	oyster
4	śambūka	conch (Tn.)
5	bhallūka	cowrie, "kapardaka"

(2.4) **pādin** (which have feet)

1	kūrma	tortoise
2	kumbhīra	crocodile, gavial; "ghaḍiyāla" = h. *gharyāl*
3	karkaṭaka	crab
4	kṛṣṇakarkaṭaka	black crab
5	śiśumāra	crocodile *(Planista gangetica)*

(2.5a) **nādeyā matsyāḥ** (freshwater fish)

1	rohita	carp *(Labeo rohita)*
2	pāṭhīna	silurus, catfish *(Wallago attu)*
3	pāṭalā	?
4	rājīva	mullet? (= 2.5.21)
5	varmi	?
6	gomatsya	?
7	kṛṣṇamatsya	?
8	vāguñjara	?
9	murala	? (Mh. Tn.)
10	sahasradaṃṣṭra	*bāchchā* catfish; "mahāpāṭhīna" (cf. Hora, p. 73: comm. of Kṣīrasvāmin on *Amarakośa*)

(2.5b) **sāmudrā matsyāḥ** (marine fish)

11	timi	(Hora: *shark* rather than *whale*; fabulous)
12	timiṅgila	(fabulous)
13	kuliśa	?
14	pākamatsya	?
15	nirula	?
16	nandivāralaka	?
17	makara	(fabulous)
18	gargara	Mh. Tn. *Pimelodus gagora*
19	candraka	?
20	mahāmīna	Mh. *mīna* (Dravidian origin)
21	rājīva	mullet *(Mugil corsula)*

Notes

INTRODUCTION: THE SAVORS OF THE SOIL

1. *Laws of Manu*, V, 29.

2. The only precise and trustworthy diagram is that by Pierre Legris, *La végétation de l'Inde: Écologie et flore* (Pondicherry, 1963), map 19. We might also mention Harry G. Champion and S. K. Seth, *A Revised Survey of the Forest Types of India*, Delhi, 1968, a colored plate. O. H. K. Spate & A. T. A. Learmonth, *India and Pakistan*, 3d ed. (London, 1967) reproduce an old version of Champion (1936) and provide a valuable summary of his nomenclature. The very approximative schema by George B. Schaller in his *The Deer and the Tiger: A Study of Wildlife in India* (Chicago, 1967), p. 21, is useful by reason of the way it is employed to demonstrate an animal ecology.

3. *Dhanvan* or *maru*, "the desert, the arid lands." Caraka very often substitutes *dhanvan* and occasionally *maru* (e.g., *sūtra* XXV, 40) for their synonym *jāṅgala*.

4. Spate and Learmonth, *India and Pakistan*, p. 139: "Malaria, 1938."

5. Conclusions of the Académie cited by Gaston Bachelard, *La formation de l'esprit scientifique* (Paris, 1938), p. 125.

6. Ibid., p. 126.

I: THE JUNGLE AND THE WATER'S EDGE

1. O. H. K. Spate and A. T. A. Learmonth, *India and Pakistan*, 3d ed. (London, 1967), pp. 537–539.

2. James Tod, *Annals and Antiquities of Rajasthan* (1829; reprint, Lon-

don, 1950), vol. I, p. 1 ("the sandy tracts south of the Sutledge, termed *Jangul dés*"); and Charlotte Vaudeville, *Les Duhā de Ḍhola-Mārū* (*Une ancienne ballade du Rajasthan*) (Pondicherry, 1962), p. 19ff. J. E. Schwartzberg, *A Historical Atlas of South Asia* (Chicago, 1978), p. 190a2: *Jāṅgaladeśa*, a medieval principality; given pp. 32a and 137a (where the long *ā* is missing).

3. A deciduous tree (dry deciduous series), very common in the plains, particularly in sandy terrains, along the banks of dried-up watercourses.

4. Hindi name (*babūl*) for the *Acacia arabica.*

5. Victor Jacquemont, *Voyage dans l'Inde pendant les années 1828 à 1832* (Paris, 1841–1844), vol. III, p. 30.

6. *Nirvārideśa* (Śabdaratnavalī), *jalanirmuktadeśa* (Viśvaprakāśa), *nirjanasthāna* (Medinī, Hemacandra, Trikāṇḍaśeṣa). Cf. Anundoram Borooah, *Nānārthasaṅgraha* (1884; reprint, Gauhati, 1969).

7. The confusion is an ancient one, as proven by the compound *Jaṅgaltarā'ī*, Jungle-Terry (the land of the Santal) attested as early as the eighteenth century, in H. Yule and A. C. Burnell, *Hobson-Jobson* (1886); reprint, London, (1968).

8. Harry G. Champion and S. K. Seth, *A Revised Survey of the Forest Types of India* (Delhi, 1968), p. 172 (Eastern wet alluvial grassland).

9. J. T. Platts, *A Dictionary of Urdu, Classical Hindi and English* (Oxford, 1930), pp. 374a and 392a.

10. The jungles of the Rajmahal Hills between Bengal and Chota Nagpur, cf. *Hobson-Jobson*, in the article "Jungle-Mahals."

11. V. Jacquemont, *Correspondance de V. Jacquemont avec sa famille et plusieurs de ses amis pendant son voyage dans l'Inde* (Paris, 1833), vol. I, pp. 143–144. This is to be compared with Modave's accounts of his travels from Bengal to Delhi, which would take back to 1774 the first occurrence of the word *djongol* in French: "There are no forests in Bengal. One can only see there open spaces abandoned, covered in strong, thick grasses, studded with a few heathers, which in multiplying will eventually form fairly bushy thickets. Djongols is the name for these unpleasant deserts." *Voyage en Inde du Comte de Modave, 1773–1776*, ed. Jean Deloche (Paris, 1971), p. 120; see also pp. 188–189 (fallow land, dry sandy moors).

12. Caraka, *sūtra* XXVII, 332–333, 336.

13. Cakrapāṇi. *ad* Caraka, *sūtra* XXVII, 331–332.

14. Ḍalhaṇa *ad* Suśruta, *sūtra* XLVI, 138.

15. Vāgbhaṭa, *sūtra* I, 23.

16. Caraka, *vimāna* VIII, 84 (2).

17. Caraka, *vimāna* VIII, 75.

18. Cakrapāṇi. *ad* Suśruta, *sūtra* XXXV, 39.

19. Caraka, *sūtra* VI, 50, and the commentary of Cakrapāṇi.

20. Caraka, *vimāna* VIII, 118.

21. Ḍalhaṇa *ad* Suśruta, *sūtra* XXXV, 39.

22. Suśruta, *sūtra* XXXV, 42–47.

23. Cakrapāṇi. *ad* Suśruta, *sūtra* XXXV, 44–45.

24. Ḍalhaṇa, ibid.

25. Vāgbhaṭa, *sūtra* I, 23–24 and the commentary of Parameśvara (Kottayam, 1950); same remarks in the *Hṛdayabodhikā* and the *Hṛdyā*, well-known commentaries in Kerala.

26. Caraka, *kalpa* I, 8. "Which abounds in free space" (*paryākāśabhūyiṣṭha*) is the equivalent of Suśruta's "free and flat" (*ākāśasama*), an open, even terrain. Cakrapāṇi. *ad* Suśruta, ibid., glosses "*gahana*" as "forest"; Ḍalhaṇa, ibid., proposes understanding *gahana* (the end of the compound) as "made inaccessible by" (the abundance of waters and the uneven ground) *etaiḥ kṛtvā gahanībhūta*. The word *gahana*, which Suśruta and Caraka apply to *ānūpa* country, denotes the dense (vegetation) and the tangled (thickets).

27. Cakrapāṇi. *ad* Suśruta, *sūtra* XXXV, 43: "The text speaks of the justified preeminence of *sādhāraṇa* in the series of the three places" (*trividhadeśe sopapattikaṃ sādhāraṇasya śreṣṭhatvam āha*). And further on: "hence Caraka: the *sādhāraṇa* place is the best" (*ataś carakaḥ-śreṣṭhaḥ sādhāraṇo deśaḥ*); this is quite inaccurate, for the expression does not appear at all in the Corpus of Caraka.

28. Caraka, *sūtra* XXV, 40.

29. Cakrapāṇi. *ad* Caraka, *sūtra* XXVI, 31.

30. We shall be returning in chapter 5 (infra, p. 129) to this notion which is common to both India and Greece in connection with pharmaceutical coctions.

31. Caraka, *vimāna* I, 22 (6).

32. Caraka, *vimāna* VIII, 125.

33. Galen, *On the best sect, at Thrasybulae*, xxxv; Charles Daremberg, *Oeuvres de Galien* (Paris, 1854–1856), vol. II, p. 451.

34. Galen, *On sects to students*, vi; Daremberg, *Oeuvres de Galien*, II, p. 384.

35. Vāgbhaṭa, *sūtra* XIII, 36; cf. Francis Zimmermann, "*Ṛtu-sātmya*, le cycle des saisons et le principe d'appropriation," *Puruṣārtha* (Paris: Centre d'études de l'Inde et de l'Asie du Sud, 1975) 2: 87–105. English translation in "*Ṛtu-sātmya*: The seasonal cycle and the principle of appropriateness," *Social Science and Medicine* XIV-B (1980): 99–106.

36. Vāgbhaṭa, *sūtra* XII, 24–25.

37. Cf. Claus Vogel, "Die Jahreszeiten im Spiegel der altindischen Literatur," *Zeitschrift der deutschen Morgenländischen Gesellschaft* 121 (1971): 284–326.

38. Caraka, *cikitsā* III, 42–47; cf. G. J. Meulenbeld, *The Mādhavanidāna and its Chief Commentary, Chapters 1–10* (Leiden, 1974), pp. 136 and 186 n. 232.

II: POPULATING THE PLAINS

1. Jean Antoine Dubois, *Moeurs, institutions et cérémonies des peuples de l'Inde* (Paris, 1825), vol. II, p. 228. He also says "these solitaries" (pp. 241, 254).

2. Charles Malamoud, "La brique percée (Sur le jeu du vide et du plein dans l'Inde brâhmanique)," *Nouvelle revue de psychanalyse* 11 (1975): 205–222.

3. Caraka, *vimāna* III, 47–48. Cf. Vāgbhaṭa, *śārīra* III, 79.

4. *Laws of Manu*, VII, 69. P. V. Kane, *History of Dharmaśāstra*, vol. III, 2d ed. (Poona, 1973), p. 132 n. 176 cites the verse in question from the commentary of Kullūka. The last quarter reads: "it overflows with cereals," where Caraka notes: "diseases there are very few."

5. *Yājñavalkyasmṛti*, I, 320.

6. E. W. Hopkins, *India Old and New* (New York, 1901), pp. 230–231. Aubréville's work is cited everywhere, but for India, see Pierre Legris, *La végétation de l'Inde: Écologie et flore* (Pondicherry, 1963), p. 76 (lower rainfalls) and p. 341 (bushes are burned every year).

7. Chāgaleya cited in Kane, *History of Dharmaśāstra*, 2d ed. III (Poona, 1974), pp. 129–130 n. 288 (means of subsistence in periods of famine).

8. *Mitākṣarā ad Yājñavalkyasmṛti*, III, 42: living by selling wild herbs and burning fuel collected in the mountains.

9. I retained Kipling's spellings: Seeonee (Seoni), Waingunga (Wainganga).

10. H. G. Champion and S. K. Seth, *A Revised Survery of the Forest Types of India* (Delhi, 1968), p. 183 (dry teak forest, Seoni division) and p. 220 (dry bamboo brakes). The bamboo brakes are indicated with a symbol on the *Wainganga* sheet of the International Vegetation Map (Pondicherry, 1971).

11. Hindi name *(karelā)* for *Momordica charantia.*

12. Legris, *La végétation*, p. 210.

13. These calculations are considered in greater detail in both books coauthored by Bridget and Raymond Allchin. These are *The Birth of Indian Civilization* (Harmondsworth, 1968), p. 211; and *The Rise of Civilization in India and Pakistan* (Cambridge, 1982), p. 318 ff.

14. Allchin and Allchin, *Rise of Civilization*, p. 320.

15. The date of Manu: R. Lingat, *Les sources du droit dans le système traditionnel de l'Inde* (Paris, 1967), pp. 109–113. The date of the *Arthaśāstra*: L. Renou, in L. Renou and J. Filliozat, *L'Inde classique* (Paris-Hanoi, 1953), Vol. II, §§1597–1598. Dates of Suśruta and Caraka: J. Filliozat, ibid., §§ 1635, 1647; and G. J. Meulenbeld, *The Mādhavanidāna and its Chief Commentary, Chapters 1–10* (Leiden, 1974), Appendix 2.

16. Burton Stein, "Integration of the agrarian system of South India," in R. E. Frykenberg, *Land Control and Social Structure in Indian History* (Madison, 1969), pp. 175–216. Burton Stein, *Peasant, State and Society in Medieval South India* (New Delhi, 1980) and in particular pp. 73–76.

17. *Arthaśāstra*, II, *24*, 5. Cf. II, 24, 23.

18. *Arthaśāstra*, VII, *11*, 3. Classic opposition between land watered solely by the rain (*devamātṛka*) and irrigated land (*nadīmatṛka*); cf. Kane, *History of Dharmaśāstra*, III, p. 133.

19. *Arthaśāstra*, III, *9*, 25, 33.

20. *Arthaśāstra*, II, 2, 7.

21. *Arthaśāstra*, II, *28*, 17, 24; IV, *3*, 6.

22. O. H. K. Spate and A. T. A. Learmonth, *India and Pakistan*, 3d ed. (London, 1967), p. 518 ("the immediate riverain or *bet* lands"). I have not identified "bar" and "bet" but J. T. Platts (*A Dictionary of Urdu, Classical*

Hindi and English [Oxford, 1930], p. 143a) lists *barr* as "dry land, desert" (of Arabic origin).

23. Spate and Learmonth, pp. 521–522.

24. Ibid., p. 520. See "Jangali" (indexed) in W. Crooke, *The Tribes and Castes of the North-Western Province and Oudh* (Calcutta, 1896; reprint, Delhi, 1975) and in particular Vol. IV, pp. 17–18. (The Musahar are divided into the Jangali and the Bearers-of-palanquins).

25. R. P. Kangle, *The Kauṭilīya Arthaśāstra*, 2d ed. (Bombay, 1972), note *ad* II, 2, 5. Charles Malamoud, Lectures 1972–73, at the École Pratique des Hautes Etudes, Vth Section; and "Village et forêt dans l'idéologie de l'Inde brahmanique," *Archives européennes de sociologie* 17 (1976): 3–20.

26. *Arthaśāstra*, II, 2: The use of the *bhūmicchidra*, literally, "gaps in the land," uncultivable zones. There is a distinction between *vana*, "wood" (woody material), and "forest" (multitude of trees), and *araṇya*, "desert" (uncultivated, wild), and "forest" (trees).

27. Vāgbhaṭa, *sūtra* VI, 43ff. (in order); Caraka, *sūtra* XXVII, 35ff. (inversions).

28. Cakrapāṇi. *ad* Caraka, *sūtra* XXVII, 56: two kinds of *prasaha*, carnivorous (tiger, falcon, etc.) and noncarnivorous (ox, etc.). Vāgbhaṭa, *sūtra* VI, 55: "The two middle groups *(bileśaya* and *prasaha)* count as *sādhāraṇa*," but further on, 61: "(The last five) groups, from *bileśaya* onward, are increasingly heavy" (so the *prasaha* are grouped with the *ānūpa*).

29. Suśruta, *sūtra* XLVI, 90–92.

30. Ḍalhaṇa, ibid.

31. M. S. Mani, *Ecology and Biogeography in India*, "Monographiae biologicae" 23 (The Hague, 1974), pp. 629–630.

32. George B. Schaller, *The Deer and the Tiger: A Study of Wildlife in India* (Chicago, 1967), p. 150. The antelope enters the monsoon forest following in the tracks of the "slash-and-burn cultivators."

33. *Śatapatha Brāhmaṇa*, VI, 4, 1, 9 (trans. Eggeling, Vol. III, p. 216). The Sacrifice fleeing from the gods wanders abroad in the form of a black antelope from which they will take the skin, ibid. (Eggeling), Vol. I, pp. 23–24.

34. On these links in ritual and mythology (for example, the two aspects of Rudra, the hunter of *mṛga*, and master of sacrificial victims), see Madeleine Biardeau and Charles Malamoud, *Le sacrifice dans l'Inde ancienne* (Paris, 1976), pp. 94–95. We shall be returning to this theme from a different angle in chapter 7.

35. The expression (which has become a truism) is Pierre Vidal-Naquet's, "Chasse et sacrifice dans l'Orestie d'Eschyle," reprinted in J.-P. Vernant and P. Vidal-Naquet, *Mythe et tragédie en Grèce ancienne* (Paris, 1973).

36. *Manu*, II, 23; *Yājñavalkya*, I, 2 (and the commentary).

37. *Arthaśāstra*, II, 2, 3.

38. A pictorial style that flourished at the end of the eighteenth century in the Himalayan valleys of the Punjab. Illustrations of this same theme in M. S. Randhawa, *Kangra Valley Painting* (Delhi, 1954), pl. 15 ("The Lament of Separation," Captain Sunder Singh collection); Randhawa, *Kangra Paintings on Love* (New Delhi, 1962), fig. 61 ("The Love-Lorn Lady," Guler, Punjab Museum, Patiala).

III: THE INDUS AND THE GANGES

1. Pierre Birot, *Les régions naturelles du globe* (Paris, 1970), p. 255.

2. O. H. K. Spate and A. T. A. Learmonth (*India and Pakistan*, 3d ed. [London 1967]), p. 43 cite A. Geddes and pp. 534–538 compile the controversial evidence for the "lost Sarasvati" and the "capture" of the Yamuna by the hydrographic system of the Ganges.

3. Suśruta, *sūtra* XLV, 37–39.

4. *Bhāvaprakāśa*, Varanasi, 1969 ("Kāśī Skt. Ser."), vol. I, *vārivarga*, 26–31.

5. Suśruta, *sūtra* XLV, 31ff.

6. Caraka (*sūtra* XXVII, 214) and Vāgbhaṭa (*sūtra* V, 13) appear to dissociate rivers from the series: lake-reservoir-*etc*. But Suśruta includes them all in the same series: river-lake-*etc*.

7. Caraka, *sūtra* XXVII, 209–212.

8. *Malava, Pāriyātra, Vindhya*, and *Sahya* are four of the seven mountain ranges that mark the frontiers of the land of the Bharata: H. H. Wilson, *The Vishnu Purana*, 3d ed. (Calcutta, 1961) I, 3, p. 141 n. 2; P. V. Kane, *History of Dharmaśāstra*, Vol. IV (Poona, 1953), p. 560n. The Himalayas are not a part of this series.

9. Suśruta, *sūtra* XLV, 21.

10. Ḍalhaṇa, ibid.

11. Cf. Kane, *History of Dharmaśāstra*, Vol. IV; D. C. Sircar, *Studies in the Geography of Ancient and Mediaeval India*, 2d ed. (Delhi, 1971).

12. Opposition formulated by A. Borooah, *Ancient Geography of India* (1877; reprint, Gauhati, 1971); and F. E. Pargiter, *Mārkaṇḍeya Purāṇa* (Calcutta, 1904), p. 354.

13. Suśruta, *sūtra* XLV, 23 (*Maru*, plural: the Marwar).

14. Suśruta, *sūtra* XLV, 21.

15. Cakrapāṇi. *ad* Caraka, *sūtra* XXVII, 209–212.

16. Cakrapāṇi. *ad* Suśruta, *sūtra* XLV, 21 (29 in the Jaipur edition).

17. Caraka, *kalpa* I, 8.

18. Balwant Singh and K. C. Chunekar, *Glossary of Vegetable Drugs in Bṛhattrayī* (Varanasi, 1972).

19. Legris, *La végétation*, p. 387.

20. *Bṛhatsaṃhitā*, LIV, 10–11.

21. See Singh and Chunekar, *Glossary of Vegetable Drugs*; P. V. Sharma, *Indian Medicine in the Classical Age* (Varanasi, 1972).

22. From a geographical point of view—rather than the pharmacognostic one which I am adopting here—I accept the classic identification which is, furthermore, confirmed by the Hindi name *asan* for the *Terminalia*. Note, however, that *Pterocarpus marsupium* is always present in the series which includes *Anogeissus* and *Terminalia*: Legris, *La végétation*, pp. 236–240; leaflet for the *Rajasthan* sheet of the International Vegetation Map (Pondicherry, 1972), pp. 79 and 81. Thus, despite the uncertainty surrounding the interpretation of one particular term, Caraka's list remains coherent overall.

23. The genera *Shorea* and *Dipterocarpus* belong to the same *Diptercarpaceae* family but have very different ecologies.

24. They are planted at the approaches to villages and temples. But *Ficus bengalensis* also appears growing wild as an epiphyte on ruined tombs and buildings.

25. Legris, *La végétation*, p. 330.

26. James Tod, *Annals and Antiquities of Rajasthan* (1829, reprint, London, 1950), I: 547–549.

27. Leaflet for the *Rajasthan* sheet (Pondicherry, 1972), p. 79ff. (*Anogeissus* and *Terminalia* series).

28. Regional variations: the *śamī* is *Acacia suma* in Bengal, but *Prosopis spicigera* in Rajasthan, and *Dichrostachys cinerea* in Tamilnad.

29. J. D. Hooker, *A Sketch of the Flora of British India* (1903), published in 1907 in the *Imperial Gazeteer of India*, 3d ed.

30. W. T. Blanford, "The Distribution of Vertebrate Animals in India, Ceylon and Burma," *Philosophical Transactions of the Royal Society of London* (B), 194 (1901), pp. 335–436.

31. Ḍalhaṇa *ad* Suśruta, *sūtra* XLVI, 54.

32. Cakrapāṇi. *ad* Caraka, *sūtra* XXVII, 45–46.

33. Vāgbhaṭa, *sūtra* VI, 43; *Amarakośa*, II, 5, 10; etc.

34. The Bombay editions give *ṛkṣa*, the Jaipur edition *ṛṣya*. Similarly, Vāgbhaṭa, *sūtra* VI, 43: *ṛkṣa* (Bombay edition), *ṛṣya* (Kottayam edition). The matter was conclusively settled by Ronald E. Emmerick, "The Sanskrit Text of the *Siddhasāra*," *Bulletin of the School of Oriental and African Studies* 34 (1971): 112. Similarly, one should read "antelope" in Macdonnell and Keith, *Vedic Index*, I, p. 463, line 4. Ḍalhaṇa *ad sūtra* XLVI, 54: *ṛkṣo nīlāṇḍaḥ "roru" iti prasiddhaḥ* is illuminated by Ḍalhaṇa *ad nidāna* V, 7: *ṛṣyo nīlāṇḍaḥ "roru" iti prasiddhaḥ / anye "ṛkṣa" iti paṭhanti / ṛkṣo "rīch" iti loke /* "The antelope with blue-black testicles is known to be [*rojh*]; others read *ṛkṣa* (variant); *ṛkṣa* is *rich* in ordinary speech." There is a homonymy between: *ṛkṣa* = *ṛṣya* "antelope," the Hindi name for which is *rojh*, and *ṛkṣa* "bear," the Hindi name for which is *rīch*.

35. Appears similarly in the *Bṛhatsaṃhitā*, Varanasi, 1968 ("Sarasvatī Bhavan Series"), LXIV, 7: *kṛṣṇāṇḍa* (applied to the goat) and the gloss *asitavṛṣaṇa*, "which has black testicles."

36. *Bhāvaprakāśa*, I, *māṃsavarga* 11 and 44.

37. R. L. Turner, *A Comparative Dictionary of the Indo-Aryan Languages* (Oxford, 1966).

38. The *śvadaṃṣṭra*, etymologically "which has teeth like a dog," is "very vicious": the muntjak (barking deer) snaps violently at the dogs which pursue it (W. T. Blanford, *The Fauna of British India*, Vol. I, *Mammalia* [London, 1888], p. 534).

39. Blanford, ibid., p. 527.

40. Raghu Vira, K. N. Dave, and Lokesh Chandra (*Indian Scientific Nomenclature of the Mammals of India, Burma and Ceylon* [Nagpur, 1953], p. xxvii) point out the onomatopoeia; J. T. Platts (*A Dictionary of Urdu, Classical Hindi and English* [Oxford, 1930], p. 434b) explains the Hindi *cikārā* in similar fashion. Another hypothesis is that of a Dravidian origin (Burrow, in M. Mayrhofer, *Kurzgefaβtes etymologisches Wörterbuch des Altindischen* [Heidelberg, 1956–1976], *s.v.* "chikkāra"). The *Rājanighaṇṭu* among others (Poona,

1896, "Anandāśrama Skt. Ser."), p. 270, associates *jaṅghāla* and *śrīkārin*.

41. Ḍalhaṇa suggests a pseudoetymology: *cāruṣkaś cāruśarīraḥ* "with a charming (*cāru*) body." But we should remember the ambiguity of *śrī-kārin*: (meat) "which fattens" (according to Monier-Williams). Is it not rather (an alarmed gazelle) "which utters *shhr*"? Similarly *cāruṣ-* might well be an onomatopoeia subsequently rationalized.

42. Schaller, *The Deer and the Tiger*, p. 43.

43. S. H. Prater, *The Book of Indian Animals*, 3d ed. (Bombay, 1971), pp. 277–278.

44. *Raghuvaṃśa*, II, 17.

45. Ḍalhaṇa: *ondraḥ pānīyabiḍālaḥ "odana" iti loke*. Cf. Hindi *ūd* "otter" (Turner *udra*). The image of the "water-cat" passed into Hindi *(ūd-bilā'o)*.

46. In India, the yak is indigenous only in northern Ladak (Blanford, *Mammalia*, p. 491). It is true that it is more widespread in its domesticated (hybrid) varieties.

47. Pierre-P. Grassé, *Traité de zoologie*, Vol. XVII, *Mammifères* (Paris, 1955), fascicule 1, p. 656. Others include the four-horned antelope and the nilgai among the *Bovinae* but distinguish them from the *Bovini*: See J. R. Ellerman and T. C. S. Morrison-Scott, *Checklist of Palaearctic and Indian Mammals, 1758 to 1946* (London, 1951).

48. In my view, the nuanced use of *mṛga* (Suśruta, *sūtra* XLVI, 54) and *paśu* (ibid., 94) is significant, although in both cases "quadruped" is the only translation possible. Cf. *Amarakośa*, II, 5, 11: *paśu* "quadruped," *paśujāti* "the quadruped class."

49. Ḍalhaṇa *ad sūtra* XLVI, 94.

50. Prater, *The Book of Indian Animals*, p. 289; Schaller, *The Deer and the Tiger*, p. 97.

51. Schaller, ibid. Cf. M. S. Mani, *Ecology and Biogeography in India*, "Monographiae biologicae" 23 (The Hague, 1974), p. 348, but figure 35, "Distribution of the *barasingha*," is incorrect: it situates the *duvauceli* in Tibet!

52. F. J. Simoons and E. S. Simoons, *A Ceremonial Ox of India: The Mithan in Nature, Culture and History* (Madison, 1968), p. 8.

53. Jacques Dupuis, "Coutumes alimentaires, sociétés et économies: le cas de la répartition de la consommation du lait en Asie tropicale," *Annales de géographie* 79 (435), (Sept.–Oct, 1970): 529–544.

54. Robert O. Whyte, *Land, Livestock and Human Nutrition in India* (New York, 1968), pp. 70–71.

55. François Durand-Dastès, *La géographie de l'Inde* (Paris, 1965), p. 78. Durand-Dastès's excellent map can be supplemented with, for example: Ashok K. Dutt, S. P. Chatterjee, and M. Margaret Geib, *India in Maps* (Dubuke, 1976), p. 29 (Contrasting areas for rice and millets).

56. Caraka, *cikitsā* XXX, 316–319.

57. Contrast between barley and rice: barley gruel (*mantha*) moistened with ghee and stirred into water (Suśruta, *sūtra* XLVI, 385, Cakrapāṇi. *ad* Caraka, *sūtra* VI, 28, etc.) as for *peyā*, the emphasis here is laid on its component, *rice*, rather than on its light consistency (G. J. Meulenbeld, *The Mādhavanidāna and its Chief Commentary, Chapters 1–10* [Leiden, 1974], p. 476).

58. Caraka, *vimāna* I, 17–18.

IV: ZOOLOGY IN PHARMACY

1. Aristotle, *Historia Animalium*, IX, 29, 618a8.
2. Caraka, *sūtra* XV, 7 (3).
3. Cf. D. M. Bose, *A Concise History of Science in India* (New Delhi), 1971.
4. Priya Vrata Sharma, *The Aṣṭāṅga Nighaṇṭu* (Madras, 1973), p. xix.
5. Suśruta, *sūtra* XLVI, 135–136.
6. Macdonnell and Keith, *Vedic Index*, I. p. 510: the whole-hoofed animal is opposed to the wild animal. Cf. *Laws of Manu*, V, 11: "carnivorous" birds are opposed to birds "which live in villages."
7. Ḍalhaṇa *ad* Suśruta, *sūtra* XLVI, 518.
8. Ḍalhaṇa *ad* Suśruta, *sūtra* XLVI, 125, and *cikitsā* XL, 31.
9. Suśruta, *sūtra* XLVI, 53–138. The prose is intermingled with distiches formed of four hemistiches (*a, b, c, d*), but in most cases it is enough to start a new line to indicate how each distich is divided into four.
10. Pāṇini (VI, *1*, 150) connects *viṣkira* with vi-KṜ. The birds in this group eat grain, "scattering it" *(vikīrya)*. They are "three-clawed"; Ḍalhaṇa glosses as "the *tryāhala* scratch (the ground) with the three claws of each of their two feet." The foot of the walking bird comprises three fingers, sometimes four, not to mention the spurs of the *Phasianidae* and the *Gallinaceae*. *Vikīrya*, the bird "which scatters" or "scatterer," is sometimes translated as bird "which scratches" with its claws, "scratcher"; see *Laws of Manu*, V, 13.
11. Wild pigeon; not mentioned in verse 67.
12. Hemistiches exceptionally with eleven syllables.
13. They neutralize the "slow poisons" (*dūṣīviṣa*).
14. Categories of hooded snakes not mentioned in verse 78.
15. "Shell": *koṣa* (verse 93) or *kośa* (verse 108).
16. *Nādeya*, "those of the rivers," to which all freshwater fish are assimilated.
17. Duckweed. The carp *(rohita)* does not excite bile too much because it never sleeps (Caraka, *sūtra* XXVII, 82d) and is vegetarian, as opposed to the catfish *(pāṭhīna)* which takes naps and is carnivorous.
18. The Bombay in-18 edition gives *sāgarasaṃbhavāḥ*, fish "born from the ocean." Everywhere else (Calcutta, Benares ed.), the variant is given: *sarasijāḥ smṛtāḥ*, "born from a lake," which prompts a hypothesis from Sunder Lal Hora ("Ancient Hindu conception of correlation between form and locomotion of fishes," *Journal of the Asiatic Society of Bengal, Science* I [1935]: 1–7) which it is hard to take seriously. For this ichthyologist, *sarasija* fish could only be those that live in mountain streams; thus (note the inverted logic), *saras*: "lake" would here mean "mountain stream."
19. "Living off inappropriate foods" *(asātmyacārin)*: the principle of an "appropriateness" *(sātmya)* of living beings to their environment *(cara)* through foods.
20. Allusion to the series of the seven *dhātu*, or "tissues": chyle-blood-flesh-fat-bone-marrow-semen, listed in order of increasing heaviness. "Chyle" is omitted in paragraph 130, leaving only six terms in the series: blood-, etc. The

series thigh-shoulder-head (in order of increasing heaviness) is repeated in paragraph 130 and verse 131 in the same order, but "rump" and "back" occupy a floating position.

21. "Equal" *(sama)*: neither too heavy nor too light (Ḍalhaṇa).

22. "Environment" *(cara)*: both nourishment and habitat (Ḍalhaṇa). Identical in Caraka, *sūtra* XXVII, 331.

23. The hare (80d) is "moderate [in its action] on wind" *(vāta-sādhāraṇa)*; cf. Caraka, *sūtra* XXVII, 77b: the meat of the hare is recommended "in cases of a relative weakness of wind in the conjunction of the three humors."

24. Paul Lazarsfeld, *Philosophie des sciences sociales* (Paris, 1970), specifically p. 367; Allen H. Barton, "The concept of property-space in social research," in P. F. Lazarsfeld and M. Rosenberg, eds., *The Language of Social Research* (Glencoe, 1955), pp. 40–53; specifically p. 50 (substruction of the property-space of a typology).

25. Suśruta, *sūtra* XLII, 8 (1).

26. Caraka, *sūtra* XXII, 12cd–13ab.

27. Suśruta, *sūtra* XL, 5; Caraka, *sūtra* XXVI, 48d.

28. Substances of a sweet savor and sweet digestion are normally of cold energy, and the same goes for milk: Caraka, *sūtra* XXVI, 45–47. Milk "in general" is of cold energy: Caraka, *sūtra* I, 107ab, and Cakrapāṇi. *ad* Caraka, *sūtra* XXVII, 217–224 *(sāmānyaguṇe śītatvam)*.

29. Suśruta, *sūtra* XX, 13; Caraka, *sūtra* XXVI, 82–84.

30. Julius Jolly, *Medicin* (Strassburg, 1901), §68, n. 4 = *Indian Medicine*, 2d ed. (New Delhi, 1977), p. 117, note, ref. *Census of India 1891*, 23, p. 366.

31. *Asiatick Researches or Transactions of the Society instituted in Bengal for inquiring into the History and Antiquities, the Arts, Sciences, and Literature of Asia*, Volume the second (Calcutta, 1790), pp. 149–158, specifically p. 156.

V: LOGIC AND CUISINE

1. Ḍalhaṇa *ad* Suśruta, *sūtra* XLVI, 53.
2. Cakrapāṇi. *ad* Caraka, *sūtra* XXVII, 35.
3. Cakrapāṇi. *ad* Suśruta, *sūtra* XLVI, 53.
4. Caraka, *cikitsā* VIII, 132.
5. Suśruta, *sūtra* XLVI, 344.
6. Ibid., 349.
7. Caraka, *sūtra* XXVII, 259.
8. Suśruta, *sūtra* XLV, 131.
9. A hemistich common to both Suśruta, *sūtra* XLVI, 391a and Caraka, *sūtra* XXVII, 276a.
10. Caraka, *vimāna* I, 22 (2).
11. Ḍalhaṇa *ad* Suśruta, *sūtra* XLVI, 351.
12. *On ancient medicine*, V, 24 and XVIII, 24 ("Loeb Classical Library"); cf. Festugière ed. (Paris, 1948), pp. 37–38.
13. Caraka, *sūtra* XXV, 36.
14. On this series: Caraka, *sūtra* XXVIII, 3; Suśruta, *sūtra* XLVI, 494; etc.

15. Suśruta, *sūtra* XIV, 3.

16. Aristotle's most precise text on the classification of animals (*Historia Animalium* I, 6) reproduces a schema already to be found in Homer. See Pierre Louis, introduction to his edition of *Partes Animalium* (Paris, 1956), p. xiv.

17. *On regimen*, XLVII, 2 and XLVIII, 2; valuable notes by Robert Joly in his critical edition (Paris, 1967).

18. Robert Joly, *Recherches sur le traité pseudo-hippocratique "Du régime"* (Liège-Paris, 1960), pp. 21–23.

19. *On regimen*, XXXIX.

20. *On ancient medicine*, XIV, 33 (*kai alla myria*).

21. Ibid., XVII, 9 (same phrase).

22. Roman Jakobson, "Linguistics and poetics," in *Style in Language*, ed. Thomas A. Sebeok (Massachusetts, Institute of Technology, 1960), pp. 350–377; quoted from p. 358.

23. Suśruta, *sūtra* XXXV, 40.

24. Louis Renou, *Histoire de la langue sanskrite* (Lyon, 1956), p. 126.

25. Jean Bottéro, "Symptômes, signes, écritures en Mésopotamie ancienne," in *Divination et rationalité*, ed. J. P. Vernant (Paris, 1974), p. 173.

26. Suśruta, *sūtra* XLVI, 352; Caraka, *sūtra* XXII, 25; XXV, 40 (5°); XXVII, 4, 87, 312.

27. Vāgbhaṭa, *sūtra* XIV, 9 and 35.

28. Ḍalhaṇa *ad* Suśruta, *sūtra* XLVI, 102: *vṛṣyaṃ śukralam*. We should emphasize this type of synonymy. The two words are interchangeable; they always indicate a production of phlegm, a flux.

29. Caraka, *sūtra* XXII, 13–14, and *cikitsā* II (4), 36 (meat-based, virilifying pills and broths).

30. Compare "with a secondary astringent savor" (*anu-rasa*) (lines 99b, 101b, 115a) with Suśruta, *sūtra* XLI, 4 (1) and (2): "a touch of astringency" (*īṣatkaṣāya*).

31. Louis Hjelmslev, *Prolegomena to a Theory of Language* (Madison; Milwaukee; London, 1969), p. 135 (Definition 64).

32. Caraka, *sūtra* XXVII, 67; Vāgbhaṭa, *sūtra* VI, 57–58.

33. See table 12: "Second paradigm", infra, p. 144.

34. Suśruta, *sūtra* XLII, and *uttara* LXIII; Caraka, *sūtra* XXVI, 14–22; Vāgbhaṭa, *sūtra* X, 40–42; etc.

35. Suśruta, *sūtra* XLII, 4; Caraka, *sūtra* I, 66, and *vimāna* I, 6–7; Vāgbhaṭa, *sūtra* I, 14–16.

36. This adjective appears in lines 60e, 81b, and 84b.

37. Suśruta, *sūtra* XLII, 7; in opposition to Caraka, *sūtra* XXVI, 53–56.

38. Suśruta, *sūtra* XLI, 7–8.

39. Caraka, *cikitsā* III, 37–39.

40. Robert Blanché, *Structures intellectuelles* (Paris, 1966), p. 56.

41. Ibid., p. 113.

42. Caraka, *sūtra* XXIII, 3.

43. Suśruta, *sūtra* XLV, 50ff.

44. Jakobson, "Linguistics and poetics," p. 35.

45. See Jakobson, "Grammatical parallelism and its Russian facet," *Lan-*

guage XL (1966), reprinted in his *Selected Writings, III (Poetry of Grammar and Grammar of Poetry)* (The Hague; Paris; New York, 1981), pp. 98–135.

46. Gerard Manley Hopkins cited by Jakobson in "Linguistics and poetics," p. 368; Hopkins, *The Journals and Papers*, ed. H. House (London, 1959), p. 84 ("Poetic Diction," 1865).

47. V. V. Chklovski, "L'art comme procédé," in T. Todorov, *Théorie de la litterature (Textes des Formalistes russes)* (Paris, 1965), p. 94.

48. Madeleine Biardeau, *L'Hindouisme* (Paris, 1981), p. 84; and by the same author the thesis *Théorie de la connaissance et philosophie de la parole dans le brahmanisme classique* (Paris; The Hague, 1964), p. 141 (absence of the idea of concept) and p. 444 (the status of medical knowledge).

49. Suśruta, *sūtra* XL, 19–21.

VI: THE FLESH OF EATERS OF FLESH

1. Ḍalhaṇa *ad* Suśruta, *sūtra* XLVI, 102; XLVI, 411; XLV, 112.

2. Suśruta, *sūtra* XLVI, 98d (supra, p. 107) "it makes flesh firm" (*māṃsadārḍhyakṛt*).

3. Caraka, *sūtra* XXII, 38.

4. Caraka, *sūtra* XXVII, 343.

5. Caraka, *sūtra* XXII, 10.

6. Jamnagar (Gujarat) is, with Benares, one of the major centers for Ayurvedic research in India. A planning commission was set up under the chairmanship of R. N. Chopra to elaborate the policy to be followed in the newly independent India with regard to indigenous systems of medicine. The Report of the Chopra Committee published in 1948 thus determined the policy followed during the 1950s. The aim was to combine the Ayurvedic system with the allopathic system (Western medicine) to produce an "integrated system," at the cost of an extraordinary telescoping of the Sanskrit texts into the facts of modern biology. The policy was subsequently abandoned, at least on the practical level; the double qualification of practitioners was scrapped, and those of each of the two systems were thereafter inscribed on two separate professional registers. The books of C. Dwarakanath are nevertheless a typical product of this attempt at an integration on a doctrinal level.

7. Bhagwan Dash (*Concept of Agni in Ayurveda* [Varanasi, 1971]) takes up the themes of C. Dwarakanath, *Digestion and Metabolism in Ayurveda* (Calcutta, 1967).

8. Bhagwan Dash (ibid., p. 83) develops Dwarakanath, ibid., p. 126.

9. Cakrapāṇi. *ad* Caraka, *cikitsā* XV, 16.

10. Aristotle, *Historia Animalium*, trans. A. L. Peck, in Loeb Classical Library (London, 1965).

11. Caraka, *cikitsā* XV, 16.

12. *Mitākṣarā ad Yājñavalkyasmṛti*, III, 84.

13. Cakrapāṇi. *ad* Caraka, *sūtra* XXVIII, 4.

14. Caraka, *śārirā* VI, 9–11.

15. Three texts: Cakrapāṇi. *ad* Caraka, *sūtra* XXVIII, 4, and *cikitsā* XV,

16; and Cakrapāṇi. *ad* Suśruta, *sūtra* XIV, 10. Cf. S. Dasgupta, *History of Indian Philosophy* (Cambridge, 1932), Vol. II, p. 322ff; Dwarakanath, *Digestion and Metabolism*, p. 126ff.

16. Cakrapāṇi. *ad* Caraka, *sūtra* XXVIII, 4.
17. Suśruta, *śārīra* VII, 3.
18. Cakrapāṇi. *ad* Suśruta, *śārīra* VII, 3.
19. Among others: Gananath Sen, *Pratyakṣaśārīram* (Calcutta, 1911); P. S. Varier, *Aṣṭāṅgaśārīram* (Kottakal, 1925).
20. Cakrapāṇi. *ad* Suśruta, *śārīra* VII, 3.
21. Caraka, *cikitsā*, XV, 1–40.
22. Ibid., 14.
23. Caraka, *sūtra* XXVIII, 4 (end).
24. Caraka, *sūtra* I, 44.
25. Caraka, *śārīra* VI, in particular 1–18.
26. Ibid., 10–11.
27. Cakrapāṇi. *ad* Caraka, *siddhi* XII, 41–44 (as an example of ellipsis, *vākyaśeṣa*).
28. Caraka, *sūtra* XXVII, 262.
29. Caraka, *cikitsā* II (1), 44–45.
30. Among others: Suśruta, *sūtra* XIV, 36; *cikitsā* XXXIV, 12; *cikitsā* XXXVI, 48; Caraka, *cikitsā* XIX, 74; *cikitsā* XXX, 101; *siddhi* VI, 82; *siddhi* X, 41; Vāgbhaṭa, *sūtra* XXVII, 43.
31. Ḍalhaṇa *ad* Suśruta, *sūtra* XIV, 36–38.
32. Red blood, a digestive hemorrhage of lower origin, as opposed to *meloena*, blood that is black because it has been digested, which has an upper origin. This distinction is unknown in the Ayurvedic texts which substitute for it a distinction between "living blood" (*jīvarakta*) and "bile-blood" (*raktapitta*).
33. Caraka, *siddhi* VI, 82–83, and the commentary by Cakrapāṇi.
34. Suśruta, *cikitsā* 82c; Caraka, *sūtra* XXVII, 58d; etc.
35. Vāgbhaṭa, *sūtra* XIV, 35.
36. Caraka, *cikitsā* XV, 209–211.
37. The "eaters of grass" (*tṛṇāda*): *Bovinae* and other domesticated animals. The eaters of flesh: tiger and other carnivores are grouped together under the heading *prasaha*. Cf. Cakrapāṇi. *ad* Caraka, *sūtra* XXVII, 56, and *cikitsā* XV, 210.
38. Caraka, *sūtra* XXII, 27; *cikitsā* XV, 210.
39. Cakrapāṇi. *ad* Caraka, *sūtra* XXII, 27.
40. But it is a name given to the tiger and also the *godhā* (lizard) in the *Dhanvantari* and the *Rājanighaṇṭu*.
41. Heinrich Lüders, "Eine indische Speiseregel," *Zeitschrift der deutschen Morgenländischen Gesellschaft* 61 (1907): 641–644. See Kane, *History of Dharmaśāstra*, II, 2, 2d ed. (Poona, 1974), p. 777 for the references to the normative texts.
42. See chapter 7, note 8 in this book.
43. See Meulenbeld, *The Mādhavanidāna*, p. 508.
44. The principal treasuries of names gloss *pañcanakha* with elephant and tortoise; cf. A. Borooah, *Nānārthasaṅgraha*. The *Mitākṣarā ad Yājñavalkyasmṛti*, I, 177 cites dog, cat, monkey, etc.

45. The *Bhāgavata Purāṇa*, III, 10, 20–24, classifies the 28 kinds of animals into whole-hoofed, cloven-hoofed, and *pañcanakha*. The *pañcanakha* are "dog, jackal, wolf, tiger, cat, hare, porcupine, lion, monkey, elephant, tortoise, lizard, and *makara*." If we remove the *makara* (a sea monster) and the names commented on above, we are left with the carnivores: dog, jackal, wolf, tiger, wildcat, lion. In reality, the beasts of prey have no less than four fingers: the hyena only four; the felines five in front and four on their hind paws; and the thumb leaves no mark on the ground. *Pañcanakha* is therefore an approximation, but I believe it may be interpreted as an approximative reference to beasts of prey as a whole.

46. Hemistiches 120a–b and 134c–d.

47. Suśruta, *cikitsā* I, 82–83.

48. Ḍalhaṇa *ad* Suśruta, *cikitsā* I, 82–83.

49. Vāgbhaṭa, *cikitsā* V, 7.

50. Caraka, *cikitsā* VIII, 149–157.

51. "According to the rule" also in *Manu*, V, 27, which will be cited below in chapter 7.

52. *Raghuvaṃśa*, XIX, 48–51.

53. Caraka, *cikitsā* VIII, 4d and 25a, and the commentary by Cakrapāṇi.

54. Louis Dumont, appendix to *Homo hierarchicus* (Paris, 1966), p. 361.

55. Caraka, *nidāna* VI, 12.

56. Cf. Macdonnell and Keith, *Vedic Index*, II, p. 182, 219, etc.

57. Caraka, *cikitsā* VIII, 189.

58. Cakrapāṇi. *ad* Caraka, *sūtra* VIII, 19.

59. Caraka, *cikitsā* VIII, 10.

60. Caraka, *sūtra* XXV, 40.

61. Caraka, *sūtra* XXX, 15; cf. Suśruta, *cikitsā* XXVIII, 28.

VII: VEGETARIANISM AND NONVIOLENCE

1. Suśruta, *sūtra* XXXIV.

2. Suśruta, *sūtra* XLVI, 446ff.

3. Dumont, *Homo hierarchicus*, pp. 192 and 198.

4. *Laws of Manu*, IV, 212.

5. *Arthaśāstra*, II, 26, 1.

6. Ibid., VIII, 4, 44.

7. Ibid., II, 2, 1; II, 29, 21.

8. Suśruta, *sūtra* XLVI, 103c (supra, p. 108) Kane, *History of Dharmaśāstra*, Vol. IV, Poona, 1953, pp. 422–423.

9. *Mahābhārata, anuśāsanap.* CXVII (critical ed. Poona) = CXVI (Bombay edition); cf. Kane, *History of Dharmaśāstra*, II, 2, 2d ed. (Poona, 1974), p. 781. Note that the stanzas expressing the point of view of the warriors and hunters *are censored* in the Gītā Press edition.

10. Biardeau and Malamoud, *Le sacrifice*, p. 134.

11. Ludwig Alsdorf, *Beiträge zur Geschichte von Vegetarismus und Rinderverehrung in Indien* (Wiesbaden, 1962), pp. 617–619.

12. Suśruta, *sūtra* XLVI, 89d.

13. Suśruta, *sārīra* III, 25.
14. Suśruta, *sūtra* XLVI, 103c (rhinoceros), 330 (precious stones); *cikitsā* XXIV, 75 (turban); etc.
15. Caraka, *sūtra* XXV, 39.
16. Caraka, *sūtra* XXVII, 79.
17. *Mārkaṇḍeya Purāṇa*, XXXII, 4 (trans. Pargiter, p. 181).
18. Caraka, *cikitsā* XIX, 4.
19. Cf. H. H. Wilson, *The Vishnu Purana*, 3d ed. (Calcutta, 1961), IV, 1, p. 280 n. 8.
20. Caraka, *cikitsā* XIX, 73–74.
21. Caraka, *cikitsā* IX, 96.
22. Caraka, *śārīra* V, 8.
23. Caraka, *cikitsā* XIX, 4.
24. Cakrapāṇi. *ad* Caraka, *sūtra* VIII, 29.
25. Dumont (*Homo hierarchicus*, p. 189) cites the *Mitākṣarā*. This is a commentary on Yājñavalkya composed at the beginning of the twelfth century, the same period as Cakrapāṇidatta and Ḍalhaṇa.
26. Ḍalhaṇa *ad* Suśruta, *sūtra* X, 3 (end).
27. Cakrapāṇi, *ad* Caraka, *sūtra* VIII, 29.
28. P. V. Kane, *History of Dharmaśāstra*, V, 2, (Poona, 1962), p. 1183.

VIII: ANIMALS IN THE SEQUENCE OF FOODS

1. Aristotle, *De Anima*, III, 414a 31 (hierarchy) and *Historia Animalium*, VIII, 1, 588b 4 (continuity). Cited by Henri Daudin, *De Linné à Jussieu (Méthodes de la classification et idée de série en botanique et en zoologie, 1740–1790)* (Paris, 1926), pp. 81–83 and 91–94.
2. Suśruta, *sūtra* I, 22–30.
3. Macdonnell and Keith, *Vedic Index*, I, p. 278; *Bhāgavata Purāṇa*, III, 7, 27; etc.
4. Caraka, *śārīra* III, 16.
5. *Laws of Manu*, I, 49–50.
6. Ibid., I, 46.
7. Ḍalhaṇa (*ad* Suśruta, *sūtra* I, 22) and Cakrapāṇidatta (*ad* Caraka, *śārīra* III, 16) gloss *bhūta*, "creatures," by *prāṇi*, "living beings." All things alive, not just the animals. But Brajendranath Seal (*The Positive Sciences of the Ancient Hindus*, 2d ed. [Delhi, 1958], pp. 177 and 181) likens the Ayurvedic texts to a passage in the commentary by Śaṅkara on the *Chāndogya Upaniṣad* (VI, 3, 1) and incorrectly translates *bhūta* as "animals"; the texts then immediately appear to be affirming the existence of zoophytes, "animals born from plant organisms." This magnificent mistake is reproduced in the chapter "Zoology" of D. M. Bose et al., *Concise History of Science in India* (Delhi, 1971), pp. 425–426 and 428.
8. Suśruta, *sūtra* I, 30: *indragopa-maṇḍūka-prabhṛtaya udbhijjāḥ*. The *indragopa* is a scarlet insect born during the rainy season. The Jamnagar team which translated Caraka identifies a trombidion by that name.

9. Suśruta, *sūtra* I, 28, in part repeated in *sūtra* XLVI, 3.
10. *Amarakośa*, II, 135.
11. See supra, p. 131.
12. Ḍalhaṇa *ad* Suśruta, *sūtra* I, 27.
13. Vāgbhaṭa, *sūtra* I, 25.
14. *Taittirīya Upaniṣad*, II, 2.
15. Caraka, *sūtra* XXVII, 350–351.
16. Caraka, *sūtra* I, 15; etc.
17. Caraka, *sūtra* XXVII, 346.
18. *Laws of Manu*, V, 40.
19. In a marginal note in *Trois énigmes sur les cent chemins* (Paris, 1956, Vol. II § 886–888), Armand Minard interprets what he calls (in French) the *filière*, the sequence moon-space-wind-rain-earth-food (*Bṛhadāraṇyaka Upaniṣad*, VI, 2, 16), from the point of view of the chain of being and cites a fine expression of Diderot's (*la grande chaîne des êtres*). The evidence he elsewhere compiles for the etymology of *oṣadhi*, § 743–747, suggests that this term expresses the idea of food or cooking.
20. Charles Malamoud, "Cuire le monde," *Puruṣārtha* (Paris: Centre d'Études de l'Inde et de l'Asie du Sud), 1 (1975): 91–135, specifically p. 95: "and one can see the narrowness and rigidity which caused Hinduism to depart from its Vedic starting point: it reinterpreted the formula "to cook the world" as "to cook for other people."
21. Cited by W. Norman Brown, "La vache sacrée dans la religion hindoue," *Annales ESC* 19 (1964): 643–644.
22. *Mahābhārata, śāntiparvan* LXXXIX, 21 (big snakes eat small ones), XCVII, 18ff. (the hero and the coward), and XCIX, 15. On the "logic of fish" (the large eat the small): R. Lingat, *Les sources du droit dans le système traditionnel de l'Inde* (Paris, 1967), p. 231.
23. *Śiśumāra* semen (Caraka, *cikitsā* II [2], 10) and *śarabha* meat are forgotten in P. Ray and H. N. Gupta, *Carakasaṃhitā: A Scientific Synopsis* (New Delhi), 1965.
24. Cf. T. A. Gopinatha Rao, *Elements of Hindu Iconography* (Madras, 1914) Vol. I, p. 1, intro., p. 44 and plate E.
25. Cakrapāṇi. *ad* Caraka, *sūtra* V, 5 (*mahāśṛṅgī hariṇaḥ*); *Dhanvantari* and *Rājanighaṇṭu* (Poona edition), p. 269 (*vyāghraviśeṣa, upavyāghra*) and p. 293 (*mahāśṛṅga, mahāsiṃha*); *Vaidyakaśabdasindhu, s.v.* "pañcanakha."
26. Caraka, *sūtra* V, 5; VI, 43ab; Suśruta, *uttara* XXXIX, 153ab; etc.
27. The *śarabha* is a wapiti in the translation of Caraka published in Jamnagar, and also in Ray and Gupta, p. 33.
28. Cf. Biardeau, "Études de mythologie hindoue, II," *Bulletin de l'Ecole Française d'Extrême-Orient* 55 (1969): 59–105; reprinted in her *Etudes de mythologie hindoue*, Vol. I, *Cosmologies purāṇiques* (Paris, 1981).
29. Edgar Thurston, *Castes and Tribes of Southern India* (Madras, 1909), Vol. V, pp. 163–164 and 166.
30. *Viṣṇu Purāṇa*, trans. H. H. Wilson, 3d ed. (Calcutta, 1961), p. 37.
31. *Śatapatha Brāhmaṇa*, VI, 2.1.2; etc.
32. *Mahābhārata, bhīṣmaparvan* IV, 13.

33. *Bhāgavata Purāṇa*, III, 10, 20 (cited supra, p. 243). Comparison with the 28 infirmities: *Viṣṇu Purāṇa*, trans. H. H. Wilson, I, 1, 5, p. 31 n. 5.

34. Cf. Francis Zimmermann, "Poiétique et matériau du savoir (Les dictionnaires dans l'Inde classique)," *Recherches poiétiques* 2 (Paris, 1976): 101–114.

35. *Amarakośa*, II, 1, 5: "solid land (*sthala*), dry lands (*maru, dhanvan*), wasteland (*khila, aprahata*)"; and 6–7: "on either side of the Sarasvati the southeast, the northwest; the borders, barbarian country; the middle country."

36. The *vanauṣadhivarga* (Section of wild plants) in this *Treasury of Amara* is on the syllabus for the examination in Sanskrit at the end of the first year; modern notions of botany are added. Cf. *Curriculum and Syllabus for Ayurvedic Education*, formulated by the Central Council of Ayurvedic Research (New Delhi: Government of India, 1962).

37. Jean Bottéro, "Symptômes, signes, écriture en Mésopotamie ancienne," in *Divination et rationalité*, ed. J. P. Vernant (Paris, 1974), specifically pp. 168–173.

CONCLUSION: UNCTUOSITY SUBLIMED

1. Cited by François Dagognet in *Pour une théorie générale des formes* (Paris, 1975), p. 41. "La géographie spirituelle" (spiritual geography) of the eighteenth century is the subject of one fascinating chapter.

2. Suśruta, *sūtra* XL, 5, and XLII, 7.

3. Jean Filliozat, *La doctrine classique de la médecine indienne, ses origines et ses parallèles grecs*, 2d ed. (Paris, 1975), p. 135.

4. *Śatapatha Brāhmaṇa*, I, 6, 4, 20.

5. Suśruta, *sūtra* XLV, 49.

6. *Śatapatha Brāhmaṇa*, II, 2, 4, 15. Cited by Charles Malamoud in "Cuire le monde," *Puruṣārtha* (Paris: Centre d'Études de l'Inde et de l'Asie du Sud), 1 (1975): 104.

7. Suśruta, *sūtra* XLV, 48.

8. G. Morris Carstairs, *The Twice-Born, A Study of a Community of High-Caste Hindus* (London, 1957), p. 166.

9. Ibid., p. 85.

10. Caraka, *vimāna* III, 43–44.

Sources

Suśrutasaṃhitā
- —ed. in-18, Bombay: Nirṇaya Sāgar, 1945;
- —with the commentary by Ḍalhaṇa, ed. Jadavji Trikamji, Bombay: Nirṇaya Sāgar, 3d ed., 1939;
- —with the commentary by Cakrapāṇidatta, ed. Jadavji Trikamji and Nandkishor Sharma, Jaipur: Svāmī Lakṣmī Rām Trust, 1939 (*Sūtrasthāna* only).

Carakasaṃhitā
- —with the commentary by Cakrapāṇidatta, Bombay: Nirṇaya Sāgar, 3d ed., 1941;
- —with an English trans., Jamnagar: Śrī Gulabkunverba Ayurvedic Society, 1949 (six volumes).

Aṣṭāṅgahṛdayasaṃhitā
- —ed. A. M. Kunte et al., Bombay: Nirṇaya Sāgar, 6th ed., 1939;
- —ed. Vayaskara N. S. Mooss, Kottayam, 1963–1978 (six fascicules).

(Other editions of these texts do exist, but the above are unanimously considered to be the best.)

Index

abhaya (law of safety), 61, 183
abhayavana (paradise), 50, 61
abhidānakośa (treasury of names), 99, 211, 215
abhiṣyandin (producing fluxes), 54, 68, 100, 102, 151–153
abstinence, 179, 188, 190
ācāra (rules of conduct), 202
adharma (rules denied), 39, 193
adhiṣṭhāna (point of application), 23, 199
āgneya (where Agni predominates), 145, 198
Agni (the sun) and Soma (the moon), 33, 131, 145, 198, 220
argriculture: and irrigation, 16, 18–19, 48–49; and metaphors, 166, 169, 223
āhāra (food), 130, 199, 201–202
ahiṃsā (nonviolence), 2, 178–179, 187–188
āhitāgni (maintainer of the sacred fires), 205, 207
Airs (On), Waters, Places, 22, 31
ALCMAEON, 31, 128
ALLCHIN B. & R., 45–46, 233 n. 13
ALSDORF L., 185, 187, 243 n. 11
Amarakośa, 215–216, 236 n. 33, 237 n. 48, 245 n. 10
analadīpana (stimulates the digestive fire), 115
anatomy, treatises, 166
ANAXAGORAS, 131
Ancient Medicine (On), 129, 239 n. 12
aṇḍaja (oviparous), 199–200
annarasa (juice from food), 163, 170
antaragni (digestive fire), 205
anubala (subsidiary force), 35
anubandha (accessory factor), 35
anūpa or *ānūpa* (marshy lands), definition, 4, 25, 28, 134
ānūpagrāma (village on the water's edge), 48
anurasa (subsidiary savor), 35, 122, 138
āppaddharma (dharma for times of distress), 41, 189
appropriateness, 23–25, 32, 205, 238 n. 19
araṇya (forest), 50, 101
āraṇya (wild), 61, 101, 214
archaeology: of representations, ix, 58; of iron age, 44–47
ARCHER W. G., 63
ARISTOTLE, 97, 131, 132, 163–164, 197, 240 n. 16, 244 n. 1
artha (material goal), 39, 181, 183, 205
Arthaśāstra, 38, 47–51, 61, 183, 233 n. 15, 234 n. 25
ārya (Aryans), 18, 39
āryāvarta (Domain of the Aryans), 61, 71
Asiatick Researches, 123, 239 n. 31
Aṣṭavaidya, 213
astringency, in jungle meats, 101, 122, 144

COMPARATIVE STUDIES OF HEALTH SYSTEMS AND MEDICAL CARE

1. John M. Janzen, *The Quest for Therapy in Lower Zaire*
2. Paul U. Unschuld, *Medical Ethics in Imperial China: A Study in Historical Anthropology*
3. Margaret M. Lock, *East Asian Medicine in Urban Japan: Varieties of Medical Experience*
4. Jeanie Schmit Kayser-Jones, *Old, Alone, and Neglected: Care of the Aged in Scotland and in the United States*
5. Arthur Kleinman, *Patients and Healers in the Context of Culture: An Exploration of the Borderland between Anthropology, Medicine, and Psychiatry*
6. Stephen J. Kunitz, *Disease Change and the Role of Medicine: The Navajo Experience*
7. Carol Laderman, *Wives and Midwives: Childbirth and Nutrition in Rural Malaysia*
8. Victor G. Rodwin, *The Health Planning Predicament: France, Québec, England, and the United States*
9. Michael W. Dols and Adil S. Gamal, *Medieval Islamic Medicine: Ibn Riḍwān's Treatise "On the Prevention of Bodily Ills in Egypt"*
10. Leith Mullings, *Therapy, Ideology, and Social Change: Mental Healing in Urban Ghana*
11. Jean de Kervasdoué, John R. Kimberly, and Victor G. Rodwin, editors, *The End of an Illusion: The Future of Health Policy in Western Industrialized Nations*
12. Arthur J. Rubel, Carl W. O'Nell, and Rolando Collado-Ardón, *Susto, a Folk Illness*
13. Paul U. Unschuld, *Medicine in China: A History of Ideas*
14. Paul U. Unschuld, *Medicine in China: A History of Pharmaceutics*
15. Glenn Gritzer and Arnold Arluke, *The Making of Rehabilitation: A Political Economy of Medical Specialization, 1890–1980*
16. Arthur Kleinman and Byron Good, editors, *Culture and Depression: Studies in the Anthropology and Cross-Cultural Psychiatry of Affect and Disorder*
17. Judith Justice, *Policies, Plans, and People: Culture and Health Development in Nepal*
18. Paul U. Unschuld, *Nan-ching—The Classic of Difficult Issues*
19. Viggo Brun and Trond Schumacher, *Traditional Herbal Medicine in Northern Thailand*
20. Francis Zimmermann, *The Jungle and the Aroma of Meats: An Ecological Theme in Hindu Medicine*

Designer: U. C. Press Staff
Compositor: Asco Trade Typesetting Ltd.
Text: 10/13 Sabon
Display: Sabon
Printer: Edwards Bros., Inc.
Binder: Edwards Bros., Inc.